SWEAR BY APOLLO

SWEAR BY APOLLO

BY SHIRLEY BARKER

RANDOM HOUSE

For

ELLA SHANNON BOWLES

From her "second daughter"

CONTENTS

I swear by Apollo, the physician, and Aesculapius, and Health, and All-heal, and all the gods and goddesses, that, according to my ability and judgment, I will keep this Oath and this stipulation. . . .

I will follow that system of regimen which, according to my ability and judgment, I consider for the benefit of my patients, and abstain from whatever is deleterious and mischievous. I will give no deadly medicine to any one if asked, nor suggest any such counsel. . . . With purity and with holiness I will pass my life and practice my Art. . . .

Into whatever houses I enter, I will go into them for the benefit of the sick, and will abstain from every voluntary act of mischief and corruption; and, further, from the seduction of females. . . . While I continue to keep this Oath unviolated, may it be granted to me to enjoy life and the practice of the art, respected by all men, in all times! But should I trespass and violate this Oath, may the reverse be my lot!

SWEAR BY APOLLO

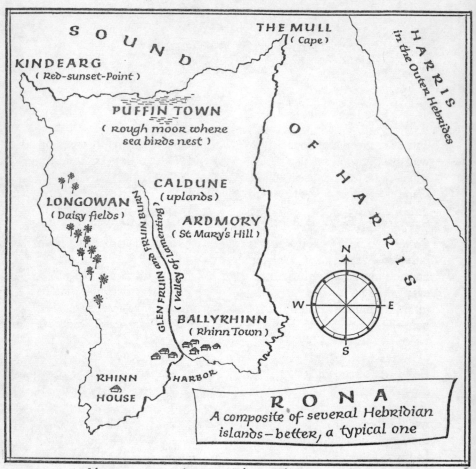

SOUND

KINDEARG
(Red-sunset-Point)

THE MULL
(Cape)

HARRIS
in the Outer Hebrides

OF HARRIS

PUFFIN TOWN
(Rough moor where
sea birds nest)

CALDUNE
(uplands)

LONGOWAN
(Daisy fields)

GLEN FRUIN and FRUIN BURN
(Valley of Lamenting)

ARDMORY
(St. Mary's Hill)

N
W   E
S

BALLYRHINN
(Rhinn Town)

RHINN
HOUSE

HARBOR

R O N A
A composite of several Hebridian
islands — better, a typical one

Names are given with Gaelic meanings

Caldune was for sheep · Longowan, cultivated land
Ardmory for cattle · Ballyrhinn, the village

Past and Prologue

THE LAST green afternoon of his boyhood, Randall Woodbury went out with his gun and his dog to walk the bounds of his father's land, just where the salt marsh meets the alder swamp below Hampton Falls, New Hampshire. A man aged twenty-one and two years married would have little claim to being a boy if he had to prove the case in court, Randall was thinking, and yet, what else had he been—so far? For he was still a son in his father's house and not uncontent to be so, working with his father to give pills and purges and set broken bones, hoping in time to know as much about the profession of medicine as his father knew. Not even when he married Sally Anne Ingle, a neighbor's daughter, had he set up for himself. Instead he brought his wife home to the great square house his grandfather had built, and his mother and sisters made her welcome there, and it had been big enough for all of them.

But as he strode through the sedge and juniper, close followed by Rocky, the ancient black and white hound, named for her habit of chewing small stones in a long forgotten puppyhood, he knew that he was his own man and would always be so—after today. September 1, 1773, it was, his life's dividing line, and he vowed that he would always mark the return of it. For they were certain now. All through August they had wondered, and this morning they had agreed that it must be so, he from a doctor's knowledge, and she from a woman's. Sally Anne would bear him a child in the spring. That meant that his place in the generations was changing now; that some day he would have to show a younger lad the blazed trees that marked these outlying wood lots, just as his father had shown them to him, not too many years ago. A man must know his property lines, just as he knows his name or what town he was born in, and perhaps the best thing he can do is to hold these lines intact, or widen them if he can, and keep the old knowledge of them alive always, from father to son.

It was this thought, too close to his heart for him to put into words, even to Sally Anne, that had drawn him out in the hot sunshine of the late summer afternoon so that he could be alone and exult in his new knowledge and think thereon. A waste of time, probably, so for his conscience's sake he would keep a sharp lookout to see that nobody had been chopping his trees down, and maybe drum up a partridge or two to bring home, as yesterday he had gone fishing in Blackwater Brook and so tonight they would have fried eels for supper.

He wandered long, and it must have been near five o'clock, he judged, by the way the shadows fell, when he reached the dead ash tree at the corner of Ben Tilton's land, turned sharp left, and headed out of the woods, uphill, across the pasture. But he was not ready to go home yet, for all the thinking he had done. And what thinking had he done? Why none at all, really. He threw himself down on the deep green moss under the spread of a blue-green cedar tree shaped like a candle flame, enjoying the good feel of the ground, the warmth of the mild air. Rocky settled down beside him, making a low sound of companionship in her throat that was neither wheeze, nor bark, nor whimper—something like a cat's purr, only that it did not repeat itself. He reached out and felt between the ears for the curve of the neat black head. Off to the left a cricket chirped at the roots of a mullein stalk, and small busy wings whirred in the tangle of goldenrod and blackberry vines above him on the hill. He lay there and smiled happily up at the blue sky growing just a little shadowy with the lateness of the day, and he was pleased with himself as never so.

Ever since their wedding he had expected to have a child with Sally Anne, had even been a little surprised that it had not happened the first year. There had been no lack of love between them all those winter nights in the great fourposter bed in the east chamber, nor in the summer nights either. She had always responded to him, close and eager and warm. And it was she who had begun their first courting. He himself had been riding over after the Portsmouth girls: Mary Sheafe, and Beth Brackett and half a dozen more. He had not thought so soon to settle on one. But Sally Anne had settled on him, and she was close by, and laughing and winsome, a somewhat spoiled only daughter. With him as with everything else, she had had her way. He wasn't really sure he would have chosen Sally Anne, but she had chosen him, and it had turned out well enough—especially now—and he could not complain. He had not thought for a long time of Mary Sheafe and Beth Brackett and the rest.

Bells rang in the white steeple a dozen fields away, and he did not count them. Rolling over, he turned his head to the west where the sun still rode high, and yet, he could almost see it move, like a wagon going down a hill. He sat up and reached for his gun. Never a bird or a squirrel to carry home with him! The girls would mock and call him "Nimrod, the Mighty Hunter," he supposed. Never mind. He had a word that would keep them still tonight. For tonight he and Sally Anne would tell the family how they were going to be lucky at last. "How would you like to be 'Aunt Betty' and 'Aunt Sue?'" he would ask his sisters. And then they would walk over to tell Sally Anne's mother and come home together in the starlight and the warm dark.

He sprang to his feet, ran a hand backward through his blond hair neatly clubbed above the collar of his rough woolen shirt, and whistled to Rocky, though she was already astir, only waiting to learn their direction. John Woodbury, he thought—Dr. John Woodbury. And his son, Dr. Randall Woodbury. And his son—another Randall? Another John? Oh, the child might well enough be a girl, he knew. Unaccountably, they often were. He had seen it happen to other men, and it could happen to him. But at least he knew his wife was not barren now, and if this was a daughter, there would be a son later on. He had much to hope for from Sally Anne.

He started up the rough slope of the cleared land with the tops of the orchard trees lifting green beyond it, then turned again for one last look at the swamp and woodland, already a fiery leaf of autumn showing here and there. In the foreground stood the cedar tree he had rested under. Maybe he would cut down that cedar tree, he thought, and drag it home, and hew and shape it in the long evenings when there were apples and chestnuts roasting, and corn parching, and snow lying white on all the fields outside; hew and shape it into a cradle for his son. Cradles of pine and oak and hickory he had seen, but never a cedar cradle. And yet, cedar was the wood women always chose for the chests they kept their treasures in. Yes, he would come back and cut down that cedar tree.

When he came round the corner of the barn, his father was washing his hands and face in a bucket by the well. He had taken off the full-skirted coat of the claret suit that he always wore for his afternoon visits and flung it on the grass, and Randall noticed sweat and dust stains on his white ruffled shirt. Dr. John was a tall man like his son, but leaner, with the same wheat-sheaf-colored hair and steady gray eyes. They looked very like. He had taken off his Boston wig, too, and laid it carefully on his coat. He was rubbing soft soap on his hands and scouring them with a rough bit of sandstone. He grinned and nodded at the younger man.

"Not a good afternoon for Latin, I take it," he said, eyeing the flintlock and the deerskin Indian shoes on Randall's feet, shoes that were no good at all save to prowl the woodlands in.

Randall grinned back. "I would say it was a damned bad afternoon for Latin, sir," he answered. "I never read a word of it."

His father's grin faded. "Well, if you have not the taste—but you will need it if you go—as we hoped—as we always talked of—to the medical school in Philadelphia or the new one in New York. To Edinburgh even. I've been selfish to keep you here with me this long. But it's about time. You're not getting any younger. None of us are."

Randall looked down and kicked a large pebble, glad that it was there for the diversion.

"I can't go to school now, sir. I got Sally Anne. Where I go I have to take her too. You want to pay for all that?"

He lifted his head, and the two men looked straight into each other's eyes.

"Yes," said Dr. John, his jaw thrust slightly upward, "I'm willing to pay for all that. I want you to go, since I never went myself. You're a good doctor. I taught you all I know. But you can learn more, lad."

In his mind Randall saw himself and Sally Anne walking down the streets of a strange city, bigger than Boston, with tall houses on both sides of the street. In his mind Sally Anne was carrying the baby on her back, like a squaw with a papoose—which of course she would never do. He thought of the fields sloping down to the salt marsh and Ben Tilton's pine lot. This was Woodburys' land and had been, ever since they came up here from Massachusetts in his grandfather's time. This was where they belonged, not in New York or Philadelphia. But then, his father did not know what he and Sally Anne knew. If he had gone when he was younger—then he had wanted to go. Maybe he would want to go still, if it hadn't been for this other thing. Sometimes when he and his father looked at each other across a deathbed in the night, knowing that their skill and knowledge had not been enough, that another loved and valuable life was slipping out and there was nothing they could do to save it, he had wondered with more hope than bitterness if there were not some other, newer practices of medicine known to more skillful men. He had thought there must be such, and that he would go out into the world and learn about them. But he had not gone. He had stayed here, following his father in the old ways. He had married Sally Anne.

He heard his father saying, "Well, think about it, son."

He mumbled an answer, filled a small stone trough with drinking water for Rocky, and hurriedly washed himself. Dr. John had put on his claret coat and tucked his wig under his arm. Together they walked toward the house, but the older man stopped just by the bed of tall, swaying golden glow.

"Oh, Randall, I was talking to Nehemiah Cram," he said.

"That so?" asked Randall indifferently. "How was Nehemiah? I hear he's bought a new chaise to travel in, now he's a Selectman."

Through the open kitchen windows came the murmur of women's voices and the smell of eels frying.

"He was afoot when I saw him," said Dr. John, "just this side of the new meeting house. He'd been to Portsmouth."

Randall looked up quickly. "He bring home any tea with him?" he asked.

"Tea? Nehemiah? Why, he wouldn't buy tea no more'n we would ourselves. He says some is on sale though."

"That was what I wondered about. Was it smuggled or East India?"

"Not East India! The company can sell it cheaper since the new act, but we'd rather pay more money and be free to trade where we please. Fact, it costs less here than in London, but we don't like to be told we've got to buy from them and not from our own."

Randall knew all this, of course, and his father knew that he knew. But the older man was proud of these sentiments and liked to voice them over.

"How did Nehemiah feel about it?" asked the son.

Dr. John smiled. "He was so upset he wanted me to bleed him. Said he felt an apoplexy coming on."

"You didn't, did you?"

"No. I don't know why. He was that red in the face he looked as though it would be a real kindness to him."

"I know why." Randall smiled and slapped his father between the shoulders. "It's a midwife's tale—never bleed on September 1st—but I've watched you six years, and never known you to do it."

His father looked thoughtful. "Truth, I don't," he said slowly. "As you say, it's only an old tale, but there may have been wisdom in it when it was made. There's wisdom sometimes in more places than a man is likely to go looking for it. No, I didn't bleed Nehemiah, and I couldn't find it in my heart to complain against the King the way he did. We're a large family, we folk with English blood in us, and in large families there be always some quarreling. This Tea Act is a family quarrel—only that. Besides, as I told Nehemiah, I have enough to do to earn my bread without trying to mind the King's business for him, and sometimes I think the way I earn mine is a damn discouraging one."

"Why? What's wrong?"

They stood on the stone doorstep now. The door was open and he could see the women moving about the table. His young sisters had mugs and tankards, Sally Anne a willow basket of roasting ears, his mother a large pewter tray.

"You knew the throat-ail was about?"

Randall nodded. "Of course. I told you last night the Philbrick children had it, and you said you'd stop by there today. Did you?"

"Yes. The littlest one is gone."

"That quick? I thought she seemed bad, but her mother said she only sickened yesterday."

"It's quick with the young. I hope we can save the others. I haven't seen it so bad since '64. But the worst time was when I was a boy. Come out of Kingston, some said, from a sick hog that was butchered up there. Twenty families lost all their children—Joe Batchelder buried twelve or thirteen. Mrs. B. couldn't remember afterward just how many she did have, but they all went. Must have addled her wits temporarily. You were two when you had it, and I swear your mother was so scared she was sicker than you were. I only hope—"

"John," said his wife behind him, "will you stop talking and come in and eat your victuals!"

Randall reached out and cuffed his mother lightly on the cheek as he passed her. Martha Woodbury, at forty-four, had soft silver hair brushed back from a girl's smooth face, and her decent wool dress covered a girl's slim figure. He guessed life had been good to his mother all her days so far, and he was glad of it. He strode on, scarcely noticing his sisters—sunburned, dimpled, roly-poly as puppies—and pulled out a chair beside Sally Anne, who had just sat down. Her face looked rosy, he thought, but her brown eyes were dull and lifeless. He held her hand under the tablecloth while his father said grace. Then everyone began talking and passing food.

"What did you do all afternoon?" he asked. "You look like it tired you."

Sally Anne laughed nervously. "It did, a little. We were plucking geese. I swallowed more feathers than I got in my bag, and they beat their wings and raised so much dust, I'm still half choked with it."

"Are we going to tell them tonight? What's the matter? Aren't you going to eat anything?"

"You want milk or cider?" asked Betty at his elbow. "You want milk or cider, Sally Anne?"

"Cider," said Randall promptly, and held his mug while Betty filled it and Susan poured milk for his wife. The food was hot and good, and he savored every mouthful of it before he let it melt away.

"Randall," said his mother, filling his plate for the third time, "a body'd think you were eating for wages. Sally Anne, you're not drinking your milk! You haven't taken a morsel of food either!"

Sally Anne played with her napkin, creasing and uncreasing it.

"I'm still choking on those goose feathers," she complained, clearing her throat huskily.

"Oh, is that it! Well, I don't wonder. Take a swallow of Randall's cider, and that will clear your pipes out. Won't it, John? Geese never like to be plucked—I'm sure I shouldn't if I were a goose—but I never saw a flock more contrary. It took the four of us all afternoon. How were all the sick folks, John? The tin peddler came by right after dinner, and he says everybody's got the flux in Salisbury."

Randall missed his father's reply, for he was watching Sally Anne. She did not seem able to swallow her milk. He smiled, thinking he knew the reason and that it was a good one. He looked over her head, past the black, old fireplace hung with drying herbs and ironware, to the western window sills where the setting sun shone through the thick crimson jars of blackberry jam placed there in a careful row. His father was talking about the flux in Salisbury. The girls were teasing each other about the bound boy on the next farm.

"I don't think, Randall—we'd best tell them tonight," faltered Sally Anne.

"Why not?"

The words leaped out before he had time to check them. Under the tablecloth he clenched his hands in disappointment. He had been waiting for this moment all day—all his life, really. Probably she did feel sick, but didn't she realize sickness was natural to a breeding woman? He did not intend to be thus thwarted by Sally Anne.

But to his quick dismay she gave one stricken look about her, pushed back her plate with both hands, and flung her head down on the table.

"My throat hurts," she wailed, so loudly that everyone stopped eating and turned to stare at her.

Though Randall was close at her side, it was her father-in-law, from the head of the table, who moved faster. He was down on them like a sudden wind, and in his hand he bore a lighted candle, though Randall never knew how he came so quickly by it.

"Hold this!" he snapped, handing it to his son.

Obediently, too startled to think for himself, Randall took the green length of bayberry wax and held it up while Dr. John lifted Sally Anne's head and gently forced her mouth open.

"Tilt your head back, child," he ordered.

With a little rasping cough Sally Anne obeyed him.

Randall had recovered himself, and he held the light deftly now, for he knew what his father was looking for within the slender gullet. He was looking for the deep crimson swelling, the grayish white patches of the throat-ail. Terror was on the young husband suddenly, and he could feel his own throat stiffen and the fetid taste of disease in his own mouth.

The doctor drew back from Sally Anne and laid her head against the chair cushion. She rested limply where he had placed her, her dull eyes staring straight before, not seeming to see.

"Your bones ache, daughter?"

She nodded. "My throat hurts," she croaked, sounding much worse to Randall now. He was still holding the candle, he realized, and he pinched the wick and flung it down, and stared at his wife. Was there a swelling at the angle of the jaw? He could not see because of the shadows gathering, and the high collar of her blue lawn dress. His father kept on.

"Your tongue prickle underneath?"

Again she nodded. Martha Woodbury came over and put her hand on the girl's shoulder. The young maids huddled on their chairs, silent and apprehensive.

"Take her pulse, Randall," said Dr. John, turning away and going toward the front of the house where he had his study.

Randall pulled his heavy watch from its tortoise-shell case and reached out for the slim hand that wore his ring. Trembling and unnerved, he lost the count twice, and when he finally completed it, he realized it was high but not unduly so. Then suddenly his father was elbowing him aside, and Randall did not need to look to see what he had brought with him. He got up to hold Sally Anne's head while her throat was painted, but Dr. John laid down the vial of nitrate and the bit of sponge fastened to the long wand of whalebone. Then he lighted the candle his son had just put out.

"You take a look for yourself, Randall," he said gruffly. "You better see."

This time he held the light while Randall searched for the signs of the throat-ail in Sally Anne. Together they bent over the half-fainting girl, then straightened up, saying no word, careful not to meet each other's glance. Dr. John lowered his arm and the shadows of twilight fell across the rosy face and soft golden-brown hair.

"Take her to bed," he ordered. "I'm going to ride up to Jos' Bartlett's for Peruvian bark. I left the last of ours with Jane Philbrick, and he'll have some by. It's a favorite dose of his. I'll be as swift as I can."

Randall followed him into the yard. The summer day was turning rapidly into an autumn night. Purple shadows thickened overhead. A white mist gathered in the low sea meadows, and the air had a sharpness that had not been there an hour ago.

"Father," he cried, too troubled now to keep the news for a ceremonial time, "she's with child! We were going to tell you tonight. Two months, I think."

Dr. John uttered a harsh sound of dismay and quickened his already hurrying footsteps.

"That makes it harder. But she's a strong girl. Go back and paint her throat. You know what to do if it starts to fill."

As he carried his wife upstairs, his mother following them with a lamp and warm blankets, Randall remembered the first time he had carried her so, the night of their wedding. That had been late summer too, and the elm trees outside the window on the landing had rustled just as they rustled now. He had seen death often and fought against it, but it had never come close to him, and he could not yet believe that it might. It was a swift disease, the throat-ail, soon done, one way or another. In a week she should be laughing up at him, reaching for his hand. But whenever he touched her bare flesh he could feel the fever rising in the veins, and he was afraid. She was his, and he loved her, and she carried his child, and she must not die. His skill might fail, and his father's might fail, but he told himself that God would surely raise a miracle up to save Sally Anne.

» » » « « «

The first night after Sally Anne's burying, Randall wandered out alone in the misty, uncertain moonlight, wanting only to be away from the house for a little while and free of the sympathetic words and glances, free of the last terrible hours he had watched beside his wife. He had seen people die of the throat-ail often enough, and it was always hard to watch, a cruel way for the soul's going, but it was different when you saw it happen to one of your own.

He did not turn toward the old cemetery on the plain above the hill, where he had gone with the mourners and the coffin that afternoon. Nor did he go down through the sloping pasture where he had lain under the cedar tree only four green afternoons ago. Never so long as he lived, he thought, would he look again at that cedar tree. He went instead where the scent of ripening fruit drifted along the soft wind that stirred through the apple orchard, and he walked among the trees to the stone wall at the end of them, and sat down and gazed into the nowhere of the dark. Rocky padded soberly behind, moving when he moved and resting when he rested, huddling against his knee, there in the crook of the wall.

If they had a hive of bees, he thought, someone would have to tell the bees. You always had to tell the bees when a person died. Not for any good reason, only that it was custom. You did not have to tell a dog. A dog knew.

All around him lay the shining fields where he and the dead girl had walked together. Off to the left ran the path through the hazels where he had kissed her first. Here they had quarreled, and there made up again. It was hard to make himself believe there was no more Sally Anne. But at least he could think about his wife; the child that had lain within her, he could not think about that.

He and she had both known it, almost from the moment he carried her upstairs; that he would go on enjoying the sunlight and all the homely, comfortable life they had grown up in, while she was going away into the dark ground. She had been angry at it, and resentful. She had fought like a trapped animal, like a cornered thing. She could have gone out easy, he thought, with a kind of unreasonable anger, if she could have taken him too, if she had not had to relinquish along with her life its dearest possession.

Three times in that last hour, he and his father had worked desperately to free her throat of the yellow mucous, the choking false membrane that gathered in larynx and trachea faster than they could clear it away. And all the time he had watched her features sharpen and the hollow look of death come round her eyes, and held his arm under her shoulders, and bent to hear any last word of Sally Anne's.

"I'll never let you go," was what she had said to him. "I may die, but I'll never leave you—never!" But Sally Anne had gone.

What did she mean by saying that, he wondered miserably, running his fingers along the dog's sleek coat, staring into the white mist now drawing close around, at the fog wreaths beginning to curve about each apple tree. Did she mean that she would stay in his thoughts so close that he could make no second marriage or be pleased with any other love? She couldn't think to come back and haunt him. Few people believed any longer in ghosts, except for children, frightened of old dark houses on Hallows' Eve. She was dead, and maybe her soul was alive somewhere, but not in this world, and so long as he was alive in the flesh he would meet no more with Sally Anne. There was this world, and there was the "Hereafter" they talked about in church—there was no strange half-world of spirits, wraiths, and demons existing in between. That had been nothing but the superstition of ignorant folk a long time ago. The preacher had said this afternoon that her body would return to the earth and her spirit unto God who gave it, and surely a spirit that had gone to God would never come back to Randall Woodbury in Hampton Falls, New Hampshire. Why would it want to come? He was sick suddenly for the merry laughter and eager love-making of Sally Anne.

The night must be growing cooler, for he could feel the chill of it working through his new black broadcloth coat. Or maybe the cold was from inside him because all his fires were banked and low. He must go back to the house in any case, or they would be looking for him, starting to search. It was custom to allow a man to be alone with his grief, but only for so long. He had visited other houses of mourning, and he knew. He rose and walked back through the foggy trees, making the unnecessary gesture of whistling half-heartedly to the dog.

The kitchen was empty, and he was grateful. He had expected it would still be full of the neighbor women who had been there helping his mother serve roast chicken and ham to the funeral guests come by chaise and horseback a long way. They must have withdrawn to her little sewing room, he realized, for he could hear the babble of voices there. He went toward the front of the house, past the wide stair and the parlor door, into his father's study, where he knew his father would be. His father was not alone. He was sitting at his tall desk, a glass of brandy in his hand, and near him sat his friends and fellow physicians, Josiah Bartlett of Kingston and Hall Jackson of Portsmouth. They were drinking brandy too, and both turned to Randall as he came in.

"It's hard, but you'll be the better doctor for it, lad," rumbled Bartlett, a gruff, kind man, near as old as his father was. "When you see it happen to others, you'll know how it is yourself, now."

"Yes, I know," said Randall, sitting down on a bench by the empty fireplace and reaching over to take the full glass his father poured for him.

"A pity we couldn't save her," said Hall Jackson, a younger man, his eyes dark with sympathy. "Times like this makes a man wish he had been a shoemaker."

"Don't know why," declared Dr. Bartlett. " 'Twas sad, but no fault of the doctoring in any way. You saw her, Hall, and I saw her, and John and Randall never left her side. Trouble is with you younger lads, you forget that no matter how good at our trade we be, there comes a time when every man must die."

"Shouldn't come to a woman nineteen," said Dr. John, his chin resting on the silk of his wide black scarf, "a bearing woman."

Nobody said anything for a few moments, and all four men drank. Then Dr. Bartlett looked sharply at Randall.

"Your father tells me you're going away, sir. I'm not sure it's needful, but if it is, why this be the time, while the grief is on you."

Randall lifted his eyebrows and looked at his father. Dr. John flushed; brandy or lamplight reflected from the Turkey-red rug, it must be. He was never the man to show embarrassment. He cleared his throat and took another drink.

"I been telling them, Randall," he explained mildly, "how we'd often talked of your going away—away to study. I told them I thought maybe the time would be now."

"I went to London," said Hall Jackson thoughtfully. "There wasn't a school of physic in all America then. Now there be two."

"But are they so good, do you think?" Dr. John's tone was scalpel sharp.

Jackson shook his head. "I wouldn't go to them myself. No, nor to London either, if it was to do again."

"Where then?" It was Randall who asked, interested in spite of himself, and then, wanting somehow to be the one to give the answer, he finished, "Edinburgh?"

He could tell by Hall Jackson's face that he was right, but Dr. Bartlett interrupted before his younger colleague could speak.

"I got my schooling in Amesbury, Massachusetts," he announced, "and it's always served. Edinburgh's far off and among the Scots. Had you thought what a venture like that would cost you, John?"

"Yes, I thought," said John Woodbury slowly. "And what I thought was this. Some men have seven sons, or six, or four; two, maybe. But I got only the one boy to set forth in the world. He can have not only his portion, but what might have gone to half a dozen other lads. From what I hear when I ask round Boston of the doctors there, it's to Edinburgh that he should go."

"You don't think," probed Dr. Bartlett, "this Tea Act, now, and the troops in Boston mean aught? To me it means rumors of wars, John, rumors of wars."

"Why no, Jos', I don't think there be aught to it."

"Has anyone, Randall," suggested Dr. Jackson smiling faintly, "ever asked your opinion?"

Randall looked over his glass and saw that his father's eyes were watching him intently. He could read thoughts in those eyes as he had never been able to read thoughts before that night he had watched so close to catch a last message from Sally Anne. He knew that his father wanted him to go, wanted him to go out and be the man he himself had never been, and do all the fine things he had never done. And he felt that he ought to vow and declare in front of these friends he would do it, but he didn't feel as if he was half the man his father was, or ever would be. And then it came to him that if he went away he would not have to look again at that blue-green cedar on the pasture hill, not for a long time. Sudden as that his choice was made, and yet in the back of his mind he knew that it was not sudden, only in the final workings of it. He had always known that when the time came he would do what his father wanted him to do.

He caught his breath and took another swallow of brandy. Then he felt his muscles relax and heard himself giving an easy answer.

"Well, no one has, unless you're asking now, and if you are, I'd say Edinburgh is the place I better go. Now that—now that I don't have to think about Sally Anne. Next time there's a ship out of Portsmouth—"

"Randall," said Dr. John, turning his head away to hide his feeling, exultation in his voice, "go get us another bottle, lad, and we'll drink to it. To the finest doctor in the province of New Hampshire twenty years from now."

Dr. Bartlett snorted a little, and that made Randall smile as he strode back to the kitchen. His mother was there putting away a platter of cold fowl. She walked up to him and laid her hand on his arm. It was the first time they had been alone together since he lost his wife.

"Randall," she murmured, her voice breaking, "it is hard, I know. But you will have—other sons."

Nothing had ever startled him more. How could she know that deep and honest and far inside him, he was more bitter about the dead child than about Sally Anne?

He answered brokenly. "I—I suppose I will. But what made you think —of that?"

"I'm your mother," she answered, choking back a sob. "I've known you a long time." She disappeared into the scullery, and he went to the cupboard after the brandy bottle. Well, he had promised now. He was going away, going away out of his own country to learn his profession and please his father, and after all, nobody but him ever had to know that he was running away from a cedar tree.

II

A Kiss and a Drink of Water

THAT the full moon of September should climb up out of the waters and shine down golden on the isle of Rona was no uncommon thing and nothing that had never happened before. Ellen Deveron had seen a good many moonrises over the hut on the shieling in the summer nights when she sat out to watch the cattle there, and she took no account of this particular moon. Sitting crouched on the headland, her shawl hanging loosely from her thin shoulders, she looked across the narrow sea to the lights on Gallen Head and dreamed of what it would be like to go there, further even, to Stornaway, or east of that to Skye, and maybe into Scotland. She could see herself walking down a fine street with a fine dress on her, and all the lads turning their heads to look.

Behind her stretched the island, rough and craggy, shaped like a bull's hide, sloping westward—the uplands of heather and bracken, below them the harvest fields and the white-sand beaches gleaming in the dark. All around strayed the shaggy, soft-eyed cattle she was supposed to tend until Lavan came to relieve her in less than an hour more. Would Kenneth come before Lavan did, she wondered impatiently. Probably not. Probably he was down there in his fine room in Rhinn House swilling whiskey like well water, as he couldn't do when the laird was at home. Why should he bother with whiskey when she knew a better thing? She smoothed her coarse plaid petticoat over the sleek flesh of her sunburned legs beneath. And what was Kenneth waiting for, she thought. Maybe to wake up and find a duchess in bed beside him—or more likely, Margery Rhinn. He was so sure he was going to marry Margery. Ellen smiled to herself in the dark, for she was not sure of it at all.

The double drone of bagpipes sounded away below her in the village streets that comprised the clachan, and she wondered if it meant that the men had come back from the Wick fishing. Six weeks they had been gone, and Rona had been dull without them, all the lanes and cottages empty, with the women down in the barley fields harvesting; but to Ellen, the women did not matter. She leaned back against the weathered walls of the hut, shaped like a stone beehive, and smelled the reek of burning kelp and dulse from the rocks below the hill. The old men kept the kilns going while their betters were at sea, and Ellen did not scruple at times to help them, though as a cattle maid she was called on to do no other work. Kelp ash was about the only crop you could get English money for.

Twigs crackled below her, and a heavy mass of shadow moved slowly up the hill. Kenneth. All the tenseness fell away from the girl, and she posed herself expertly, arms flung backward, leaning on them, her face held up to catch the moonlight, and her eyes seeming to look at something too beautiful and far-off for common folk to see. She had expected he would throw himself down on the bracken beside her, and he did, but she had not expected him to catch at her loose tawny hair and draw her forward roughly. She gave a little cry of displeasure and stared into his face, handsome enough, but marked less with tenderness than with passion.

"So," he cried, his voice deep but unpleasantly mocking, "what's on the wind out there for ye to be peering at? Did ye think that perhaps, being your mother's daughter, ye have the sight? Maybe now ye'll soon be as able as she is, to see a man come out of a tavern while he's still sitting inside, and coffins passing, and a death's-head in every looking glass. Oh never think it! Devil's not that fond of ye, Ellen!"

"Devil wouldna' bother with me," she retorted, "so long as ye're about. They say he himself once kept a school in Scotland and ever since has an uncou' love for all schoolmasters."

"Dinna' taunt me with being a schoolmaster. It willna' be for long."

"And what is it then? Laird of Rona ye're thinking to become?"

He smiled with his wide handsome Highland mouth and dark blue eyes, and all the scorn went out of Ellen, and she could feel herself stirring with a different fire.

"Need we travel over that again, lass?" he urged, bending closer.

No, she thought, he had not been drinking the laird's whiskey.

"It's a grain that must be winnowed one day," she told him, a firmness in her voice, but a provocative softness too. "Has he writ lately— or she? Are they coming home?"

"Come here and I'll tell ye," he answered teasingly.

"No. I willna' do that till ye answer me."

"Ye say 'I willna'' to Kenneth Crary?"

He was suddenly on her like a hail storm from the north swooping among the poor sea birds in Puffin Town. Half fierce, half playful, he flung her backwards, running his heavy hands over her face, her skirt, her breast, as he laid it bare, crushing his mouth on hers. They could never be many moments alone together without the storm rising between them.

Finally, shaken and spent by it, he pulled away from her, and sat up against the wall of the stone hut, clawing the silk scarf knotted at his throat and wiping his forehead. Ellen drew away too, smoothing her skirts with all the daintiness of a cat tidying itself after a feast of cream.

"By God, Ellen," he muttered. "There's na' woman like ye. I've thought of ye all day."

"Your thoughts didna' put ye in any haste to get here," said Ellen sharply. "It's a wonder Lavan didna' come on us, ye tarried that long."

"If she had, she would ha' gone away again. She has before. And now I'll tell ye what ye asked me. We've the winter ahead. I'd a letter today from Rona himself. They be in Edinburgh, and mean to stay there till spring."

"And then home here for her wedding—is it?"

She tried to seem angry but it was hard to, her body felt so sated and content.

"What else?" he shrugged. "Will things be the worse for us—after that?"

"Not for some, happen they won't. Ye'll be lying up there in Rhinn House, abed with your wife, the laird's daughter, Miss Margery, the fine lady. Oh I know she can speak French and sew flowers on satin and sing Italian songs to a spinet! I've known her all my days, half brought up with her, as I was, and I swear to ye I could make a better woman out of a cabbage, did I try it. Ye'll be lonely in her bed, and think of the shieling, and wish that ye was there. And where, all the while, will be I?"

He was looking straight at her in the moonlight, unhappiness in the set of his head, and a bitter twist in the words he spoke.

"And what's to happen else, my lady? We live on old Rona's bounty, ye and yur mother as much as I, or any other body in Ballyrhinn or the island here. Ye want silk gowns and gold in your purse, for ye have told me so. Can I give them to ye before I get them myself? Could we live on a kiss and a drink of water?"

A quick smile lighted his dark face and then ebbed wistfully away. "Sometimes—I think we might."

Ellen stood up and shook her petticoat. "No," she said, "I'll not live on a kiss and a drink of water—for Kenneth Crary or any man."

They heard quick light footsteps beating upward through the heather.

"Tomorrow night, Ellen?" he asked, climbing to his feet, half crouching above her.

"So soon again?" she taunted.

With a curse he half struck at her, and then went crashing off through a dwarf oak thicket. Ellen stood there, smiling to herself. Between them was never love, only love and war wherein all things are fair, and she could always defeat him because she held his body bound, and she was in noways bound at all. She turned to meet the slim, dark-eyed girl come for the night watch at the shieling.

Lavan was breathless from her climb up Ardmory—Mary's Hill, named in the old days of Popery before the coming of the Kirk.

"Ye better go home," she said in the soft speech of the islands that was nothing like the English tongue Ellen and Kenneth had used. "Your mother—she's seeing before her again."

Ellen's face sharpened and her gray-green eyes narrowed and gazed slant-wise, not at the other girl, but down the dark moorland rutted with water courses to the scattering lights in the village near the shore. She spoke now in the island tongue.

"Did ye see her? Or did someone tell ye? Did she cry out?"

"Oh no! I think she did not see a mighty *taisch*—only a little one. I stopped by your house to leave her the buttermilk my mother sent, and she was sitting by the fire, staring across it—so. Ye know how she looks when she sees before her. She did not hear me call."

"'Tis not much she's seeing then. Maybe someone of the old is like to die, or the laird's best cow has broke her leg in a bog hole. I'll go down to her. There's nowhere else to go. The beasts are restless tonight, as they always be when the moon's full. Ye'll get little sleep. Too bad all the lads are away at the Wick fishing."

"I can do without the lads," said Lavan, a faint scorn in her voice and her pretty lip drawing back. "Did I just see Schoolmaster going away?"

"Well, now, ye might have," said Ellen airily. "Your big eyes will make ye trouble yet, Lavan."

Lavan's smile was cold and so was her voice. "Oh I have big eyes, Ellen, but no mouth at all. I'll have naught to say. I plan to dance at Schoolmaster's wedding when he marries Miss Margery."

"Well dinna' fast yourself until he does," called Ellen, starting to pick her way down the hill. The path lay clear in the moonlight, but she would not have needed the moon, for she had come down Ardmory many times in her eighteen years, and no black midnight or sudden storm wrack could confuse her on such familiar ground. Away from the heathery upland, she entered a winding glen that let the waters of the burn flow down to the sea. Her mind was not quite empty as she walked along, but nearly so. She noticed neither the beauty of misty gold poured on the landscape nor the eery movement of shadow among the crags and stunted trees. She had already forgotten her encounter with the schoolmaster, the only man on Rona who seemed to offer the possibility of any escape from it. There was no depth of feeling in the girl, and no real wickedness, nothing but a relentless desire for the furtherance of Ellen Deveron in the world.

After she had come a half mile or so, the glen widened out, and she turned away from the waterside and skirted the tiny outlying fields between the clachan and the wild land. Kale and turnips and potatoes were stripped from the poor thin scraps of sod between the crooked dykes now, and the women could reckon up whether there would be enough to eat in Ballyrhinn this winter or no. Ellen had known hunger, but she did not fear it, for when any discomfort overtook her, she would curl up like a cat and go to sleep. And besides, whatever was going, her mother was sure to get a share. Midwives were never allowed to starve. If only she did not have the sight—the uncanny thing! It was lucky, thought Ellen, that it never overtook her when somebody's bairn was coming into the world. And maybe some day it might, you never could tell. She sighed, longing desperately in her heart to be forever away from Ballyrhinn.

She passed the first stone cottage on her right, and then another. They were not set orderly along a street like the houses in Stornaway on Lewis, the only town she could remember having seen. They were tumbled hit or miss about the hill running sharply down to the stone quay and crooked wooden wharves in the cove below. Few of them had any windows, but here and there the light of a whale-oil lamp streamed through an open door, and the murmur of voices came from inside. Whoever had been playing the bagpipes had left off now. One of the old men it must have been—Johnny Dweeney, maybe. He was always boasting how when he was young he went to the bagpipe college in Skye and piped in the old battles of the Forty-five, when the Stuarts lost their claim to Scotland's crown.

Her mother's house was near the water, away from the slips where the boats tied up and near to the cockle and mussel beds half awash with the incoming tide. A mat of woven rushes hung across the slit between the stones that served as a doorway, and Ellen snatched it aside and walked in, letting it fall to behind her. The stone floor felt cool to her bare feet. The laird had had that floor laid to pay her mother once for dosing a fever out of his daughter Margery. She looked around to see that all was in order, not that she cared much or expected to find it any other way. Sleepy hens roosted high under the thatch at the far end, and she heard the breathing of the two small shoats her mother was trying to strengthen before the autumn rains began. She stepped forward to the peat fire burning in the earth pit in the center of the room.

Andra Deveron crouched there on a three-legged stool, her eyes wide open, gazing into the fire. Even Ellen's unloving eye could recognize that her mother had once been a beautiful woman, and this always filled her with resentment, for she knew that she herself was not beautiful and never would be. Nor had she her mother's healing gifts and wisdom. For her advancement she would have to depend on another thing. And that she had. She went over and touched the dark red hair under the linen cap, let her hand fall to the shoulder beneath. It was limp and not tensed. That meant that the taisch, the vision, had gone. That was one gift of her mother's she would not care for—the sight. Herself, she had rather have the leaping ague.

She felt her mother start and shudder slightly.

"Ellen," she whispered vaguely, and then in a brisker tone, "Are you home early? Or did I sleep longer than I meant?"

"Ye know ye were not sleeping," said Ellen, pulling up another stool beside the low fire and sitting down. The place smelled of peat smoke and herrings and the tufts of heather piled on the roof. A whiff of Margery's Paris scent would be sweet to the nostrils, would it not, but the last little gift vial was used up and gone.

Andra smiled, quite herself now, rose and went to a bucket of water on the stone shelf near the doorway and drank deeply. Rona had offered her whiskey once, Ellen remembered, when she had had a bad taisch and he had been there and seen. But her mother had pushed it away. Taischers never drank whiskey, they were sober folk, but they always wanted clear water when they came to themselves again.

"What did ye see this time?" asked Ellen, pretending to yawn indifferently, but really curious. She could never tell—she always had hopes—if only her mother would see her setting off about some wondrous thing. "Is old Nanny Dweeney going to die at last? Or Meg Munro's daftie?"

Andra turned and fixed her sea-blue eyes on her daughter, the cup still in her hand.

"Why you know, Ellen, it was strange, what I saw. I doubt that it was in Scotland at all."

"Why did ye think it was not? Where was it then?"

"I do not know where it was. But I think it was in some far country because of the trees. They were tall—tall as the church spires I saw

when I was young, in Belfast and Aberdeen. And here and there I saw
a scarlet leaf on them."

There were few trees in the Western Islands, save for a stunted copse
here and there, and plantings, like the yews and rowans in the garden
at Rhinn House, tended as if they had human souls to them. Ellen allowed her surprise to show.

"Scarlet leaves on a tree?"

"Yes. And the talk I heard was strange. I could understand the words.
They were English words, but spoken all awry."

"What words were they, and who spoke them? Did ye see a funeral
as ye always do?"

"Yes. It was a funeral. Very much the same as here. Mourners behind a coffin. I do not know whose. A woman, I think, and young. But
the lid was nailed. I could not see."

"Was it the mourners who made the strange talk?"

"No. They were silent. Some of them wept a little, but they said no
words. At their head was a young man."

"A man?" Ellen's thin vixen face came alive in the firelight. "Was he
handsome? Did he have a fine coat on him?" Some good might yet come
to her of a taisch, you never could tell.

"Yes. Handsome, but not so handsome as Schoolmaster. His hair was
the color of wheat, and he had a black coat. He was the chief mourner,
I think. Then the others faded out, and I saw him all alone, but only
the face of him."

"Was it then he spoke? What did he say?"

"There seemed to be a light about him, a light shining downward on
something red. And he spoke in that twisted tongue."

Ellen waited, her eyes fixed on her mother's face. Again Andra drank
from the cup. Then she put it down on the ledge and came back to the
fire and stood there looking down.

"He said, 'Edinburgh is the place I better go.'"

Ellen drew a peevish sigh. "Oh," she murmured. "I wish he had said
he was coming here. Ye do see strangers coming sometimes. Ye saw that
shipful of flea-bit sailors who brought us the bloody flux three years
ago. Are ye sure it was Edinburgh he said?"

"Yes. It was Edinburgh."

Again Ellen sighed, went to a rude cupboard and took down a bit of
dried fish spine and began to comb her pale hair. "If it was Edinburgh,
we're not likely to see him here. Ye might as well ha' spent your evening carding flax. It would ha' bettered us more."

"Ellen," said Andra soberly, "you know I cannot master the sight. It
comes and goes as it will."

"I know ye say it does, but I should ha' thought ye might ha' learned to put it to some use. And what did ye mean—" a sudden thought struck her and her eyes narrowed "—by saying he wasna' so handsome as Schoolmaster? What has Schoolmaster to do with us, pray?"

But her mother's face remained open and innocent. "Why I only drew the likeness. I meant nothing. Is it harm to mention Schoolmaster?"

Ellen subsided. "No. I suppose not."

She went on combing her hair before the dim fire. Outside a seal barked from the rocks, and then the noise of it died away, lost in the beat of the surf. Andra went to the stone ledge and drank deeply once more, then she crept into the straw pallet and drew the blanket over her head. Her daughter lay down beside her after a little while, and there was no more sound in the clachan of Ballyrhinn except the old wind walking through.

III

A Handsome Bucko

"WOULD YE no like a wee dram, Miss, to waken yersel' wi'?"

Margery Rhinn opened her wide hazel eyes slowly and gazed at the angular face peering in through the striped curtains of the box bed in the fifth flat of Tait's Land, high up over Edinburgh though not half so high as many of the flats around. Then she drew down her mouth at the corners, closed her eyes again and shook her head firmly. Scottish as she was, by blood and birth and proud of it, she could never get used to the horrible Scots custom of breakfasting on whiskey. Maybe it was living so long in Paris, in the old happy days when her mother had still been alive, that had taught her to prefer a roll and a cup of chocolate. She opened her eyes again, and Meg, the serving woman, still stood there with the bottle in her hand, well-meaning, insistent.

"There's many ladies do," she urged with a touch of petulance.

"Let them," said Margery smiling gaily, now that she was wide awake. "There's ladies in Edinburgh likes snuff, and tobacco too, for that matter, and the less I take of such victuals, the more there'll be for them, and the same with whiskey. Couldn't you get me a cup of tea now, Meggy?"

Muttering about "foreign airs," Meggy withdrew her head, and Margery heard her bare feet thudding off across the stone floor and into the passage. She yawned, shook up the satin bolster and settled into it again. She did not want tea really, only to lie under the covers in that warm, dreamy state, and think about the dance at the Assembly Rooms the night before. Now, which had been the pick of her partners? she asked herself, resting lazily, and fastening her glance on the foot of the bed, where the counterpane had fallen aside allowing her a glimpse of one of her own slender great toes. Margery considered the great toe, the left one, the one with the scar on it from the stone bruise she got one summer on the crags of Rona when she was a little girl. Andra had bound some sort of leaf upon it, and the stinging pain had gone. It would be good to see Andra, she thought, when the winter broke and they could go home again. But that would not be soon. She looked through the window at the cold blue sky and snow lying like swan's-down on the sill. She tucked the great toe under the counterpane and went back to her memories of the evening before.

Supper, with green turtle stewed in spices and lime punch. Then the dance. She gazed apprehensively at the floor. No, it had not been a dream, it was true then. There lay her best gold brocade slippers, kicked hastily off last night, the sole of the left one quite worn through. Well, she would go to the Luckenbooths this afternoon and order another pair of slippers. And again, her partners. Who had been the choice of them, and was there a choice? The young advocate whose father was a Lord of the Sessions, who tripped so spry in the galliard and swung her about as if she had been a little thing? Margery stretched herself full length, knowing she was not a little thing, and not minding that. Tall and slender she was, supple rather than stately—unless occasion called for stateliness. "Like a rose swaying on its stem," the young advocate had said. No, that had been the slightly drunken poet from Johnny Downie's in Libberton's Wynd. It had been a pretty compliment, but she decided not to count the drunken poet. Better the young man from Glasgow who was said to have made a fortune in something—soap or harness leather—she had forgotten which. Her father would have liked her Glasgow partner, called him a "canny lad." And then the medical students from the College, too many to count, poor and unfashionable— not that she minded that, but they were always apt to suspect you had a fever when it was only a touch of the rouge pot, and given to the most dismal conversation. Why only last night that hulking oaf from Pittenweem had offered to name her bones for her! As if she wanted her bones named! 'Twas enough to put an ache in every one of them!

Meggy came back and reported gruffly that the larder held no tea. She still carried the whiskey bottle. She was not one of their own people from the island, only hired for the season as they had hired this flat, to serve them through an Edinburgh winter. Perhaps she would learn their ways, and if she did not it would not matter for long.

But Margery had another thought now, and she sprang out of bed and dashed to the window. Looking up across Parliament Square to the north, she could see the clock on St. Giles. Only the clock itself, its spread-eagle hands and their horrid message. She wasted no time considering the square stone tower with its bulbous top and frail spire, nor the towering "lands" or tenements about it in the High Street. Far away across the Nor' Loch, the Firth of Forth ran out in a long thread of blue the same color as the winter sky, with the snow-clad hills of Fife

rising behind it. But Margery saw only the clock. Each and every one
of those dancing partners had wanted to wait upon her this morning,
and she had told each and every one of them to come at eleven, having
no intention of being at home when they came. Now it was half after
ten. She began to scramble into her clothes as fast as if the whole flat
was ablaze behind her.

A few minutes later she was hurrying across the towered square, past
the law courts and into the High Street below the gray massed buildings
under the shadow of the great church. Here she paused for a moment,
smoothed the thin wine-red silk of her polonaise and drew her short
furred cape more closely about her to shut out the sting of the weather.
On her left stood the ugly weathered bulk of the Tolbooth, the city
prison, cleaving the street in two, and that way also waited the Luckenbooths crowded under the buttresses of St. Giles. Here were the shops
of the milliners, and hosiers, glovers, and jewelers, and bauble-sellers.
Margery felt in her purse. As usual there were plenty of coins in it.
A morning's shopping might not come amiss. There were the slippers
to replace. She needed a fichu for the new white taffeta. Gold, she
thought, or scarlet, or peacock color. And besides, if she went to the
Luckenbooths, she might meet with company. But then, and she tilted
her head upward again to look at the fatal timepiece, she had promised
to meet her father at the Royal Infirmary at eleven. Her father and his
friend, Dr. Cullen. No, she would have to wait till afternoon before
she went shopping. She started down the High Street, along the razor
back of the ridge that ran from the Castle to the Canongate, drawing
her slim shoulders together inside the velvet mantle, keeping her face
well sheltered within the rim of her quilted hood.

But this was only for a little way. In a few moments she was so used
to the cold that it no longer existed for her, and she shook the hood
back impatiently on her dark silky hair and walked along over the uneven cobblestones with her head up, facing the world and smiling at it.
She was happy to be Margery Rhinn, walking down the High Street of
Edinburgh on a fair day with the sun shining. Maybe there were luckier
women somewhere, busy about finer things, but this was enough for
her.

On both sides of the street towered the tall stone houses, rising up
twelve and fifteen stories on the blue air—houses with round turrets
pointed on top, and pointed gables so far up they might be looking
down from heaven upon the goings-on of mortals, and carved wooden
balconies tapering to the high flights of stone steps at every front door.
Margery hardly saw the houses, for they were old and well-known to
her, and she could tell which family of the fashionable set had wintered

in this one or that one, last year, two years ago, three years ago. But the faces she met in the street were always changing, and she kept her eyes fixed on the passers-by, hoping to see a friend, seeing none. Probably still home abed, the lazy wenches, and no reason, for many had taken far more rest against the wall last night than she. In fact, not even for one moment of one dance had she rested there. The "Town rats" in their russet uniforms, with muskets and Lochaber axes, ranged about in pairs, but there seemed little need for constables on a morning like this one, when everybody was frozen into bed apparently. Small, ragged, ruddy-faced errand boys, the "caddies," ran to and fro, darting out of the crooked wynds along the High Street—ill-smelling alleys, even in this clear clean weather—and the water carriers in their red coats toiled up and down the turnpike stairs built outside the tall flats, or stopped at the public wells to thaw their frozen cans and buckets. Here and there a gentleman or a black-gowned advocate hurried by, or once in a while, a knot of high-colored, stuff-gowned old ladies, mouthing toothless oaths among themselves in perfect good nature, waving their muffs and reaching into their pendulous bosoms for their snuff pouches.

She had passed the Royal Exchange, and stepped into the shadow of the dingy, Dutch-looking tower on the Tron Kirk, before she met anybody she knew.

Then gay voices hailed her, and she turned to look across the street. Two pretty, dark-haired girls in red-heeled slippers and fur capes were standing in the doorway of a tavern, The Full Cup, hardly more than a slit in the beetling stone walls that reached up for ten stories over their heads. Her cousin, Helen MacNeill, and their bosom friend, Anne Farquharson! With a little cry of pleasure, Margery caught up her polonaise, showing her trim ankles to the nearest town rat, since nobody else was by to see, and ran across the cobblestones to join them. The three girls kissed, though they had been apart only since the ending of the dance the night before.

"You caught us, cousin," smiled Helen, dimpling. Helen was plump now and would probably be too plump later, Margery reflected, as the other girl chattered on. "We know 'tis not to be thought on—without an escort—to go to a public house. But we were on our way to the Luckenbooths to match some silk, and we grew so cold! We were going in for a cup of tea. There'll be no one to see us there at this hour. Will you come—?"

"Of course I will," nodded Margery. "All that wretched Meggy had in the house was a black bottle, so I've not breakfasted yet. It will make me late meeting Father, but he's waited for me before."

They stepped into the dusty little taproom, tenanted only by a dour-faced leathery old man, sipping whiskey at the bar, and a faded woman in a clean apron, who brought the tea and sweet cakes they asked for. Seated at a table near the wide black hearth, they were soon amusing themselves with inconsequential feminine chatter.

"Peggy Lachlan's just back from France," said Anne, "and she tells me the Dauphin's wife is disgusted because farthingales are out, and she says when she's queen she'll bring them in again, so huge that every doorway in Paris will have to be widened so she can go through."

"I wouldn't widen my doorways for her," said Margery, studying the tea leaves in her cup and trying to read fortunes there, which she was never able to do. "I hate farthingales. In truth, they're the worst curse can come on a body for being born a woman. If farthingales come in," and she stared tragically across at her friends, the sun through the diamond-shaped windowpanes making patterns on her hair, "I shall retire me to Rona and live out of all society and fashion there in nothing but a plaid petticoat."

"I thought that was what you meant to do anyway," said Anne, biting a honey-filled scone with small, even teeth. "I thought you were going to marry a Highland laddie who keeps a school there and—"

"I saw him once," said Helen, licking sugar paste from her wide mouth. "Once when he and Uncle Rona were in Glasgow together. I thought him sullen and ill-natured—but a handsome bucko!"

Margery stood up suddenly, pulling on her gloves and fastening her cape. Her eyes looked like shuttered windows with the light gone out behind.

"I'm late," she murmured. "I have to meet Father."

But her cousin had words to say. "Anne's right. You told me you were going to marry him. Kenneth Crary, the schoolmaster. You said I could be first of all the maids in your marriage procession. You'd best not put it off any longer, Margery. You're none so young."

"I'm eighteen," retorted Margery, "eighteen last Michaelmas."

"Nineteen!" shrieked Helen. "I remember—"

"That was what I said—nineteen," replied Margery, smiling guilelessly. "Do not urge me, cousin. There is still time."

"Ah, I know, but he was a braw lad," Helen babbled on. "I'd an eye to him myself, did I know you meant to dangle him and maybe let him get away. If Aunt Gillian was alive, you'd be none so coy. She would have you fast married to him with a ring before he could change his fancy. She knew a man when she saw one, Aunt Gillian did. He seemed like a rare Stuart kind of lad, and that would ha' pleased her."

Yes, thought Margery to herself, if her mother had been alive, perhaps she would be married to Kenneth by now. But then, with her mother alive, so many things would have been different. In her thoughts she was suddenly back ten years in the high-ceiled room in Paris with the long windows overlooking a little square, set with flowering chestnut trees. Here in the bleak Scottish December, she could feel the soft May wind blowing out of that other time, stirring the white and gold curtains of the carved bed where her mother had lain down to die, feel again, with a shudder even now, the grief and terror that had gripped her child's heart.

You knew, when you were nine years old, that people died, but you did not always know the wherefores of it. One time, in the years between, she had asked her father. It had hurt him to have her do so, and she had known that it would. It hurt her, too, but she had to know.

"But Father, why? Was it some disease she had? She was young."

"Aye, lass," he had answered, twisting his pipe nervously in his square brown fingers, "she was young. And she had no disease the doctors could find, or that anybody knew. But she was weak from bearing, and it saddened her that none of her bairns lived, after you. But I sometimes think it was more that she missed the old way o' things. There's a whole new world come about since she was the age ye are. There was more died at Culloden than the men who fell."

"What do you mean?" she had asked him. "Was she one of those?"

"Aye, I think she may ha' been. If the Stuarts could ha' fought their way down to London and climbed on the throne that belonged to them, and set the country free o' the bloody German thieves—I think the old ways o' Scotland would ha' lasted, and she would ha' been happy in them as she always was, and not let herself go down to death. For a while she hoped, as many did, that Charlie would come again with better luck. Myself, I had no hope for it at all. And God forgive me, once I told her; which I shouldna' ha' done. 'Gillian,' I said, 'the Stuarts is past and done and put away. We must live in the new time.' 'Twas the only sharp word she ever spoke to me. 'No, Comyn,' she said, 'ye are wrong. The Stuarts will come again. But I canna' wait.' 'Twas almost the last she ever said."

He had gripped the pipe stem in his two hands then and snapped it apart. Margery had not asked him any more.

Yes, she supposed, her mother would have favored Kenneth, for from what she had heard of the lads who were out in the Forty-five, they looked and spoke and thought very much as he. It was that knowledge that had first drawn her to him, and their meeting had been at a time when she was weary of the beaux she met at balls and concerts and assembly rooms. They were like marionettes who bowed and wigglewaggled when she crooked a finger. Kenneth had been crude and surly

at times, but he was not a poppet. He was a living man moved by his
own will. And Helen was right. He was handsome. And it had seemed
to her a fine romantic thing to turn from all the polished gentlemen of
London and the Continent to love a Highland lad of her own country,
come of the same race as she. It had given her a deep, blissful satisfaction to feel that she was choosing as her dearly-loved mother would have
wanted her to do. But she did not feel blissful now. She felt troubled
and uncertain. She had not seen him since early last summer, having
been abroad with her father all that time. Perhaps when they met again
in the spring, she would be as eager for their wedding as he. For he
was eager. He kept writing her so. Many lads had been eager to marry
Margery Rhinn, but so far she had not desired to marry any man at all.

Far up the town she heard the bells of St. Giles playing the foreign
tunes as they did every day a little before twelve. She turned swiftly
away from the other girls and started toward the door.

"Good-by. I'll see you both at the Assembly Rooms tonight. I really
have to go."

Helen and Anne followed her.

"If you're going to the College, we'll see you safe there," smiled
Anne. " 'Tis no telling what fine sights we might meet on the way."

"I think the fine sights will be all in their classes now," laughed
Margery, her mood changing, "but I'll be glad of your company there."

Still chatting, they walked down College Wynd, past the ugly halls
weathered black as old iron, piled hit or miss against each other. Ahead
of them reared up the dingy hospital, sunken between tall buildings as
if set at the bottom of a shallow well, an ornate central block with
scrolled pillars and cupola on top. Margery shuddered, thinking of all
the ailing, feckless people within. She usually called at this place at
least once whenever she visited Edinburgh, because it was a haunt of
Dr. Cullen, now Professor of the Practice of Physic at the College.
Years ago when he had been a young doctor round Glasgow, he had
cured her father of a deadly fever there, and the two men had kept up
the acquaintance without ever seeing enough of each other to become
intimate. For Comyn Rhinn had spent the last twenty years in the service of the East India Company, traveling all over the world, and Dr.
Cullen had stayed in Scotland to become a leader in his profession. But
they liked to meet, and dine, and drink whiskey together, and muse over
how different their lives had been.

As she stood now in front of the dismal structure taking her leave of
the girls, a young man came down the street and walked past them, up
the high, narrow steps, disappearing inside. She noticed that his hair
was sleek and golden under his black three-cornered hat, his head bent

a little, so that she caught no idea of what his face was like. He carried books in a strap like a grammar-school boy, and his black cloth suit did not look to her like the work of any tailor in any country under God. She would have laughed at him, she thought, if there had not been a squareness and a dignity about the set of his shoulders that kept her from doing that. Instead she turned to the other girls, lifted her eyebrows questioningly, and said in tones that she knew would not carry after him, "What was that passed by?"

Helen and Anne were still staring in his wake. Anne shook her head. "I'm not sure," she said thoughtfully. "He wasna' at the Assembly Rooms last night. If he had been, I would ha' known."

"A handsome bucko," said Helen grinning. "I think, Madge, I shall go with you, after all. There's a sudden yearning to see my Uncle Rona takes me."

Margery laughed openly and shook her head. "And I'm taken with a sudden yearning to go alone," she answered. "Good-by, Anne. Good-by, cousin. Many fine sights to both of you on the way home."

She ran up the brown stone steps and into the Infirmary.

She knew the way well enough, and she swung open the heavy oak door, crossed the vestibule and stepped into a tiny waiting room, with one dirty window high up and no furniture except a bench built into the wall on three sides. She was a little surprised not to find her father already there, and Dr. Cullen, somewhat fretful over her lateness. Perhaps they were away together in the gloomy interior of the place. It had happened so before. But the little room was not empty. It had an occupant she was not at all surprised to see there. In the middle of the right-hand bench sat the young man with the gold-colored hair and ill-cut clothes. He looked up as she came in, and she saw that he had steady gray eyes set wide apart, straight features and a firm mouth. He had unstrapped his books and laid them on the bench beside him, with a sheaf of papers on top. He had one book open on his knee and appeared to be reading it. Flashing a quick look at the page, Margery saw a drawing of a human skull with fine lines and arrows leading to Latin phrases in the margin. The young man smiled faintly at her, then turned to his book again.

Margery smiled back and sat down with a great rustling of wine-colored silk, and only the heap of books between the two of them; smiled and sat down, and waited for him to begin the conversation, which he did not do. The cold of the stone floor bit through her thin slippers. The place smelled like a charnel house, she thought. Somewhere down a corridor off the vestibule she heard a harsh moan, then quick footsteps, then a wail full of pain and terror. She moved restlessly and gave an audible sigh. The young man kept on reading his book. She let her gaze rest idly on the sheaf of papers protruding from the books between them. They were covered with square, angular, very black writing, so plain it cried aloud for you to read it.

"Scrofula of the vital organs, palsy, malignant pleurisy, extra-uterine foetus, angina suffocativa, worms in the liver, gout, natural decay," she read to herself. The words had a sick sour taste to them. She wished her father and Dr. Cullen would come. It wasn't that she especially wanted this young man to talk to her. It was just that her feet were cold, and she felt restless, and she wanted somebody to talk to, just anybody at all. Well, he had won. He wouldn't begin, so she would have to. She smiled sweetly at him.

"You're a medical student, aren't you? Are you homesick in Scotland?"

He looked up, startled, laid a finger across the line drawing in his book.

"Why should you think I am homesick in Scotland?" he asked quickly. "How did you know I wasn't Scots myself?"

She could not say it was because of the cut of his clothes and the way he wore them, so she answered, still smiling at him, "You did not talk like a Scotsman."

"But I hadn't said anything," he pointed out. "I hadn't talked at all."

"I know," she answered demurely.

Then they were both laughing.

"It's right," he said. "I'm not from Scotland. I'm from Hampton Falls."

She widened her hazel eyes and questioned him. "Is that near Hampton Court?"

"I doubt it. Where's Hampton Court?"

Then suddenly they were both laughing again.

"I tell you," he said, "when I first came here two months ago, a body'd ask me where I came from, and I'd hang my head and say, why I came from the colonies—from the town of Hampton Falls in the Province of New Hampshire in America. But I found that seemed to amuse them. So now I say, all proud-like, 'I'm from Hampton Falls,' and if they be so ignorant as not to know where that is, why then I have the advantage, and I'll not be bothered to inform them."

She nodded, her laughter gone. "I know. I felt that way when I was a little girl and my mother took me to Paris first. I had always lived in the Western Islands—in a little rocky town at the edge of the world, and I did not know the ways of the Paris folk. At first I was shy. But after a while, when they would point to me and laugh and say 'Oui, oui,' I would tell them 'Wee' was what pigs said at home."

He had put his book quite aside and taken his finger off the page, turned halfway toward her. But he was waiting . . . She did not intend to let silence come between them. She said, "Do you like Edinburgh?"

"I don't know. At first I thought it looked like the sort of thing you see in dreams when you've eaten too many fried pies for supper. It's well enough. Still, they run it too high up in the air. I'm inclined to favor Boston."

"I've never been to Boston," she answered thoughtfully. "I've been in many cities, but never there. My father says it's a rebel town. He says it's seeking for trouble."

"He may be right," agreed the young man. "Can't tell which way that cat will jump—yet."

Again there was silence. Then he broke it.

"I saw you, you know, on the steps as I was coming in."

"Oh yes," she replied quickly. "Anne Farquharson and my cousin, Helen MacNeill, were with me. We had been for a cup of tea."

"I thought they were pretty girls," he answered shyly. "I thought you all were."

"Oh thank you. They are pretty. Helen's my favorite cousin, and Anne's so spirited. She's a niece of Colonel Anne, you know, in the Forty-five."

He looked bewildered.

"Colonel Anne—but you're an American, maybe you never heard. She was Anne Farquharson, too, and she upset a kettle of boiling kale all over her husband, the MacIntosh, so he couldn't fight against Charlie. So they called her 'Colonel.' She—"

The young man smiled ruefully and interrupted. "She might have made a good colonel, but she wouldn't make a wife I'd care for. My wife wouldn't have—!"

"Oh!" cried Margery in very small tones. "Do you have a wife? Did you bring her to Edinburgh?"

He spoke harshly. "I did have a wife. She's dead now."

"I—I'm sorry," said Margery gently, and he looked so bleak she really was sorry. She did not quite know how to go on with the conversation. After a moment he remarked in a careless tone, "What was the Forty-five, and who was Charlie?"

"You—you don't know what the Forty-five was?" asked Margery blankly.

"I've been trying to think. It was in '45 we took Louisburg away from the French. But you don't mean that, do you?"

She was still groping for words when her father and Dr. Cullen stepped into the waiting room. The doctor looked a little older than she remembered him. He had thick lips and piercing eyes and wore a bushy peruke and a cloak that made him seem hunched at the shoulders. Her father, lean, and sandy-haired, of middle height, was such a well-loved and familiar figure that she hardly saw him at all.

"Well, Margery," said the doctor, putting out his hand. Then his gaze darted past her to the young man who had climbed to his feet and was holding out a white envelope. "What's your business, Woodbury?"

The young man handed the envelope to the doctor. "Professor Fergusson asked me to give you this, sir. It came for you after you dismissed classes, and he thought you should have it at once. He bade me try your lodgings first, and if you were not at home to come here looking for you."

Dr. Cullen took the envelope.

"Thank ye, sir. Margery—Comyn—this is one of our men from the colonies. One of their best, I think. He comes recommended by Hall Jackson of Portsmouth, who went to study at the London Hospital and showed them a better way to treat gunshot wounds than they'd ever known before. There's good mettle in some of these colony lads. Let me make known Dr. Woodbury, Dr. Randall Woodbury. Sir, this is my friend, Comyn Rhinn, Laird of Rona, and his daughter, Miss Margery. She knows French, music, dancing, sews neatly, makes shellwork, and can milk a cow. Are ye not afraid of such female erudition?"

"I'm glad she can milk a cow," said Randall Woodbury, smiling at Margery and putting out his hand to her father.

"Ah well," muttered the doctor, "get ye gone, sir, or ye'll miss Botany lecture, which ye can ill afford. Comyn, ye and Miss Margery are to come home with me for a bit and drap, and I won't take nay from ye."

And it seemed that none of them would say nay to Dr. Cullen, as willy-nilly, they dispersed themselves much as he had suggested they should.

After the bit and drap, Margery walked back to Parliament Square beside her father in the late afternoon. Cold purple shadows lay in the drifted wynds, and icicles hung on the wooden balconies above the High Street. Probably they made the town look more than ever like a bad dream to the young man from Hampton Falls, New Hampshire, she thought. More and more she thought about him, murmuring inside herself.

"What did ye say?" demanded her father, cupping his hand to his ear to shut out the harsh December wind whistling down from Castle Hill.

". . . . a handsome bucko," repeated Margery, her gaze fixed afar off.

Comyn Rhinn, Laird of Rona, shook his head. "Lass," he said, "I lived a long time, and I ne'er heard Wullie Cullen spoken of as a handsome bucko before."

Margery crooked her fingers round his upper arm and drew close against him as they started up the turnpike stair at Tait's Land.

"I wasn't thinking of Wullie Cullen, Father," she said.

IV

A Good Evening

COMING HOME through the dark wynds and closes that followed the rambling remains of the old Flodden Wall, built almost in a single night, he had heard, to protect the city while a battle was going on, Randall walked with his head up, enjoying the fresh March wind, the clean smell of wet stone, and the sunset dying away red in back of Castle Hill. After five months in the medical school it was an increasing trouble to him that so much of his time was spent with books and lectures and so little in acquiring further experience in the actual treatment of disease. All his life, he now discovered, he had been taught medicine according to the principles of the Dutchman, Boerhaave, of whom he had never heard. He had heard of Boerhaave now, but he still did not know a better way to treat a flux or a fever, and he was beginning to doubt that these wordy Scots doctors were ever going to teach him a better way. One thing he could do, and that was to return to the Infirmary in the late afternoon when the rest of the College was having its tea, and spend his time in the paupers' ward, working with the almost untended sufferers there, and observing ravages and torments more varied than he had ever met with at home.

The ghastly results of vice and squalor were ills he had never treated and hardly seen. The pox now, was almost unknown in the clean-living country town where he had grown up. Once, indeed, his father had taken him to Portsmouth to observe a sailor who was almost dead of it, one of Hall Jackson's patients. He could see the man now, lying in a bed all foul with the matter from his own running sores, his human shape slowly leaving him as his bones collapsed in decay. He had been young then, less than sixteen, and the pity and shock and hopelessness in his heart must have shown in his face, for the older men had taken him to a tavern afterward and bought him brandy. Well, he was alone now, on the other side of the world—or almost—with no one to take him to a tavern and buy him brandy, and he had just come away from a worse case, for which there was little he or any man could do. Wrack with mercury and burn with caustic, and then anodynes to ease their going out. It was the same in America as here.

Through the stone streets around him flowed the rough, glittering, boisterous life of the city, and he tried to lose himself in it as he walked homeward to his lodgings and forget the patients he had left in paupers' ward as the twilight settled in. All the small, sooty windowpanes were shining with lamplight now, and the shopkeepers' signs creaked on their hinges as the spring wind set them swinging overhead; first the painted wooden likeness of a barley loaf, and then a periwig, followed by a cheese, a butter firkin, a pair of stays, and a petticoat. Then the gilt and scarlet fiddle over the door of the music shop, and the next door was his—a gapping arch with a crest cut into the top of it, fantastic animals reared upright on their hind legs, and the motto *Blesset-be-God-in-al-his-giftis* underneath. Thomson's Land in Rowan Tree Wynd, it was, and he felt his spirits rise as he toiled up the crooked turnpike stair. The first flat was let to a dowager, and the second to a minister of the Kirk, and the third to a dancing master. He had long since learned that old Edinburgh had piled itself up this way toward the sky, all kinds of ill-assorted folk scrambled together, because there was not ground room enough within its walls for everybody who wanted to live there. But times were changing now. They were draining the Nor' Loch and building out beyond the walls, broad streets and squares and bridges. He wondered if he would be in the city long enough to see these new workings completed, and he did not think that he would. He put his hand to the latch of the door on the fourth landing, swung it back, and stepped inside.

A low smoky sea-coal fire burned in the center of a tiny grate, and the lads were sitting in front of it with no other light, though both of them looked as if they had been at home a long time, sprawled in the only two cushioned chairs the room afforded, their pipes drawing well. Sandy MacCrimmon from Skye and Tom Culpepper from Caroline County, Virginia, turned their heads and grinned a welcome at Randall.

"Tally-ho!" called Sandy, speaking as English as you please, the chief accomplishment he had brought back from a year in the London Hospital. Any Scot who had the least desire to be well thought of, Randall noticed, spoke as much like an Englishman as he could—whenever he remembered it. Lank and pale-haired, Sandy just missed being a fop, but he was a good roommate, always easy and affable, in and out of pocket like the rest of them, but when he had it, most generous to pay.

Tom's lean, dark, good-looking face lighted with a happy smile as he waved a claret bottle. Randall went quickly forward, took down a thick cracked tumbler from a corner shelf and strode up to Tom.

"How did you come by that?" he asked, holding the tumbler out.

"Lawrence, my cousin, God bless him. He sent me three pounds credit for books and instruments." Tom poured the clear red wine with a free hand. "Sit down, sir, and account for yourself. You've been in some tavern moistening your clay, I'll warrant."

Randall flung himself on a strip of worn carpet before the fire and rested his head on the fifth edition of the *London Pharmacopoeia*, that happened to be lying there. There was a weariness in him, he realized as he lay stretched out, the weariness of tense nerves slowly relaxing, aftermath of the last two hours in the hospital. He watched Sandy shake his head at Tom.

"Arrh, Thomas, you know he was at the Infirmary, was you not, Randall? Bessie now? Is she gone yet?"

"She may be," said Randall, very low, straightening up long enough to take a heavy pull at his claret. "She was alive when I left. Asleep. At least I could do that much for her."

"Who's Bessie?" asked Tom, the dandy of the three, given to silver buckles and fancy waistcoats and sword-carrying. Poor relative of a rich family, Tom was trained in all the graces and welcome at every tea table in Edinburgh. He was not likely to know the name of a dying harlot in paupers' ward. Still, Randall had spoken of her often enough during the last week or two. Neither young nor old, ugly nor beautiful, Bessie had been, when in health, he thought, a pleasant-faced woman, brown and comely. But there was nothing brown about her now except her sick eyes, nothing from top to toe but a mass of red-rimmed sores, even her hair bleached and fallen away, so that she was in a worse plight than the Portsmouth sailor he remembered from long ago. The order had gone out that no more drugs were to be wasted upon her, and there was nothing Randall could do except sit by her filthy pallet sometimes, and talk a little, and try to make her believe that no soul is ever quite alone. But that afternoon she had burned in such utter torment that he had given her what little opium he had about him, knowing well that it was not enough. He should have stayed with her, he thought. But he had not stayed. And Tom, already forgetting Bessie, had the reason.

"Are you going to Stewart's with the rest of us, Ran'? Who's your lady for the evening?"

"Yes," said Randall, watching the fall of firelight and shadow on the plaster walls of the low room. "I'm going to Stewart's. I'm meeting Margery Rhinn."

Tom flung his empty pewter cup at Randall, missing him narrowly, as he intended.

"Why, damn your eyes, sir! And to think I was proud as Cock Robin to have worked myself so close to her as her cousin Helen! How do you manage it?"

Sandy reached past Tom for the claret bottle, perched on a three-legged stool all by itself. He poured out another drink and entered the conversation.

"Why, Thomas, lad, at their first meeting he struck her with a cat-alepsy from which she has not yet recovered. He told her—Margery Rhinn, the MacNeill's granddaughter—that he'd never heard of the Forty-five and Charlie!"

Tom leaned back on the frayed cushions. Outside the casement window facing the Nor' Loch and all Fifeshire spread beyond it, the sky had gone from pale gray to purple black with a few stars sprinkled through. St. Giles's bells chimed for six o'clock.

"You're not speaking Greek, for Greek I studied with my cousin's tutor before I was table-top high," Tom announced thoughtfully. "But I do not catch the sense of you, if there be any. Why should it captivate a woman to show her you're ignorant in what she's fond of?"

"Why sir, 'twas the sheer novelty of the thing," retorted Sandy, sipping his wine with almost feminine daintiness, "and the brazen effrontery of it! Here's she, brought up in Scotland's last tradition, still hoping in her heart that the Stuarts will come back. And here's this whooping red Indian from the frozen swamps of North America comes up and tells her he never heard of her bonny Stuart. 'Twas like a club knocking her senseless. She's fixed as with the eye of the basilisk, and she cannot tell him nay."

"Who are the MacNeills?" asked Randall, his empty tumbler put aside, still lying flat on his back with his head on the *Pharmacopoeia*. He had seen Margery Rhinn many times that winter since she had sent him a prim little note about a week after their first meeting, asking him to tea at her father's flat in Tait's Land. He had squired her to concerts at St. Cecelia's Hall and dances at the Assembly Rooms, enjoying her company, not unduly troubled by the fact that other men shared these decorous favors too. He knew a deal more about Scottish history now, knew that in the eyes of many people besides Margery the country had fallen to utter ruin with the defeat of Prince Charlie on Culloden Moor after the uprising of 1745. He knew that was the end of the old, proud Scotland, and that the kingdom was humbled now under England's dreary Georges. Slowly he had learned all that, by the stray word spoken here and there as he moved about in the social life of Edinburgh. The old men liked to deliver lectures on it over their whiskey, but Margery's talk had been more like a ballad than a lecture. She made him see waving banners and plaided troops marching. But she had not mentioned her own family. He had never heard before of the MacNeills.

His roommates lounged in their chairs and Sandy went on talking, staring dreamily into the fire, which woke green flashes in his pale eyes, almost slipping out of the identity of the young medical student from Skye, becoming the troubadour, the bard, the ancestral storyteller.

"Why first of all," he told them thoughtfully, "this special MacNeill was a breeder—a prime sire of daughters. He was famous for that. My father told me they were the most beautiful women in Scotland. I do not know, for they had all gone out of the country before I was of an age to notice women. There was Helen married a Lindsay from the border, and Maisie married a Frenchman, Sir I-dinna-ken-what, and Gillian married the Laird of Rona's heir, and that was Comyn Rhinn. Beautiful women they were, and proud, too. That was the MacNeill in them. Why 'tis said that in Flood-time the MacNeills refused to take passage with Noah because, they assured him, they had a boat of their own. 'Tis said, too, though I canna' vouch for it, that the family herald used to go forth and stand upon the crags of Barra with a golden horn and blow. 'Hear ye, oh ye people, and listen, all ye nations! The great MacNeill of Barra having finished his meal, all the people of the earth may dine!'"

Tom guffawed. "Well," he said, "what else did the gentleman do? We set no great store by the breeding of daughters—in Virginia."

Randall lay silent, thinking of the differences between Margery's mother and his own. Martha Randall from Pickpocket Mill! Daughter of Caleb Randall, always called "Thief"—not that he had ever stolen anything in his life—because of the ancient name that went with the land he owned. "Thief" Randall, famous for his apple trees and the use he made thereof. "Hear, oh ye nations, and listen, all ye people! 'Thief' Randall of Pickpocket Mill has pressed his autumn cider, and now all the people of the world may drink!"

But he could not laugh as Tom could. You could laugh at such stories in America. Not here.

Sandy straightened up in his chair and the far-off light died away from his eyes. His storytelling mood seemed to have ended before it had well begun. "When Charlie came from France," he finished, "'twas just north of Barra he touched first foot on Scotland. Many of the lairds thought he had bonny prospects then. Many of them died. But that was near thirty years ago. Didna' the bell ring for six a while back? Should we keep the lassies waiting?"

A few moments later, their Scots friend left behind them in the outer room, Tom and Randall crowded each other at the narrow mirror in the sleeping quarters of the flat, hardly more than a cupboard, furnished with a box bed, a cot, and a stout oak wardrobe that reeked of black pepper, which a thrifty landlady said would keep moths away. Both were trying to tie their new muslin cravats in the fashionable bows, both cursing a little and making ill work of it. Randall no longer wore his mourning suit. He had a well-fitting pair of doeskin breeches now, and a dark blue velvet coat with black-banded sleeve. Finally edging Tom away from the glass, he started to brush back his fair hair, sleek-lying enough already.

Tom spoke very low, just at his shoulder.

"Did you have word from home lately, Ran'?"

Randall narrowed his eyes and shortened the strokes of his brush.

"Why?"

"Oh, I thought maybe your father had written you—or something like."

Randall put the hairbrush down and turned all the way round to look the Virginia man full in the face.

"My father did write me. You had a letter from your cousin, too. Did he say—? Had he heard about—?"

"Boston?"

The word was out between them.

"Boston," repeated Randall, keeping his voice too low for Sandy to overhear. "He didn't say much. The letter was a long time coming. He wrote it just three days afterward. What'll come of it he wasn't too sure. He said it was too early to tell."

"What did happen?" asked Tom. "Lawrence wrote something about somebody stealing some tea. Said Boston had taken things into their own hands, and he thought, by God, it was about time for us to do the same."

"Way Father heard it," explained Randall briefly, "there was three ships full of the East India Company's tea off Griffin's wharf, and nobody'd move it either in or out until tax was paid. There it sat, 'cause nobody'd pay tax. Then comes a band of Narragansetts down through town, all blankets and war paint under a bright moon, and threw every last leaf of that tea overboard. Providential, wouldn't you say?"

"Ah, the noble savage!" Tom cleared his throat and winked. "Providential," he agreed, with a sanctimonious nod.

"We've no call to tell MacCrimmon or the girls," cautioned Randall. "They're from this side of the water, they might see things a different way."

"I doubt they'd care much," said Tom. "In their eyes we're all red Indians from the world's end, and 'tis no matter what we do. It will not disturb his Gracious Majesty. Yes, MacCrimmon!" He lifted his voice in answer to a complaint from without, "Stop nagging at us, you old horse godmother of a man midwife! We'll be with you anon."

» » » « « «

Stewart's oyster cellar near the bottom of Fishmarket Close was only a few steps away from Thomson's Land, and the three young men covered the distance quickly in the sharp spring night. Down a flight of crooked steps they went, into a long narrow room, dark and dingy, lighted with tallow candles in crude sconces and a great fire blazing on a hearth at the far end. The room was almost filled with a long narrow table—so much its own peculiar shape that it must have been built there, the boards and trestles carried in separately—and benches ranged along each side. Round the table, gay in bright coats and dresses, sat as goodly a company of young folk as could be found anywhere in Edinburgh that night, students from the College and young advocates from the law courts, girls from James Court and Parliament Square, helping themselves to wooden bowls of raw oysters and mugs of porter. In a cleared space before the hearth, two fishwives from Leith rocked about in an awkward dance with much rump-shaking, their creels tangling in their striped gowns.

It did not take Randall's eyes long to find Margery, and in a moment he had slid to a place on the bench beside her. Tom likewise sought out her cousin Helen, and Sandy was welcomed by a slender red-haired girl seated near the fire and clapping in time to the fishwives' dances.

"You're late, sir," said Margery with a soft little laugh, pulling away and then leaning close again.

He smiled gallantly. "Well, the loss was all mine, wasn't it?" he retorted, thinking that he had come further in six months than across the ocean. He never would have thought of talking to the Portsmouth girls that way. Or to Sally Anne. Sally Anne seemed to him now like someone in an old story, no one he had known himself. A bitter old story. One that had an unhappy ending. He suddenly flicked his hand across his eyes as if he were brushing cobwebs away. He felt Margery touch his sleeve.

"What is it, Randall? Did ye see a ghostie or aught like?"

Coming out of his revery, he noted with amusement that she had spoken in broad Scots, the old-fashioned country tongue. She did not often do it. Somehow it pleased him.

" 'Twas a dust mote settling past," he told her lightly, motioning at the stained and dingy rafters overhead.

"I hope it was only that," she answered soberly. "You looked as if it were a graver thing. Like Andra when she sees before her."

"Who is Andra?" asked Randall.

Halfway down the table one of the lads who had been sitting there drinking too long overset his porter. Tom cracked a broad jest to hide the embarrassment. The two fishwives had stopped dancing now, and somebody called for Margery to sing.

She jumped to her feet eagerly. "Oh I will," she cried, "but not alone! If Jess and Kate and Nancy—" And in a moment she and three other wide-skirted belles with jewels in their high-piled curls were standing where the fishwives had stood and singing the old songs of Scotland. They were not new songs to Randall now, he had heard them often that winter. They sang "Green Sleeves and Pudding Pies," and they sang "The Flowers of the Forest," and a plaintive air that was sweeping the town called "Auld Robin Gray."

And after the singing they came back to their seats, and jests and laughter went round till the last oyster was eaten and the waiters brought in melted cheese and apple puffs and brandy, whereupon the lads started to toast each other.

"God bless him! Give him sons and no daughters!"

"May fools grow wise and knaves honest!"

"Here's to us! Who's like us? De'il a one!"

Looking around him, Randall saw that the moment had come, as it came to most parties in Edinburgh, when the gentlemen should leave the ladies, if they were able to do so. It looked like the start of a roaring night for the other lads. He determined not to share it. He turned to Margery.

"Shall I take you home now?"

She smiled in agreement and they extricated themselves from the bench and found their cloaks, hung on hooks near the stairs leading up from the cellar. Walking along the High Street, he held her elbow in the palm of his hand, clinging tighter sometimes so they would not be separated, for other folk were hurrying home too. It was almost ten, the hour when all the tall flats opened their windows and flung their slops and refuse into the streets below. Everyone would take shelter wherever he was, the moment that deluge started, and the nearer home he was, the shorter journey he would have afterward through the filth and muck.

They were breathless when they reached the head of the stairs at Tait's
Land.

"Will you come in for a cordial?" asked Margery, her manner friendly
and honest, with none of the exciting femininity she sometimes displayed. "My father is here, I think."

But Comyn Rhinn was not there when they entered the high-ceiled
room with leather-paneled walls and heavy old-fashioned furniture. Randall had come here often before, and he felt at home enough to go
directly to the brass grate and blow up the sea-coal fire smoldering on it.
Margery put off her cloak and went herself for liquors, not disturbing
Meggy. When she joined him again, she had a tray with a squat bottle
and two glasses, and was soon pouring out a pale green liquid.

"What is it?" he asked, as they sat together on an ancient damask sofa,
and lifted the glasses up.

"I do not know," she told him. "My father brought it back from the
East. Stronger than wine. Not so strong as brandy. If you do not care
for it—"

"It will do," he said, sipping. It had a honey taste, he thought. There
had been bees and flowers in the making of it, he'd wager.

Margery leaned back and closed her eyes, then opened them, smiling
at him.

"It was a good evening, Randall," she said. "Do you like Edinburgh
better now?"

"Better," he said, still not completely yielding the point, still thinking
in his heart that he preferred Boston, and wondering what was going
on in Boston. "But—yes it was—a good evening."

He looked at her slender hands lying in her satin lap and thought of
taking one of them in his, then decided not to do it. He was not shy,
the other thing, rather, but he knew well where such games ended, just
as he felt sure Margery did not know. Having no wish to frighten or
offend her, he kept both his hands cupped carefully round his wine glass
and set himself to make conversation.

"A thing you said tonight," he began, "I wondered about. You mentioned someone named Andra. Does she live in Edinburgh? And what
did you mean by saying she sees before her?"

Margery put her own glass on a small carved table by the sofa.

"You do not know what it means 'to see before you?' Oh, but of course
you would not! I have heard folk lose the power when they cross the
sea, that it never happens in America."

"What power?"

"'The Second Sight' some call it. Those who have it see things that
have not yet happened but that will—or things afar off. Andra is a

woman in Ballyrhinn who has the power. I have known her ever since I was a little girl. Her daughter Ellen was my playmate."

"Does Ellen see before her, too?"

"No, Ellen does not see before her, nor anyone else in the island, though many do in that part of the world. It is not thought of as a gift, but as a curse, Randall. It does not make folk happy. To think of it frightens me a little when I am away from there—but at home on Rona I am never afraid."

He was about to tell her impatiently that such things could not be, that he would bet he could cure this Andra of her powers with a good bloodletting, but she looked so serious and troubled that he had no heart to say anything that might unsettle her further. He was sorry he had asked about the woman. He gulped his cordial—whatever it was—and fought an increasing desire to draw Margery to him, to kiss her lips, to touch her breast, to take her with him into the deepness of love. It was hard enough to have to hold himself back, without trying to chat gaily while he did it; an actual relief to him when Comyn Rhinn stepped into the room, rubbing his hands and hastening to the fire.

"Awrrrr, it's a cold night for spring. How be ye, lad? Margery, could ye no find more of a man's drink in my house than what he's holding? Join me in a whiskey, sir?"

Randall shook his head, put down his empty glass and stood up. "Thank you for your kind offer, but I think I'd best say good night to both of you." He turned and bowed toward Margery. "There's still a deal of studying ahead of me before bedtime, if I'm not to be a dunce at tomorrow's lecture."

"Dinna' hurry, lad," said Comyn, fetching a whiskey bottle from a lacquered cupboard in spite of the young man's refusal. "And ye, wench," he spoke firmly to his daughter, "be off to your chamber. It's now my turn with the lad, and I have somewhat to say to him. We can do without your presence. Good night to ye."

Margery gave her shoulders a saucy tilt and made a face, but she went, smiling wryly as she flung her good nights back over her shoulder.

Randall settled again on the sofa and found himself drinking the proffered whiskey in spite of his protest. It was good whiskey. It warmed the throat going down and sang in the blood a few moments after. The Laird of Rona did not come quickly to his point, but his guest made no attempt to hurry him. He could relax now as he had not been able to do when Margery was so close, lie back and enjoy the warm rich smoky room, the yielding cushions, the liquor, and the companionship of a sharp, kindly man he liked and trusted.

Finally Rona said, "I hear ye're not overfond of Edinburgh and the ways of the College."

"Won't say as to the town," answered Randall, choosing his words cautiously. "The school, I'll admit, is a disappointment to me."

"Why is that? Do ye know more than your teachers, do ye think?"

"No," said Randall, willing to tell the truth and trying to be sure he knew just what the truth was. "It's not that I know more than my teachers. But that so often I do not know less. It seems they study more to range knowledge in patterns than to advance it. I spend my time making lists of diseases that may afflict the spleen, but I want more to learn what to do when the spleen's afflicted."

Comyn Rhinn nodded. "I think I see your trouble, lad. Part of it is because ye ha' already practiced medicine and find it hard to go back to naught but the book. And part of it, I hear, is true. There's too much of theory and system and too little of practice in the College here. I've been about the world some, and I've talked of it with men who know."

"Don't mistake me, sir," said Randall uneasily. "'Tis God's truth, I know little enough of medicine, but I question, am I like to learn more of it here?"

The Laird of Rona went on as if the young man had not spoken. "And ye be an American! Their wit has a different color and edge to it. Sir, I think your country will be a match for us in a hundred years."

"Thank you," replied Randall, wondering if perhaps the two countries were not already matched in Boston Harbor, thinking that he ought to be there and have a part.

But his host was speaking of medicine. "Wullie Cullen tells me now that your doctors have their own excellencies. Fever, he says, and the rheumatism. Those diseases be treated better there than here."

"I couldn't say that," said Randall. "I haven't been here long enough to know. We do what we can for them. They're among us a-plenty."

"Fevers, rheumatism and smallpox! He says ye're past masters in the inoculation."

"It's a common practice," Randall told him, "in New England. There's few lives lost by it now."

"Ye're apt in it?"

"I can do it well enough."

Rona was looking into the fire. "The Laird of Muck hired a young doctor last year," he went on, "hired him to come to his policies and inoculate his people—the crofters, every one—for six shillings two pence a head. Would ye think that was fair enough wages?"

"Where was his—'policies,' you call it? How many crofters were there?"

Rona was smiling at him. "Lad," he said, "I'm not speaking now of his people, but of mine. And I'd not quibble at pence and shillings. My crofters round Ballyrhinn are poor as the dust they're made of, and it's little enough I can do for them, but when I saw how Muck kept his from disease last year, I thought—this is one thing I can. 'T has been in my mind ever since then to take a young doctor with me when I go there next month; to have him inoculate every man-jack and woman-jill on Rona before he goes away again. I didna' know where to find such a man. I was to ask Wullie Cullen. But now I've a different thought. If it be ye're none so happy in the College; if ye'd like to leave your books and go back to doctoring again—for a season?"

It came to Randall as a flat question. He suddenly realized that his wits were so mellow and all awash with whiskey he could not tell any man nay. He wondered if Rona had intended that. Then he was ashamed of his suspicion. He stood up, reassured that his feet felt steady under him.

"I'll tell you tomorrow, sir," he said. "I'll be round and tell you to-morrow."

Rona walked to the door with him. "Sleep on it well, lad," he counseled. "Do not say I tried to urge ye."

Going away from Parliament Square, Randall did not turn directly homeward. Instead he went down the broad stone steps into the Cow-gate and walked past the squalid shops there, picking his way over heaps of old rags, fish bones, potato peelings, and worse offal. He thought of the clean fields round his father's house where the night wind smelled of sea salt or pine boughs, depending on which quarter it blew from. There would be sea salt and maybe pine on Rona, he thought, an island far west and beyond Scotland, beyond Skye, Sandy had told him, west of the very Hebrides. An island looking straight at America across the great sea. And on Rona there would be Margery. He thought how troubled he had been in her presence tonight, so close to all the warmth and sweetness of her, the two of them together, so secure and alone. Well, he had not touched her, and he would not. He had been a mar-ried man, and he could not go back to being a schoolboy, to stop with kissing a woman's mouth.

"A good evening to ye, sir."

A scrawny little girl with pale eyes and wispy hair was tugging at his coat sleeve. At first he did not understand.

"Would ye no come in out of the cold, sir? I'm called Jeanie, and I've a tidy room, clean and warm. And for a handsome young gentle-man like yersel' 'twould no cost—"

He could not mistake her now. The horrid thing was that as he looked

at her face it seemed to change. Her leanness turned to delicacy, her
pale eyes softened, brightened, and a shine of gold came on her hair.
She had full red lips, he saw, and a rounded bosom. She was there beside him, and his for a few shillings, and he needed her. Sally Anne
was dead, and Margery could never be his, it wasn't likely—not the
granddaughter of a MacNeill of Barra. In vain he tried to remind himself of Bessie, to tell himself he should warn this girl, as a physician,
what a short distance it was from the streets of Edinburgh to paupers'
ward. He stood there not saying a word, looking down.

In the end it was Margery who saved him, the words of a gay little
song she had sung earlier that night in the oyster tavern. A ribald little
song, he had thought it then.

> The lassies of the Canongate
> Oh they are wondrous nice!
> They will not give a single kiss
> But for a double price.

It was the double price that stopped him. He was willing to abandon and
degrade himself for one night; he surmised the pleasure would be worth
that much. But not for every night all the rest of his life, and he knew
the memory of what happened—if it did happen—would not let him rest,
not ever. He did not think Tom would have hesitated, nor Sandy. It
was probably a mistake to be born to the puritan code of Hampton Falls,
New Hampshire. But that mistake he had already committed. It was too
late to retrieve it now.

He wrenched himself away and felt in his pocket for the largest coin
there.

"Go home, Jeanie," he muttered, "and sleep to yourself tonight. Here's
the price of it."

He pressed the money into her hand and stalked off, aware that she
stood peering after him. And well she might! He was probably as sorry
a sight as anything abroad in Edinburgh.

He walked down to the Infirmary to ask after Bessie, learned that she
had died and already been carted off to the dissecting table.

He walked back to Rowan Tree Wynd, but this time he did not enjoy
the starry night nor the fresh wind that blew between the gray old houses
with a promise of spring. He was wondering what was a man to do who
could not have Margery and would not have Jeanie. He was wondering
how much of himself and his life he had buried with Sally Anne.

V

A Man's Errand

If a man could, while still alive in the flesh, swing out between two worlds, this would be something the way of it, thought Randall. He stood at the prow of the little fishing boat that scudded over the gray water in the early April evening, its brown sails full of a rainy wind that blew from the Long Island behind it, from hills and moors and harbors all black with rain. Ahead of him, beyond the western edge of the storm wrack, he watched the sunset flare up in a great arc of crimson fire. Here on the wide sea, between the dark and the brightness, borne swiftly forward through no power of his own, he had a sense of great things coming to pass, of excitement and adventure, and he in the heart of them, ready to cope with all that came, to cure any sickness, or throw any man wrestling, or court any girl. He felt a little as he had that afternoon in September under the blue-green cedar tree, but now it was in a different way and for a different reason.

It went back to that morning a few weeks ago when he had walked from the College after classes, up to Parliament Square to give his answer to Comyn Rhinn; an answer that would settle nothing. He had asked the laird to wait while he wrote home for his father's advice, but Rona had eyed him shrewdly and shaken his head.

"I canna' wait that long, I fear. Neither would I. There's a time, lad, when every man must decide for himself, when he is no longer ruled by his father. If ye've no come to that time, I dinna' want ye. I will na' send a boy on a man's errand."

He had spoken the words softly, but that had not taken the sting out of them. Randall had looked down, at first, and felt his face redden, and studied the short golden hairs on the backs of his lean hands. Then he had lifted his head and met Rona eye to eye, and told him that he would abandon his studies and go. A new feeling of strength and self-confidence had risen in him, as he said it, and had never gone away. In any case, he thought, while trying to justify his choice to himself afterward, the session was ending. It had cost him twelve pounds, and some earnings of his own would not come amiss. He would be back in Edinburgh in September for the start of Michaelmas term. Meanwhile he would see a part of the world he had never seen before, and he would be doing the work he loved, in the ways he was used to doing it. And he would be with Margery.

He did not need to turn his head now to know that she was there, sitting with the helmsman in the stern of the little boat in order to keep its balance true, since her father wanted to stand at the front and wanted Randall beside him so that he could point out to the younger man the first landmarks rising up on the bright sky. The three had come north by a leisurely route, sailing out of Leith on a packet bound for Aberdeen, and at Aberdeen they had transferred to a smaller ship that beat its way north and west, past the gray sea lochs and misty blue headlands of Caithness and Sutherlandshire. Last night they had slept ashore, in Stornaway, a slate-roofed fishing village in the Outer Hebrides, and this morning gone aboard a tiny herring boat that would take them the last of the way home.

They had left most of their gear in the town to be sent after them tomorrow—Margery's silk dresses, and Comyn's provisions and brandy; Randall's books, and the small deerskin chest with brass nails that he had brought with him all the way from America. It was made from the hide of the first deer he had ever killed, when he was nine years old, roaming the woods behind his grandfather's cornfields near Pickpocket Mill. He wondered suddenly, with a pang of uneasiness and doubt, if he had chosen wisely enough when with Rona he had purchased the drugs for that little chest; if everything he would need had really gone into it. He had heard young Dr. Jarvis of Boston say that he wanted nothing but opium, antimony, mercury, cantharides, bark, and the lancet, but Randall had chosen to provide himself with a somewhat ampler store. Still—. Of course he was prepared to do the inoculation, but illnesses were bound to arise, and he would think it his duty to treat them as they came on. He hoped the island had a midwife. If his nerve ever failed him it was in the practice of midwifery. He wondered what he would have done when the time came for Sally Anne. He cleared his throat and bent his head toward Rona in order to make himself heard in the rush of the sea wind whistling by.

"Are they a healthy folk mostly, sir?"

The Laird of Rona kept his eyes fixed on the white-flecked waters cleaving before them. He had flung aside his cocked hat, and his hair was wet with spray. He answered promptly.

"Aye, mostly. Hard to purge and easy to cure of green wounds. Fevers they have, and jaundice, and the stone; smallpox and scurvy, worms, sometimes, and spring fluxes. But no gout nor palsy nor consumptions. And no vapors and barrenness in the women."

"Is there a midwife amongst them?"

"Aye, and a good one. Ye'll have naught to do with lyings-in. Our lassies are modest. They'd no want ye meddling about them at such a time."

Randall was grateful for their modesty. Had there ever been a doctor there, he wanted to know.

"Never a one," came the answer. "I meant to speak of it to ye before, lad, so we'll no frighten them at first before they get to know ye. Ye come here as my friend. Your business we'd best delay a bit. There— see yon shadow on the sea? Low there—where the purple cloud drifts across? That be Rona—our isle of Rona. Margery, go back! We'll be o'erset and drowned do ye shift about so!"

She had crept forward and come to stand beside them, and she laughed a little at her father's chiding, but she did not go away. It warmed Randall's heart to know that she was there so close, but he did not look at her. He felt his mouth curve in a smile, but he narrowed his eyes and shielded them with his hand, and peered ahead, over the darkening sea. They were drawing near to a low rocky coast, hidden before by the glare of the setting sun. Comyn kept on talking, trying to tell his young guest what he wanted him to know.

"Scotland's not what it was when I was a lad, sir. The clans were all for cutting each other's throats and killing each other's cattle then. The King's writ runs in the glens now, and things be better ordered, though there's still many who sigh for the free old time. But on Rona there's no change. All is the same as it was in my grandfather's day. The crofters are still poor, growing a little poorer—through no fault. A man be no richer than his land, if it's land he lives by. Tumbled out of Scotland I was, because my wife wanted to live abroad with the Stuart followers, and make my way there I could and did. But 'tis in my heart now to return. If I've not stood by my people as I should ha' done, maybe 'tis none too late to try now."

He paused for a moment, as if expecting to be challenged, then went on.

"I'm for the East no more. The Company's all corrupted, and 'twas no honest to start. 'Twas always a knave's business, and I weary o' being a knave. Kilns I've built for our folk and set them to burning kelp, for its ashes that go to the glassmaking. There's a glassworks in Greenock I've an interest in, hoping to keep them a steady market there. But just when the sun shines out and we've two coins to rub together, then all

the plagues of Egypt come down. First the barley fails, and then falls
the putrid fever, and then the emigration, and everybody would be off to
America! Ah well, such as go are such as can be spared, I say! Now lad,
if ye look to the right, ye'll see a bit of high country, and that's Ardmory.
And below it's the town and port of Ballyrhinn, and to the left—"

The words of his host flowed on like a mountain stream, but Randall
was no longer listening, for Margery had put her hand on his arm and
lifted her face up.

"Look," she said.

She turned and gazed straight ahead of her without saying any more.

They stood together, watching the isle of Rona take shape slowly out
of the April dark.

Randall strained his eyes trying to see it all at once because he felt she
wanted him to. He could really see very little, for the sunset had died,
and moonrise was still an hour away. On the right, the crags came down
to the water, black and shadowy. To the left, the land sloped gently upward, and on its crest shone out the lighted windows of a house, large
and low, he thought, though he could not trace its outlines in the gray-
green dusk. Straight ahead opened a broad crescent of cove rimmed with
white, either sand or breaking surf, and beyond the cove a few lights
were scattered across a rising hillside. Beyond that lay only darkness, and
a thin fog, and the curving arc of night sky full of stars, losing itself
far out past Rona in the curve of the western sea.

Still scudding before the wind, their boat moved swiftly into the cove,
and Randall became aware of other boats riding at anchor on the flood
tide. Then a cry went up on shore, and torches flared along the water
line.

"They're waiting for us," murmured Comyn, a quiet happiness in his
voice. "They've not forgotten—though all the rest of the world be set on
new ways."

"There goes the bonfire," said Margery, and sure enough, a spreading
patch of flame leaped upward in the midst of the torches.

As the boat drew to a small crooked wharf, Randall glanced up the
hillside, through the flickering lights of welcome, and saw the town of
Ballyrhinn. The scattered, improvident cottages looked to his New England eyes to be half stone wall and half haystack, and out of these mean
dwellings came a clamorous crowd of folk, all sizes and ages, running
forward eagerly, shoving each other and calling in a hoarse, throaty, foreign tongue.

The helmsman made the boat fast, and Comyn leaped to the wharf,
his arms outstretched, advancing to meet the island people. Randall
turned to Margery and smiled, bewildered.

"They'll think I'm a liar," he said, "if I ever try to tell them about this when I get home to Hampton Falls. We wouldn't turn out so to welcome the King himself, not if he came over with his crown in his hand."

"And I'm not sure they would either," she retorted. "They love my father, for he's one of them. They don't love the King."

Randall stepped to the wharf and turned to offer his hand to Margery when he felt himself rudely thrust aside. Recovering his balance, just short of pitching into the sea, he watched a burly young man with a handsome face and a scarlet plaid waistcoat as he swept the girl into his arms and kissed her lips and hair. Margery writhed away from him and managed to get her feet on the rough planking.

"You've not changed, Kenneth," she murmured, breathless from the onslaught. "Still the whirlwind coming down the glen—"

"And master of all it blows on," he finished. "Was ye forgetting that? Ye used to say that, Margery."

Watching her closely in the uncertain glare of the torches, Randall saw her smile stiffen and her eyes turn restlessly this way and that. If she had only looked at him pleadingly, he thought, he would know what to do, and he clenched his fists at his sides. But she did not look at him. Just then a group of girls in coarse bright dresses ran out from among the villagers and surrounded Margery, catching her hands and greeting her excitedly in the island tongue. For a few moments she gave them her whole attention, while the two men stood staring at each other. Randall felt as welcome as sour ale in summertime. He shifted about restlessly, wondering who this insolent stranger was, and why neither of the Rhinns had spoken of him before.

Finally Margery freed herself from the island girls and joined her former companions, catching an arm of each and trying to draw them together.

"Lads," she said, "let me make you known. Randall Woodbury, this is Kenneth Crary, the schoolmaster, who lives with us in Rhinn House. Kenneth, this is Randall, a friend from Edinburgh, and our guest."

Randall gazed into the hostile dark blue eyes, trying to take the measure of the man behind them. Instinctively, without really meaning to, he put out his hand. The schoolmaster hesitated. Then he took it and gripped it so hard Randall thought his bones would crack. He released it slowly.

"Margery," he growled, "ye've no call to make friends in Edinburgh."

A line furrowed Margery's smooth brow. "And no call not to," she retorted. Then she stepped forward, her arms still linked with theirs.

"Come, lads, we must go to Father, or he'll take you and knock your heads together."

Standing beside his host at the edge of the blazing heap of dried furze and bracken, Randall could not shake off the sense of unreality that had been with him ever since he stepped ashore. It was as if Comyn and Margery and this half-wild island man glowering beside her might vanish at any moment in the white mist beginning to rise from the sea. Around them gathered the people of Ballyrhinn: square-built men smelling of fish oil and cattle dung, smoke-dried, sturdy women, and the young folk all freshness and bloom like young folk everywhere. He could not understand their speech, but he could tell that they were happy; laughing, and singing, and making holiday. A little way off stood a flat stone with a handmill mounted on it, and propped secure against the stone was a keg with the top knocked in and a cup hanging from a nail, waiting all comers. Both men and women alike visited it, often, but not unduly so, and no one seemed to grow any the worse thereby. Suddenly through the open doorway of one of the cottages poured an unearthly sound, rising and falling from raucous shriek to faint moan, dying away and then reviving again.

Randall gripped the hunting knife that he would always wear under his jacket, no matter how many seas he crossed or cities he studied in.

"God's sake, what was that?" he exclaimed blankly. Then he realized that Margery stood at his elbow.

"It's only Johnny Dweeney's bagpipes," she told him soothingly.

"Bagpipes? No! I've heard them before. In Edinburgh I heard them. MacCrimmon used to play them when he'd been drinking. But they didn't sound so! Not like stuck hogs at Martinmas."

"Oh, but you've never heard Johnny's bagpipes. Nor that tune, maybe. It's Father's favorite. Once the MacDonalds of Glengarry shut up the Culloden men in a church and set fire to it, and that was the tune they played whilst 'twas burning."

"You don't make it sound any better to me," said Randall with a shudder. "Where's yon jolly lad, the schoolmaster?"

"He's gone to fetch Ellen," she answered, drawing away from him. "We're going to the house for supper now, and Ellen and Andra always come on our first night to share—"

"Aye," boomed Comyn behind them, "fetch Ellen and Andra! And we'll have another pair to sup with us tonight, lass. Iver and Lavan! They tells me they was married last New Year's Day."

Randall turned to his host, who stood between a slim girl and a flaxen-haired young man, his arms around their shoulders.

"There was many got married through the winter," said the girl in halting English, her eyes cast down. "But we was the only ones to be married on New Year's Day."

Keeping his arms about the young couple, the Laird of Rona strode off through the village toward the slope where Randall had seen the lighted windows as he came ashore. Margery started after them, and he walked beside her, following a rough cart track that wound upward through wild shrubs and budding fern. In their wake straggled the townspeople, with Johnny Dweeney's bagpipes wailing, and the torches lighting up the thatched huts and barren hills till it looked to Randall like a scene from an earlier world, caught here forever in this curve of the ancient sea.

They came out finally on a strip of greensward with a rambling stone house in the middle of it. Mellow lamplight streamed from the leaded casements, shining on a daffodil bed, and here and there a clump of dwarf holly or clipped yews. He looked down at Margery.

"Is this—?"

"This is Rhinn House. Come round to the front. They will not take leave of us till we're through the door."

Rhinn House, he discovered, was on a craggy headland looking south. Two bay windows faced the shining water under a newly risen moon, and between the windows, in a wide doorway, Comyn stood alone, waiting for the rout to overtake him. When he saw Randall and Margery he moved aside.

"Go in, lass," he told her. "I'll be with ye when I've said good night to all."

Looking at Margery, Randall thought she was going to cry. She bit her lip and closed her eyes a moment and swallowed painfully. Thinking he knew the reason, he followed her into a wide hall, stone-floored, hung with dull tapestries and lit with a score of iron lamps in wall brackets. He overtook her and caught her by the sleeve.

"You don't need," he said, clearing his throat with embarrassment, "to come in because of me. I can wait here. Go back to them."

She smiled; but he had been right, there were tears on her lashes.

"It's no that, Randall," she said. "Your being here makes no difference. 'Tis the usage of the place. I would stand there with him, yes—if I were his son and inheritor."

"I'm sorry," muttered Randall.

"Aye, we are all sorry, but there's no helping it. 'Tis only for him that I mind. A sad thing, for a man to have no son. My brothers were still-born. Come to the table. There's company there."

Together they crossed the great hall of Rhinn House, two stories high with a stairway at the rear leading to the galleries above. Turf burned fragrantly on a wide hearth, and not far from it stood a table set with linen and silver and queen's ware. The hall was old, he thought, old as the craggy hills and rude huts, and the quiet-eyed, timeless folk of Bally-rhinn. The supper table and its appointments were new, and fine, and fashionable, in the latest taste of Edinburgh; and maybe Paris and London, for all he could tell. Five people had already taken their places, in black old carven chairs, and sat waiting for the meal to begin.

Iver and Lavan crouched side by side, uncomfortable and shy. Across from them Kenneth Crary loomed between two women. One was young, and one was older. One wore a blue dress and the other a green one, like the shapeless dresses of all the island women. Randall noticed nothing further about them at that time. Margery did not sit down at once, and he stood awkwardly beside her, waiting.

"Andra," she said gaily, her tears all dried away now, "and Ellen! You know how I'm glad to see you! You know I always am!"

Then she gave a quick look at him, and turned as quickly to the others.

"This is Randall Woodbury, our friend from Edinburgh. Randall, you have met with Kenneth already, and with Iver and Lavan Gall. Now you must meed Andra Deveron. She is our midwife and our wise woman. Would you be angry if I said she knew more than all the doctors of Edinburgh?"

"Why, no, I'd say it could be that she did," he answered gallantly.

Andra was the older woman. The one, he remembered, who was supposed to have the second sight. Maybe she was having it now, for she was certainly staring at him—almost like she had seen him before. He felt himself shudder. He knew that Margery must have noticed it, for she spoke so quickly, or perhaps it was only to cover the fact that the midwife had made no reply to the introduction.

"And this is her daughter. We did not live on Rona much, while I was growing, but whenever we did, Ellen was my playmate and stayed here in the house with me."

Ellen gave him a long appraising look out of narrow eyes. Hardly a pretty girl, he thought. Too thin, with hair that could be called either pale red or dark, tawny yellow. She bent her head and said no word, any more than her mother had. Then she lifted her eyes again. Suddenly he and she were conversing amply in the old wordless language of sex. He knew that Ellen would never be without a man; she knew that he understood this perfectly, but that for himself he had no desire to be concerned therein. He looked covertly at Margery, grateful for the innocence of her open smile. With all her poise and sophistication, she had not understood this interchange in an elemental tongue.

Outside he could hear shouts and cheering, lifted three times in rapid crescendo, then dying away. Margery seated herself at the foot of the table and motioned him to the empty chair on her right. Kenneth glared at them. Then Comyn came in. He took his place facing his daughter and sat there upright, knife and fork in hand, beaming all around him.

"They're gone away now," he told his guests, "but I've promised them I'll be out and amongst them tomorrow to see how it fares with all. Andra, lass, ye're as bonny as when I first saw ye, near twenty years ago. Are ye no married yet, Ellen?" His eyes held tenderness for one woman but none for the other.

"Not yet," said Ellen demurely.

"Ah, well, if ye wait long enough at the ferry, ye'll get across some-time. Margery, where's our own house folk? If they will na' turn out to welcome us, they can at least fetch us somewhat to eat."

"It's strange they're not waiting," said Margery looking uneasy. "Call for them, Father. They must have heard us—with Johnny's bagpipes and all the cheers."

Ellen explained. " 'Tis Caitlin," she told them. "She's been ailing all winter and must keep Leitis by her side. When we came through the kitchen just now, Sim was there all lonely, trying to prepare."

Lavan stood up, blushing, looking at her bare feet. "I'll go," she murmured. "I'll go and help Sim."

Randall suddenly realized that the woman Andra had spoken no words at all.

Lavan opened a door to the left of the staircase just in time for a russet-faced elderly man to stagger through it. He carried a tray full of covered dishes and managed to get it to the table safely and ease it down. Then he turned toward Comyn and bowed low. The laird reached out and gripped the old servant's hand.

"Why did ye no shout for aid, man? None of us were too good to help ye. Where be your sister and wife?"

"Why my sister is bedfast, sir, and my wife canna' leave her side, but I bid ye welcome home. Ye and Miss Margery. I was never no cook, but I've contrived for ye some pullets with prunes in the broth. Ye've fared better, but ye'll no starve thereon."

"It will taste wonderful, Sim," said Margery reassuringly, "and I'll go to Caitlin tonight, if it will help her. Would it, do you think?"

"Aw the poor soul be out of her pain and sleeping now, and ye canna' aid her at all. Eat your supper, Miss Margery. Ye've come a long way. Merciful God, but I've forgotten the whiskey! I'll go for it now!"

Sim hastened from the room and Comyn started to serve the pullets and thick-sliced barley cake. Then he paused and put down the dripping ladle.

"Look to your mother, Ellen!" he said.

Randall did not need to be told to look at Andra; he had been doing so for the last five minutes. The woman sat upright in her chair gripping the arms, but now her eyes that had been gazing straight before her were rolled back in her head. He glanced around him uneasily, to see how the others felt about this strange behavior. They were all watching, but no one seemed excited or disturbed.

Ellen sighed impatiently. Then she put her hands to her mother's face and pulled the eyelids down with her fingers. Andra shuddered and twisted against the back of the chair. Her white linen cap fell off, and her glossy dark red locks slipped down on her shoulders. Then slowly the light of consciousness woke in her face. She shook her head slightly and gave a faint smile. Lavan was bringing her a cup of water.

She took the cup with a steady hand and drank thirstily. Then she spoke in a soft deep voice that made Randall think of honey bees in the fields on a summer noonday.

"Welcome home to Rona, sir, and you, Miss Margery."

She gave Randall a long slow look, not patent like her daughter's. There was meaning in it, but what it was, he could not tell.

Comyn leaned forward curiously above the platter of steaming food. "What did ye see, Andra?" he asked.

She gave a nervous little laugh. "Nothing, sir. Nothing so much."

"Ye mean ye saw emptiness? Space, then?"

He sounded as if her evasion had nettled him, so she gave over. Randall had a feeling that this had all happened many times before.

"Why, I did not see anything of sadness or evil. I think it is good, what I saw. I cannot tell why. But I think that good will come out of it for all of us."

"What was it, Andra?" asked Margery.

Ellen began to chew down a piece of barley cake and eye the dish of birds still before Comyn.

"I saw four men. They were sailors, coming ashore from a boat with double sails, like the boats of Stornaway. Double sails, one brown and one red."

"Did ye know their faces?"

"No. They were strange to me. They were carrying a little chest. It was covered with a pale hide, nailed together with brass."

Randall swallowed. He felt Comyn and Margery turn their eyes toward him, but he did not look up. He lifted a heavy silver fork and pretended to examine its chased handle. He felt shivers slide up his backbone and a prickling at the roots of his hair. His chest of drugs, this woman was seeing! This woman in the Hebrides! His chest that he had brought from America!

"It seemed strange," said Andra, "that four men should carry it, when it could scarce have been a burden for one. Such a little chest. Not big enough for Miss Margery's jewels. But they bore it as if there was frailest glass inside."

"Was that all ye saw, lass?" asked Rona, beginning to serve the chicken.

"Yes, only that," replied Andra simply.

In spite of the long voyage and the many hours since he had last eaten, Randall did not enjoy his first supper in the old stone house between Ballyrhinn and the western sea. Here he was, with no wisdom to lean on but his own, withdrawn to an island whose people belonged to an older, simpler world than the one he had grown up in, a people whose speech he could not understand. Somewhere, hidden away in the stone wings of the mansion, lay a sick woman, perhaps a dying one. Across the table, eating her food heartily, sat this Andra, and maybe she was a sick woman too, or maybe a sibyl out of his despised classics book. Well, if she was a prophetess, she was a false one. True, she had described a chest like his that was due to arrive tomorrow from Stornaway, but it was most unlikely that four men would carry it ashore. Realizing the unlikeliness of it made him feel better, and the tension and vague disquiet that had plagued him ever since he had set foot on Rona began to ebb away.

But then he looked at Kenneth. Kenneth was watching Margery with the unmistakable air of a man surveying something he holds jealously to be his own. Beside Kenneth sat Ellen, and her eyes meeting Randall's made him turn hot and red. Take all things together, he could understand why Comyn wanted a man for this errand. There were matters afoot on Rona that could not be entrusted to any boy.

VI

Ugly Goes to the Bone

"I CANNA' tell you nay in your father's house, Miss Margery," said Leitis, the old serving woman, "but Sim and I would take it kindly did you leave the poor soul alone with her pain."

Margery stood in the low corridor that led to the chambers on the upper floor of the stone wing which housed the granary and store rooms beneath. Sim's wife barred her way now, keeping her back from the visit she had meant to pay to Caitlin, his ailing sister. They spoke together in the island tongue that came as easily to the laird's daughter as the quick French of Paris or the careful English of Edinburgh.

"Of course, Leitis, I will not go to her if she does not wish to see me. If there is nothing I can say or do to help—"

Margery turned from the worn brown face and somber eyes of the old woman and gazed through a small dormer window that looked down to the clachan of Ballyrhinn. Morning sunlight shone through the leaded panes, lying soft on the green hillside and thatched cottages with peat smoke curling above them, dappling gold on the water beyond the crooked pier. She longed to be out in the April weather, up in the hills where Randall and her father had gone, or walking along the shellfish pools by the craggy shore. But the thought of illness and suffering under her own roof was a trouble to her, as discomforting as a cold wind or a cloud across the sun.

"There is nothing ye can do, Miss Margery," said Leitis simply, still barring the way.

Margery gazed steadily back, a pleading in her voice put there by her own intent, but coming, nevertheless, from her heart.

"Leitis," she said, "you treat me as if I were a stranger, and it hurts me. When I was born on Barra and they took me from my mother first, did they not give me to you?"

"Aye, they did, Miss Margery," said Leitis, wetting her lips and turning her eyes away, "and believe me, 'tis not unkindly meant, and ye must not grieve. It is only that she is sick to her death, and a sad sight for those who look on her with love. We would spare ye that sight, since it can in no ways help her at all."

"But are you sure, Leitis?" persisted Margery. "Sure that there is no cure for her? Is it a fever or a pleurisy or—what does Andra say?"

"Nay, it is all within," explained Leitis, "much pain and much wasting and a little illness, but nothing one can name or see. Andra comes here every day, but she can do little. She says it is beyond her skill."

Margery's eyes shone and she leaned forward intently.

"Leitis, we did not mean to tell folk yet, and the word must not cross the threshold of this house until we are ready. But we have brought a doctor with us. One of the university men. He may have means of which Andra has never heard. He has gone out with Father to walk the policies now, but when he comes in—let us take him to Caitlin. Let him try—"

Leitis gazed through the window at the shining water and brown-sailed fishing boats headed for the open sea. Then she shook her head and twisted the corner of her apron in her rough hands.

"I have seen him, Miss Margery. When he walked out with your father this morning I saw him go. He is a man, and young. Caitlin has stayed always a maid. Born on Rona, as ye know, and never been away. Why no lad ever fancied her, I canna' tell, but it always has been so, and she has kept much to herself. If I were to bring a young man to her chamber, she would die of shame."

Impatience burned in Margery's soft eyes. "You talk like a daftie, Leitis! As well die of shame as of an illness within. He would be gentle with her, and not familiar or rude. He would understand. I am a maid too, but if I were ill I would not fear to have him treat me."

But Leitis shook her stubborn peasant head.

"Ye are used to all the world's wickedness, Miss Margery, but we scarce can yield ourselves up to it here. I will speak to Sim, and to Caitlin when she wakens—but I doubt—! Now I must go to her. Forgive me, pray."

She curtsied awkwardly, turned, and walked down the corridor, through a doorway and out of sight.

Margery stared after her thoughtfully. What should she do, she wondered. She could complain to her father and insist that the sick woman receive Randall whether she would or no. A cruel outrage, but surely justified if Caitlin's life could be saved thereby. But could it? Perhaps Andra would know. She would go down to the clachan and see what the midwife had to say.

A few minutes later, wearing brogues and a short petticoat like any other island girl, she left Rhinn House and hurried down the slope and

along the curving sand. She met no one, nor had she expected to. A few
old wives sat on the doorstones minding the bairns who were too young
to be where Kenneth kept school in a loft over the cattle barn. The
younger women would be out on the wide sandy plain, the machair,
sowing oats, and the men pulling kelp or fishing for cod and ling. When
she reached the little stone hut by the cockle bed, Ellen was standing at
the door.

Margery went up to her smiling, much of her trouble dissolved away
in the clean tang of the sea air, the warmth of the sun.

"Oh, Ellen! I did not know you would be at home, but I am glad.
We could not talk by ourselves last night, with the men there and all.
But it's been so long, and there's so much to say!"

Ellen looked her up and down, but she did not smile.

"If there is," she answered, "then ye're the one to say it. Ye been about
the world, and I been in Ballyrhinn."

It was almost an accusation, and again Margery felt as if clouds had
gone over the bright sun.

"Where's your mother?" she asked. "I came to speak to her about Caitlin. She's very ill, you know."

"Caitlin's dying," said Ellen flatly. "I'd ha' died years ago, had I been
left on the bush like she."

"Oh, but you'll never be left so, Ellen," Margery hurried to reassure
her. She peered through the open doorway into the cottage, and decided
Andra was not at home. Ellen followed her glance.

"She's away," she said. "Up on Caldune gathering simples. But she'd
tell ye the same as I. Caitlin canna' last. Be the ladies' gowns longer
this year?"

Margery closed her eyes a moment, not wanting to look any more at
Ellen, but seeing her all the same. She was tall and Ellen was not. Last
year when the fashions changed she had given the cattle maid a whole
sheaf of discarded gowns. Now it was in Ellen's mind to hint for more,
without a care for the sick woman up the hill. Ellen is greedy, she
thought; Ellen is mean. And then she was as quickly ashamed of herself.
Of course Ellen wanted finery; so did every other girl. Ellen was restless
in Ballyrhinn and longed to be away. Margery loved the island, but she
knew she would not want to spend all her days on it. Ellen was unhappy. Margery could not remember that she had ever known anybody
who was greedy or mean except unhappy folk.

"The gowns are much the same," she answered evenly. "But I've a
new blue poplin with garnet bows that does not suit me at all and would
suit you very well. Come up this afternoon and if Leitis can spare the
time from Caitlin we will get her to change the hem for you."

A delicate flush of pleasure came to Ellen's cheeks and she looked almost pretty. Her mouth softened.

"Sit down," she invited, her voice a little mellower now, lowering herself to the patch of scurvy grass that ran along the cottage wall.

Margery sat down on the wide stone before the door.

"My trunks will be here today," she went on eagerly, happy that her old friend had warmed to her at last, "and you must help me unpack them. There will be many things—silk flowers and thread hose and Brussels lace—"

Then she stopped, stricken. Was she, Margery Rhinn, suddenly grown so poor in friendship that she had to bribe and buy?

Ellen's eyes glistened, and she did not notice the pause in the conversation. Silence lay for a moment between the two girls. Margery looked down at the rings on her fingers and Ellen stared idly at the blue bay. Then an idea seemed to come to her, for her face grew tense and the line of her jaw sharpened.

"Trunks!" she muttered. "They're full of wedding things! Ye're going to marry Schoolmaster!"

"No," said Margery slowly. "I did not bring any wedding things, Ellen. When I will marry—I cannot tell."

"He says ye're promised to him."

Margery's sweet mouth thinned to a harsh line. "Ellen," she said, "you will speak no more of it to me."

"Your pardon, my lady," answered Ellen with a sneer.

Margery felt close to weeping. "Oh, Ellen, do not quarrel with me! It is sad for friends to grow apart, and between us it must not happen. Tell me about yourself. Have any of the lads finally pleased you? Many have tried, I am sure. I want to hear."

Ellen began shredding a blade of scurvy grass in her fingers.

"Let them try. Ye're not daft, Madge. Ye know there is no one here for me."

"But one will come, Ellen. I am sure one will."

"Then he had best be quick. Do ye know what Johnny Dweeney said to my mother yesterday?" Her voice broke with bitterness. "He pointed at me with his stick, and he said, 'Daughters and dead fish are no keeping ware.'"

Margery gave a little cry of pity for her friend. "Oh, Ellen, the old are cruel sometimes. They do not mean to be, but they are. They are jealous, I think, because for them it is all behind. But I am sure someone will come. It is strange, I have noticed, how folk will go across the world to find each other, not knowing all the while if it is meant they should."

There was a wistfulness in Margery's tone, but Ellen did not ask her to explain it, or question the meaning in what she said. Again the two girls fell silent.

Finally Ellen asked, in a voice that implied it mattered little, "That incomer at your table last night—I forget his name? Does he mean to stay long? Is he an Edinburgh lad?"

"Randall? He will stay the summer, I think. He comes from America."

"America! They say there's gold in gowpins there, waiting for a body to pick it up. Many have gone from Skye and the Highlands this year. Has he talked of the gold?"

"Gold? No, he has not talked of gold. He came to study medicine at the College, as many do."

"Is he bespoken?"

"No," answered Margery, suddenly aware where Ellen's questions were tending, filled with uneasiness and disgust which she could not explain to herself. "I do not think so. But really, Ellen, I have not asked him. He had a wife in his own country, but she died. When do you think your mother will come home?"

Ellen shrugged her shoulders. "When she's hungry, I do not doubt. Perhaps not till dark. Will your trunks be here today?"

Margery stood up. "I think so. Tam MacVean in Stornaway promised my father. Come whenever you will."

"At the flood tide," said Ellen. "I canna' come before. I must go now to pull kelp so long as the rocks are bare."

Margery took leave of her friend and walked slowly homeward across the worn turf of the clachan. Then she stopped. The sun was high. Randall and her father had left soon after dawn to circle Rona, and they should be returning by now. They would have gone west to the machair, sunwise, as travelers must always go, according to the ancient belief of the islands; then crossing over, through the green knolls and burrows of Puffin Town, and homeward along Ardmory and the rough crags sloping down to the beds of kelp and dulse that rimmed the sea. She would walk up Ardmory, she thought, and meet them, and she turned her steps that way.

She did not follow the burn, but chose a steeper path through the young heather, coming out on the long ridge that led to the shieling hut and the moors where the cattle would be turned out in late May. Never, she thought, did any homecoming of hers have such a sour taste to it. First, there was Kenneth. She could never marry him, she knew now, any more than she could marry one of those great black snarling creatures in the Paris bear garden. But she had given him her word. The word of Comyn Rhinn's daughter. The word of a MacNeill of Barra. Then there was Caitlin's illness and Ellen's cold welcome. Margery began to cry.

She held her head back and her face lifted up, her eyes streaming. But it was only for a moment. She arranged her features in a wan smile and walked upward through the heather.

To the east, the land fell sharply away in cliffs of seamed and weathered rock, and the path Margery had chosen took her along the edge, where she could look down at the small black figures toiling in the kelp beds that spread their glossy red-brown streamers on the crags below. Smoke drifted upward from the stone kilns, and faint human voices, hailing and answering each other. She felt her heart lift as she walked along. Once again the bright weather cheered her. A body who could be sad in the midst of an April day on Rona, she thought, wouldn't be happy at the right hand of God's very throne.

In a cleft of the moorland she came suddenly upon them, taking their rest in the heather, her father seated against a rock all green and gold lichens, and Randall flung prone on the ground, lying so he could see nothing but the flight of gulls across the blue sky.

"I tell ye, lad," her father was saying with stubborn assurance, "and ye may depend upon it. Ye canna' judge a lass by her face, 'tis said—but sometimes, ye can. Beauty's only skin deep, but ugly goes to the bone."

Randall answered lazily, and as if he did not much care.

"You were speaking of Ellen Deveron. Do you mean to say that about her? I should not think she was so ill-favored as all that."

Margery had been ready to run forward and greet them, to ask Randall what he thought of the island and if he had seen the whole of it. But her father's words had a strange sound to them, as if it were another man talking, a man she had never known. She paused uncertainly and stood very still.

"Aye, it was Ellen I meant. A lad will mend and change his ways, but with a lass it is never so. There be Kenneth now. Studying for a minister he was, at the College in Aberdeen, and taken up by the watch one night for being o'erfull in a tavern and roistering thereupon. The Kirk wouldna' have him after that, but I was in town at the time, and heard o' the commotion, and went to see him. He seemed to me to have no fault, save for being a hot-head and young. So I offered him a post on Rona, for five pounds a year and a pair of shoes, and he serves in it well. Some day he will make peace with the College again."

"I wondered how he came here," said Randall. He was sitting up and leaning forward, his arms lying loosely on his bent knees. "I wondered if it was as Margery's friend that he came."

"Nay, not my lass. Ye may hear talk there be somewhat between them, but 'tis false. 'Tis plain to me who knows her she has not yet settled her fancy. Ah well, though he will na' do for her, as I tell ye, Kenneth is

a good lad and will mend. But the lasses are like lambs; born black or
white, and there's an end on 't. About Ellen now. 'Tis an ugly little
story that none but a knave would repeat. But I never scorned to be a
knave if 'twas to serve a cause I thought honest and good. And it seemed
to me better that ye know—"

Margery stepped forth from the outcropping ledge that had hid her
presence. She knew perfectly well all of Kenneth's misadventure, but
she had no idea what her father was going to reveal about Ellen. She
meant to hear whatever he had to say, but she would not stoop to eaves-
dropping.

"What is the ugly little story, Father?" she asked soberly. "I know no
harm of Ellen. You never told it to me before."

Rona started, flung up his head quickly, and stared at his daughter.
"What are ye doing a-creep on the heath like an old woman? I didna'
know ye was about? What be ye after?"

"I came to meet you," said Margery simply. "What were you going
to tell Randall about Ellen, Father?"

Randall got to his feet, flicking a bit of moss from his doeskin breeches.
He entered the conversation. "Maybe it will keep until later, sir. The
sun's overhead, and breakfast was a while ago. I'm about to be a rude
guest and say I'm hungry." He turned to Margery and smiled. "We
started a red deer back in the hills," he motioned toward the north of the
island and the scrubby uplands of Caldune. "There'd be venison for dinner, if I'd had my gun with me."

"There's guns at the house, lad. In the attic along with the targes and
claymores, weapons the Rhinns used in battle in old time ere ever the
Georges came out of Germany," answered Rona, grateful to the young
man for trying to distract Margery's attention. "Ye've the eye and nerves
of a good marksman and—"

"What about Ellen?" insisted his daughter.

"Well, if ye willna' leave it rest, I'll tell ye the kernel of it and no
more. 'Twas called to my attention once that she was too free with the
lads, and she being scarce out of her childhood at that time. There 'tis.
I'll have no more to say on 't."

"I know when it was," cried Margery. "It was that fall of the great
rains when I brought home the swan with the broken wing, and he
lived in our fowl house all winter. We were twelve years old that fall,
Ellen and I. You had always said before, that when the time came you
would send her to school in Inverness so she could be trained to teach
a laird's children in a fine house somewhere. But that fall you called her
to you and told her she could never go, and must bide as she was, for
all of you. I have always wondered why, Father."

"Ellen hasna' wondered why," he answered with a grim little smile. "Come, lass, did ye no hear Randall say he needed victuals? To the house with us!"

He strode off in the way Margery had come. She stood looking at Randall.

"Forgive me," she said contritely. "If we use you so, and quarrel amongst ourselves before your face, you will wish that you had stayed in Edinburgh."

Together they started after Comyn, away from the cliffs and down the steep path to the cottages below.

"You were not quarreling," he assured her easily. "After all, 'twas a matter between the two of you, and since chance brought it out, 'twas well to settle it there. One thing though, I think he is wrong in. I would not argue with him, and still—"

"What was that, Randall?"

"About girls not changing. I think they can. I remember a woman or two at home—good wives and church members when I knew them, but my father told me that when they were young they were the talk of the docks in Portsmouth. When they married they gave up their light ways, and so will Ellen, no doubt. I should not worry about her."

"I am glad, Randall, glad you believe it will be so. I have known father had no liking for her, but I never knew why. She seems worse than she is sometimes, because she is so unhappy. She finds it lonely in Ballyrhinn with no lad of her own."

They were picking their way between the scattered cottages now, drawing near to the cove where half a dozen fishing boats stood in from the bay.

"She should get a lad with no trouble," replied Randall. "She's as fair as most, if not uncommon fair. Her mother is a strange woman. Could it be she scares them away?"

"Oh no! No one on all the island is loved as Andra is—not even my father—surely not me! She is at the bedside when they are born and again when they die. No soul can pass either in or out of life, they believe, unless she is there to ease its way."

"Has she lived always on Rona? Where did she get her skill?"

Margery tripped lightly ahead of him as they crossed the stepping stones set in the burn just before its sluggish peat-stained waters flowed into the sea.

"Oh she is an incomer—one not born on the island—though it seems strange to think of her so. She came from 'round Banff, I think, and had lived in Ireland, and was on her way home when her ship went to pieces here. It was before I can remember. But she never went away.

Look, Randall! That's Tam MacVean's boat bringing our things from
Stornaway. Oh Randall—see!"

She caught his arm and motioned for him to look toward the wharf,
looking there herself, never taking her eyes away. Then she felt him
start and shudder, and knew that he had seen what she saw.

The laird waited at the end of the crazy platform, watching while the
crew of a small boat with double sails of red and brown unloaded its
cargo. Beside him rested his daughter's trunks and a disorderly heap of
bags and boxes. Four men were gingerly climbing out on the wharf,
carrying between them Randall's small medicine chest, a pair of hands
clutching it at each corner.

"Word of God!" muttered Randall. "It's what she saw! It's what that
woman told us of at the table last night! The four men with my chest—
the double sail!"

Margery glanced quickly up at him, surprised that he should be so
shaken.

"Why, yes, it is just as Andra saw it, but that is nothing new. Nothing
to be afraid of. She often does so. On Rona we are used to it."

"I'm not afraid," retorted Randall. "I'm going down there. I want to
find out."

He strode swiftly toward the dock, and she hurried along behind him.

"What—what do you want to find out?"

"Why it takes four men to carry what's less than two stone weight."

Breathless from trying to keep up with him, she ran down the uneven
planking till they reached her father. Rona, too, seemed curious, for he
was questioning the men in their native Gaelic, nodding gravely at their
answers. Still unable to form any words herself, she heard Randall say,
"By God, it gave me a start, sir! What's the meaning of it?"

Rona smiled widely and motioned the men to go on with their work.

"Why there's naught strange about it, and 'tis easy understood. Someone in Stornaway, Tam MacVean, likely, heard us talking among ourselves and learned ye were a doctor and the chest had your drugs and
instruments in it. Doctoring and magic, for folk in these islands, sir, be
much the same. The lads chewed the matter betwixt them whilst they
was crossing, and none of them wanted to be the one to bear it ashore,
lest it slip and fall from him, and its contents break and bring curses
down. In the end they agreed they would all put a hand to it. 'Tis not
strange, Randall. Ye're pale, lad, as if your grandmother's ghostie had
bespoken ye."

"I wouldn't have minded her," muttered Randall, "for she was a good
kind woman living, and would turn no different after. But that could
not be. We do not much believe in ghosts in my country, nowadays.

And I never knew a creature of flesh and blood who could shut her eyes and see what will come to pass! I'll admit, it fair distracts me."

Rona made a careless gesture. "Ye'll na' take it so ill next time, will he, Madge? Come to the house, lad. I'll pour ye no French slop this time, but usquebaugh, as was distilled from our own barley. It'll turn your legs to willow wands and sing in your blood like music. Andra's a rare lass, and 'twill no seem so ghoulish to ye when ye've talked to her and know her well."

Margery had her breath back now. She moved between the two men and linked her arms with theirs.

"Father's right," she said. "Let's go home."

On the cart road just above the clachan they met Ellen. She curtsied and stood aside for them to pass, giving Randall a slantwise look from her narrow greenish eyes. But Ellen had said she was going to pull kelp, thought Margery, and here she was, coming from Rhinn House! Well, perhaps she had only gone to take milk or a cheese, or herbs for Caitlin. And in any case, what harm was it if she had been there? What harm if she had changed her mind? It was a common thing to do.

They greeted the cattle maid briefly and walked on, and Margery thought Randall had missed the sly glance aimed at him, but a moment later she knew that he had not. That was when he threw his head back, and his eyes smiled without merriment, and he spoke to Rona.

"Did I hear you say, sir, that lasses are born white or black, and there's an end on 't?"

"Aye," agreed his host warily. "I might ha' said such a thing to ye."

"Then I say you're wrong, sir, begging your pardon. Black and white they may be born, but that's never the end of it—only the start."

VII

A Matter for Women

SHE HAD told him there were more Ronas than one in the Western Islands, that it was a common name amongst them, an old northern word meaning "bare rocks in the sea," but Randall was finding Margery's island home anything save rocky and bare. Sometimes he felt almost overwhelmed by the teeming life of it. No matter how early he wakened, the men in the clachan and on the circling farms were up before him, calling to each other as they strode off for the machair, to scatter rotting heath and burnt seaweed on the crops of oats and barley already laid down. And in the evenings they gathered in little groups on the doorstones or worn grassy places, smoking their pipes and plucking their fiddles, gossiping, and whittling small animals out of horn and bone, or merely sitting relaxed, staring contentedly into the dark. They were a quiet, dignified people; shy, not unfriendly, given to bursts of rich laughter, loving a jest or the rhythm of a song; good seamen, at home on the water as if their ancestors had been a web-footed folk. He had gone among them often during the month he had been on Rona, learned their names, and enough simple phrases of the Gaelic to make himself understood, discovering somewhat later that most of them could use English themselves when they chose, a rough, reluctant, workaday kind. His physician's eye noted that they were prolific. Many of the women carried suckling children into the fields with them, and Kenneth's school over the byre was crowded with sturdy lads and solemn little girls, sitting on the crude steps that led up to it, because there was such scant room for them inside.

Nor were the lesser forms of life missing. Overhead, from moor and crag and sea beach, the birds kept calling all day long; gulls, gannets, kittiwakes, strange birds he had never seen before, and many familiar birds of home. Red deer cropped the heather, and blue and orange and purple shellfish clung to the rocks in the shallow coves. To go a-fishing was to come back with nets full of cod and ling. Small dark cattle grazed on Ardmory, and black-faced sheep and rams on the middle uplands of Caldune.

Only the land he distrusted, poor and stony on the crofts round the village, and a reach of glittering white sand beyond the daisy fields in the low-lying west. Could it feed all the people who must rely on it, he wondered. He thought regretfully of his mother's table—the good roast beef and mince pies, stewed cranberry and pumpkin—and doubted if there would be any such ample fare for the folk of Ballyrhinn to warm their insides with when winter came.

Some of these rambling thoughts he tried to put into a letter to his father one night in late May, sitting alone in his room on the upper floor of Rhinn House. Supper was long over, but the sky had not yet grown dark, for it seemed as if twilight lasted forever here. He had opened the casement looking west over the gray-green curve of the island to the low gray sea, and a soft wind cooled his face and ruffled a lock of his blond hair. It was enough to make him lay his pen down, and turn his back on the candlelight, and stare off into the misty world that would never be real to him as Hampton Falls was real. Hampton Falls, he thought, and then other familiar names rang over like a chime of bells; Dover, Barrington, Exeter, Haverhill, New Castle—and he remembered with a start where last he had heard that music played. It was in a letter from his father he had received that morning, the letter he was trying to answer now.

When John Woodbury sat down to write that letter, he had not known of his son's decision to leave Edinburgh, and he had addressed him at the house in Rowan Tree Wynd. Either Tom Culpepper or Mac-Crimmon had sent it on. He had been disturbed when he wrote it, and apprehensive of troubles greater than could come to the son of any one man. It was rumored, his letter said, that Parliament was at work on a whole spate of new acts to punish the colonies for destroying the Company's tea. That Lord North complained Boston should be knocked about the ears, and he would send four or five frigates to do the work. That Lord George Germain wanted to abolish town meeting! At home, Governor Wentworth had tried to calm the Assembly and tell them how happy they were under the King, saying that their taxes were light, the French war was paid for, and the treasury had a surplus of five thousand, eight hundred and seventy pounds. But he had not convinced the New Hampshire men who listened to him. Their ears were cocked for rumblings from Massachusetts and Virginia. There was talk of rallying to defend Boston, in Dover, in Exeter, in the others, the old towns.

"It is like when there is a black wind blowing off the sea," John Woodbury had written, "when the sky draws down and hides the Isles of

Shoals, and you know a storm is coming, but what will come of the storm, you do not know. Will your house have a roof when it is over, and your cattle and your children be still alive? You are on that side of the water, lad. For God's sake, write and tell me, what is the truth of it? What are they doing there?"

Randall smiled bleakly as he stared out into the night. He was eight hundred miles from London and his father was three thousand, but his father knew more of what they were doing than he. He had withdrawn into an island. He had retired from the world and set his face to another life. But had any man a right to do that? The thought troubled him.

Below on the terrace he saw Margery coming out of the garden. She wore a full-skirted white dress, filmy and thin, her hands were full of sea pinks and she was singing.

> *"Oh I gang like a ghost, and I care na' much to spin,*
> *I dare na' think o' Jamie, for that would be a sin—"*

Sometimes it seemed to him that Margery was the only being on Rona who did not "gang like a ghost," who was made out of the real substance of the earth. Even Comyn Rhinn, sturdy and matter-of-fact as he was, had lived long in the old East, and sometimes a foreign word on his tongue or a quick-hidden light in his eyes caused Randall to stir uneasily, as he imagined hot jungles full of swollen flowers and great snakes festooned from the trees like streamers of flecked brocade, disturbing slant-eyed women, knives and incense and temple gongs. There was so much in the laird's consciousness that was not in his and never would be.

He blew out the candle and ran downstairs to join her on the terrace.

"Oh, Randall," she cried, as they stopped and stood still, smiling at each other. "I was going to take these to Caitlin. Do you think it would disturb her if I carried them up now?"

He frowned, looked past her at the squills and primroses beyond the stone pavement, all the same soft colors of mauve and ivory in the evening light. "You know I cannot tell you," he said. "You know Caitlin will not see me."

"Oh, but Randall," she spoke gently, as if she sensed the wounded pride in his voice and sought to comfort him. "It is only because she is so modest out of all reason, and you are a man. It is not you she distrusts. It would be so with anyone. But I saw you talking with Leitis today. I thought she might have told you—more than she tells me."

"I do not think even Leitis knows all of the trouble—only that there is pain. But I was asking her what medicine Andra leaves. I was curious to know that."

"Did she tell you?"

He smiled. "Yes. It is simple enough and seems to work as a palliative. Chopped nettles mixed with white of egg to smooth on her forehead and make her sleep."

"Oh? I never heard of it myself, but then, I am not wise in such matters. Is it a remedy you use in America?"

"I am afraid we would put no great faith in it there."

"But does it really help?"

"Sometimes, Leitis says, unless the pain is too great."

"You have never talked to Andra herself?"

"No, and I should like to. Could you arrange it, do you think? She might be more friendly if you were there."

Margery looked thoughtful. "She might talk to you about Caitlin," she answered finally. "She never keeps her medicines secret. She says they are for folk to know and use; that she had the recipes from her grandmother who is long dead, and wants others to have the good of them when she herself is gone. But she might fear you would question her about the sight. That, she does not like to talk about."

"She tells her visions. I heard her, that first night I came."

"Yes, but not always. And sometimes before she is quite awake again. And that night—my father commanded her to, that night. He never means to, and he is always sorry after. But he often does. He wants so much to know."

Margery's voice died away, and Randall was conscious of a little wind stirring the rowans in the garden, and the beat of surf on the crags below the house. Now at last the dark was settling down. Over the sea hung a crescent moon.

"You know," she spoke hurriedly, as if she wanted to finish the speech before anyone could stop her, "I think he is always hoping that Andra will have a word from the dead. The taischers never do. But he loved my mother so much he cannot let her go. He—"

"He might as well!" Randall spoke sharply and then was sorry when he saw the hurt in her eyes. But of course he could not explain. He could not explain even to himself how he felt about those dying words of Sally Anne. And yet, he was still not sure how he felt about Margery. If he had been a lusty young bachelor, he thought, a man who had not known marriage for what it was, he would have shown her a thing or two about courting that her loutish Highlander seemed unaware of, shown her and had her answer weeks ago. But he had been married once, a marriage that he had not chosen, but that had happened to him, like losing his childhood voice or growing a beard. It had happened, and it was over, or appeared to be, for he still distrusted that last threat of Sally Anne's. Next time he did not mean for it to happen. He meant to choose. He sighed and glanced about him restlessly, at all the peaceful beauty of the dark island, the faintly glimmering meadows of the sea.

"Come," he said, "let us go in. Play me a tune on the spinet. Not what you were singing about 'Jamie.' It's too mournful for a fine night. Play the Greensleeves air."

Heavy steps moved determinedly across the flagstones and Kenneth appeared out of the shadow. Margery turned to him with a playful greeting.

"And where have you been, sir? Out all alone contemplating the moon? Are we to believe that?"

Kenneth looked startled, Randall thought, like a boy caught stealing apples, but the look passed quickly from his face and perhaps had never really been there.

"Down in the clachan," he replied, scooping the sea pinks from Margery's grasp. "Give me your posies, lass, and tell me where ye want them put. I canna' hold hands with one so cumbered." He paid no more attention to Randall than to the little stunted rowan tree by the garden wall.

Margery forced a laugh that ended on a broken note. "Bring them into the house," she told him. "We were just going in."

The schoolmaster bent toward her and was about to utter another pleasantry when Rona came hurrying around from the lawns by the front door.

"Hoo, lad!" he cried, coming straight for Randall. "Get down to the clachan! There's a lass there like to bleed herself away!"

"Who is it?" pleaded Margery. "Oh, who is it, Father?"

"Lavan," he said, and stood still, his face mottled red, trying to catch his breath.

"Why Lavan was—Lavan was—"

"Yes. Lavan was with child. And she fell—going up Ardmory to spell Ellen. They brought her to Andra's. Get ye down there, lad."

Hurrying upstairs for his little deerskin chest, Randall felt almost overcome with inner rebellion. He did not want to go. It was not, he told himself, that he had seen the schoolmaster's arm fall about Margery's shoulders as he turned away from them. It was the unlucky chance that his first trial of skill among the island people should be in a branch of his profession in which he felt least qualified. He tried to reassure himself. He knew what should be done. He had seen it done, done it himself. But not in front of a witch woman like Andra, not to a patient who looked on magic and medicine as much the same. He cheered himself with the thought that they might not let him in.

When he descended again to the hall of Rhinn House on his way out, Margery was not there, having gone to her room or to Caitlin, perhaps. Kenneth stood by the cold hearth frowning, and Rona sprawled in a chair, still panting and calling for whiskey, which Sim was bringing from a sideboard as big as a corn bin.

"Get down to Andra's wi' ye," he ordered Randall. "There's a mort o' women there, and ye'll send one of them for me if there's need, but dinna' send for my lass. Such sights are not for her."

"If it's as you say, I'll need no help from either of you," Randall told him soberly. "Andra will be the one. Perhaps between us, we can save the child."

The laird shook his head. "Save the lass herself," he muttered, and "we'll be in debt to ye. Ah, Sim! Thank ye, lad! 'Tis the breath o' life ye're bringing me, as none can deny."

As Randall strode down the cart road through the soft island night toward the lighted cottages by the water, he tried to order his thoughts for the work ahead of him, like lining up the men of a trainband on muster day. Dr. John Burton's book on midwifery, considered in Edinburgh to be the latest word in such matters, was somewhere in the niche of stone shelves in his room at Rhinn House, but you could not go to a patient with a book in one hand and take a pulse with the other. Better to try and think what his father did that time the bound girl was bleeding to death in Seabrook, and the doctor there would not treat her because she was unwed. It had taken her master so long to send, and them to ride down, they had almost lost her. As he followed the winding lane along the white beach he could sense a hush unusual that early in the night. The women and children were not on the doorsteps. Here and there a group of men smoked and chatted, watching him uneasily as he passed, but no fiddles played, and even Johnny Dweeney's obstreperous bagpipes were still. He greeted the loungers briefly, and he read in their eyes that they knew his calling now. Rona had told them, doubtless, that he was a book doctor from Edinburgh. They would wait, skeptical, perhaps, but willing to see what he could do.

He had sometimes thought to himself when he walked alone at night beside the sea, either here, or in the old days at home, that hidden away in every man there are many men the world does not know about, and at least one child—the child he was before his beard grew and he learned to fire a gun and hold a plow and make his way in the world; the child that he will carry to the grave with him, that is never wise, nor disciplined, nor grown. In his soul he could feel that child now, stir, and tremble, and cry out, and turn to run from a challenge too great for it. Stubbornly he forced the child down and held to his course through the silent clachan.

Before Andra's house he paused. He could hear a murmur of voices within, and a light shone under the matting that hung across the doorway. He tapped against the crude stone of the wall.

"Andra," he called softly, and then with greater firmness, "Andra!"

When she pulled the matting aside and stood looking at him, he stared into her sea-blue eyes and pale ivory face, and suddenly it was as if his own blood turned and all his strength and confidence came flooding back. Andra, he thought with surprise, was indeed a magic woman to affect him so. He cleared his throat.

"Andra, I am a doctor of medicine. Perhaps Rona told you. He said Lavan was very ill here and you needed help."

Andra bent her head ever so slightly. "Lavan is bad indeed," she answered in English as proper as his. "Rona told me what you are, and that you would come."

She stood aside for him to enter the cottage.

At first the smoke hurt his eyes, and he could hardly see more than the blurred outlines of female figures clustered in one corner, but he was aware that all talking among them had ceased, that a breathlessness hung in the air, as tangible as the blue fragrance of peat smoke. He stood still and brushed his hand across his eyes, and gradually the room all came clear.

It was more like a cave than the clean kitchens the women kept where he had grown up, not dirty or littered but windowless, almost without furniture, the walls of gray, discolored stone. A fire burned in an earth pit in the center, and two straw pallets stood at the far end. One of them was covered with a clean blanket, and on the other lay a huddled form. A few of the women crouched, animal-like, near it, and two small iron lamps smelling of fish oil burned on a shelf above. He thought regretfully of the bright sunlit room with its scrubbed oak table where he and his father had spread the unconscious body of the bound girl to do what must be done. He thought of the rosy-faced kindly New Hampshire housewife in her starched dress who had stood by to help. He stepped forward and pulled back the blanket, aware that all eyes were following him, the patient, deep, far-seeing eyes of the island women.

At first he thought Lavan had died, she lay so still and clay-colored, but then she stirred a little, and he noticed a faint beating in her throat. She was covered with only a shift, and all about her curved a sort of nest of woolen rags, dark and blood-stained toward the center. Lavan writhed, as if to escape from what he knew must be an almost unbearable, heavy, grinding pain. She was shivering. He pulled the shift away and laid bare the delicate young body. It must have been early days with her, he thought, for there was no swelling to betray her condition, and he remembered that she had only been married at New Year's, and Lavan was a girl of good name. Now it was almost June. The child could date from any time between. He suddenly remembered the husband.

"Where is Iver?" he asked without turning his head.

"At sea," someone murmured, "fishing for ling below Stornaway. Three days he has been gone."

He stared down at the body of the girl, the softly curving belly, the loose and flabby bosom, the depressed nipples that in health must have been so rosy and firm. He realized that Andra stood beside him and that he was glad to have her there. It was as if his mother had come to the aid of the child he was, the frightened child, hidden secure in bonds of iron within. And maybe a man's mother was a better help than his father at such a time, or than the wisest doctor ever born. It was a woman's season and crisis, a matter for women.

"Has the child—?" he asked.

Andra shook her head. "No."

"Can it be saved, do you think?"

She shook her head again. "No. I think it should not be. Once I saved such a child, and it came to a monstrous birth. I have not tried to do so again. But we cannot make it pass."

Slowly, tensely, while the women watched him, he examined Lavan. Whenever she stirred, blood welled in the rags about her. He knew what he must do now, and he hated doing it.

"You are right. It must come away," he said.

He opened his deerskin chest and took out a metal rod with notched prongs on the end, and began to rub it with sweet oil. Suddenly he caught an hysterical murmur in Gaelic from one of the women.

"What does she say?" he asked Andra, still stroking the narrow instrument.

"She says, 'It is the magic staff of a warlock,'" replied Andra tonelessly.

He fumbled for the words himself and then gave up. "Tell her I am no warlock," he ordered. "Tell her it is a tool—like a harrow, like a plow, like a spindle—such as she uses every day. It is to open the mouth of the womb and draw away what would have been the child. The bleeding can be checked after that. I know no magic. We will use no magic here."

As he bent over Lavan he could hear Andra calmly repeating his message. Then he called to her to help him as he drew the tender flesh apart.

The climax of his task was surprisingly easy. The young wife had sunk too deeply into unconsciousness to feel pain or offer resistance, and in any case, the foetus was near ready to pass of itself. He noticed that it was a well-formed child, a boy. Perhaps Lavan had a little anticipated her wedding after all. He could not be sure. At least, he would not allow the question to arise. He caught it up quickly in a rag of stained wool. "It is dead," he told Andra harshly. "Burn it."

Bending again to the sick girl, he was dimly aware of the midwife carrying out his orders at the fire pit behind him. He thought of Iver Gall, who had hoped for a son, perhaps; of another lad who had hoped for a son once, long ago, under a blue-green tree on a New Hampshire hill.

He delivered the membranes easily and adjusted wads of clean linen in case further bleeding should occur. Lavan twisted herself again, and writhed, and muttered. Randall held her head up so that she would not choke, and gazed at her slim arms flung limply outward, at their soft flesh all waxen pale in the light of the reeking oil lamp. If he followed the custom of his profession as it was practiced both in America and in Edinburgh, he would lift one of those arms now, choose a likely vein and draw blood; establish the little bleeding there to draw the flow away from the great arteries that fed the womb. But he could not bring himself to do it. Lavan had lost so much blood. Then he straightened up and spoke to the huddled women who watched him with their quiet wise eyes.

"Go home now. She must have rest and stillness about her and clean air to breathe, unpoisoned by so many breaths. We cannot tell yet how she will fare, but now there is no more to do. You will be called—if there is need."

He was prepared for protests and excited speech, but no one demurred. Instead they crept silently past him, out of the cottage, their patient heads bowed and their glances all cast down. Finally he was alone with Andra and the sick girl—and that last undying danger out of the old dark, that will always win in the end, but that a man must always fight.

"We shall watch together now," said Andra, bringing him a three-legged stool. "First I shall make her bed clean and dry."

He sank down on the rough wooden seat placed just behind Lavan's head and leaned wearily against the stones of the cottage wall. He could feel their cold through his woolen coat, almost feel the moisture seeping through.

"Do not move her too much," he said.

Andra did not reply, and he watched her expert fingers pull the stained rags from the bed and draw clean ones gently under the still body. When she had finished she stood a moment looking down at the results of her work, then she went to the fire and heaped on another sod of turf.

"She must not take a chill," Andra told him, "and we dare not have more than a thin cover over her while we watch, lest the bleeding start again and we be unaware."

He nodded in agreement. She pulled up another stool and seated herself by the narrow bed.

"May I see it?" she asked, holding out her hand for the instrument he was cleaning to put away.

He gave it to her, and she examined it carefully, then handed it back. "It served you well," she told him. "It opened the womb as the child's head could not do. A dead child has no power to stir, only the dull weight of itself bearing down. I never saw a device like this before."

"I do not like it," said Randall. "Childbed fever too often follows its use. And I cannot see why, for it is always washed in warm water and kept clean. You must watch her for some days, to be sure the fever does not start."

Andra nodded silently, and for the moment he felt too exhausted and relieved to make any further talk. He was content to sit with his back to the damp wall, closing his eyes sometimes, not in sleep, only to shut out the unfamiliar sight of the squalid hut and the gaze of the woman's eyes, so quiet and keen, asking so much of him, and offering so much strength and confidence in return. Then he grew alert and tense again, watching Lavan, waiting for the clean rags around her to turn red and darken. But she lay quiet, not writhing or muttering any more, and the redness did not come. And then he grew restless with the long night going by them, and he felt reassured and himself again. He turned to Andra and spoke.

"You have seen this happen to women many times, have you not?"

She shook her head.

"Not many times. It is uncommon here. You must have seen more of it than I."

He smiled at her. "Andra," he said, "I'll be honest with you. At midwifery I'm no better than a blacksmith. You should see Sandy MacCrimmon catching pauper bairns at the Infirmary. He's but to curve his hands and call, and they creep forth like snails after a rain. But when I'm confronted with a bearing woman, the Devil himself couldn't scare me more."

She looked at him with a quiet smile on her lips but her eyes did not change. "Yes," she said thoughtfully. "I can see it might be like that for a man."

"You—can see?"

Andra, he thought, must have understanding, a greater gift than the second sight.

"Yes. I can see. Bearing is a matter for women. How can you think to aid us, when you yourselves cannot give life?"

He smiled again, somewhat wryly. "We have our part in it," he said. "In the pleasure, yes. But not in the time of pain."

Suddenly he wanted her to know that he, too, had once almost had a part in the great miracle of life.

"Andra," he said. "I know that pleasure. I had a wife, but she died before our child had quickened in her. She died of the throat-ail."

Andra nodded sympathetically. "That was hard, yes. But you are young. You will have other sons."

He cried out, startled. "That was what my mother said to me! Did you hear my mother say that? Did you see me before I came to Rona? Did you, Andra? That first night when I came to Rhinn House, you looked at me as if you had seen me before."

Her eyes met his steadily across the body of the unconscious girl.

"I saw you," she murmured uncertainly, like a person waking from sleep. "I saw you, but I heard no such words spoken. I heard you say, 'Edinburgh is the place and I better go there.' I saw something red upon the floor."

"The Turkey carpet in my father's study!" he breathed. "Here—half-way across the world you saw that! You heard me talk! By God, I think —I think I am afraid of you!"

Then he was shocked at himself. He sank back on the stool, muttering an apology.

But Andra spoke calmly, seeming again to understand.

"Many have been," she said. "At first there was no one more afraid than I. But never, after that first time, have I feared what I saw. It is not held a matter for fear in the Highlands. There is a clachan on Eriskay where everyone has it. I have heard that in Skye there are those who offer to teach it for a pound of tobacco."

She reached for Lavan's wrist and began to rub it gently as she talked. "You are young and wise in all the ways of the world and its new learning. But you are in an old country here, where time moves slowly and customs linger, and there is little change."

He had heard the same from Rona and Margery, he thought, but there was something about Andra that made him go on listening to her.

"The old beliefs stay, like the old mist that hides the hills even in broad noon and never quite fades from them. We believe many things here that the professors in Edinburgh say are not so, but when you find they are wrong, you must not be afraid."

Now she was lecturing him, he thought, and he was nettled by it.

"How do you know," he asked, hating his own rudeness even as the words left his mouth, "what the professors say in Edinburgh?"

Andra smiled, ignoring his insolence.

"I do not know," she told him, "but I know well how they used to talk when I was young in Aberdeen, for my father was one of them. I think the city scholars of today are likely much the same."

"Margery told me," he said, interested in spite of the cold stones at his back and the heaviness of sleep about his eyelids, "that you were not born on Rona; that you came from away."

"Ah, Margery! I was as young as she is, once, and our ways in life were not so far apart. I was not a laird's daughter, but my father owned houses in the city and a country place in the hills east of Banff, by the little river Deveron that we take our name from. My father taught Hebrew and Greek at the College. I was a pretty girl. You would scarce believe it."

"You are beautiful now, Andra," he told her, and he meant what he said. "It shows in your face that you have lived beautifully—healing and comforting all."

Still smiling, she shook her head in denial and went to pour fresh oil from a clay jug into the iron lamps. Then she returned to her place by Lavan's side.

"Many would say my life has been ugly and mean," she resumed. Her eyes looked straight at his but did not seem to meet them, stared, only, at the wall behind. She might have been talking to herself rather than to him, but she was telling the thing he had wondered about ever since his first night on Rona, and if the thatch over his head had taken fire, he might have stopped listening, but for no lesser interruption.

"I was a girl in the country house I spoke of. My brothers were grown and well-placed in the world. 'Twas thought I would marry well. I wish I could tell it all over as it was, the wonderful safe feeling of being a lass in my father's house, fair and desired and young. The wind would whip through the little Scottish firs at dusk, and in winter the snow would cling like eiderdown to the pointed turrets, and my father's students would ride out to take tea or wine."

"And there was one lad out of all the others," he prompted her. "There is always one."

"Yes. There was one. The young men are brave and bonny nowadays, as they were then. But they are not the same as he, and they never were. There was a difference on him. We were much together and thinking to be wed. But then—lad, have you ever been in a country that fell to war?"

Randall considered.

"If you count fighting Indians," he told her. "My country's never out of that. Likely won't be, in my time. But war between nations—no."

"This was fighting all amongst our own, and that is the bitterest kind.

The old and the new, fighting to see who should have Scotland. Many lads marched south with Charlie and did not come back, and among them was mine. 'Tis stale gossip now, for it was many years ago. Perhaps in America you have never heard."

"It is not much talked about in America, but I have been near nine months in Scotland and heard little else. I know the route of Prince Charlie's army as well as you."

"Not as well as I, for it is my heart that knows it. One afternoon I was sitting in the great hall with my family, all in a white dress with my hair down."

Randall remembered Margery moving across the terrace, her hands full of sea pinks, her white dress standing out against the dark. Andra went on.

"I was at the spinet, and the others were drinking tea. And it was then that the vision came. No one knew I had the sight. It had never afflicted me before. My grandmother was a Manson of Cromarty, and the Mansons were always famous for seeing what was not there but would be. My mother did not have it. 'Tis said to be in every red-haired daughter, and her hair was brown."

"What did you see that first time?" He gave a hurried glance toward Lavan, but she seemed to be in a natural sleep now, and no fresh bloodstains marred the whiteness of her bed.

"I saw my lad, all thin and pale, lying in a prison chamber with his hands bound. Near him stood an older man, dark-bearded, and his hands were free. He offered my lad a cup of water, but he could not swallow and his head fell back. It seemed I saw him die. I screamed then, and wakened, weeping, and trembling, and all a-sweat. My father was a man of the new day, just as you are. He tried to tell me I had had a dream. But my mother knew. Later—only a week it was—the strange man in the vision came to our door. He told us how my lad died in the prison at Carlisle, just as I had seen. They had fought side by side and been taken together, but the one had perished with gaol fever and the other been freed and sent home. He promised that he would seek me out and tell me the way of it. He could not know I had seen it all before."

She sunk her head on her breast and huddled silent on the stool.

"But after that?" Randall asked her gently. "Ellen was not his child. For Ellen is only nineteen, and that was near thirty years ago."

She had turned away from Lavan and sat staring into the fire, and he feared that she might be seeing before her, but she was not. She finally roused herself. He could hear gulls screaming from the waterside, and a thin line of morning light lay under the matting at the door.

"It makes sorry telling, the rest of it," she answered. "My father turned me out, after that. I had fallen ill, and he swore that I was with child, and he sent me to his cousins in Ireland. He said it was to save my name before our friends at home, but I think he was troubled that I had the sight, and wanted me out of the way. His cousins were of the Old Faith, and they gave me to the nuns to become one of them. Lost and grieving as I was then, I knew it was not in my nature to be a nun. I ran away and lived in Belfast as I could. Sometimes I spun at the looms. Sometimes I did not spin. I did not care what became of me. Ellen's father was a sailor from Bristol. He had a wife in England, I learned later, and we were not together long. But with a child to care for, life began to matter again. My strength came back to me, and my pride came back. I would not rear her to the streets and looms. We started home to Scotland, but our ship ran ashore here in a northeast gale. Some of those who had traveled with me were sick or injured, and I nursed them. I remembered my grandmother, Jenny Manson, was a wise woman of the glens, and many of her cures she had told to me when I was a child. I found I remembered them. Then the island people called on me when illness came. I have always thought that when the last one was well, I would go home. But—" she flung out her hands, smiling ruefully at him, "you are a doctor. You know how it falls about. The last one is never well before another is stricken down."

Lavan stirred and called faintly for water. He stood over the bed while Andra held a battered cup to the girl's lips. Faint color crept back under the pallid skin.

Andra touched him on the shoulder. "Go home," she said, "and sleep. Ellen will be here soon to help me if there is need. There should be no more trouble now."

Lavan stirred again, and he heard her murmur a desperate question. He did not want to be there when Andra replied to it, to tell her the child was gone. Hurrying to make his escape, he stumbled at the threshold and Lavan's bitter crying overtook him. It was well enough for Andra to say that bearing was woman's work, but he felt he knew better than she did how Lavan was feeling now. He thought he could not bear it as he strode through the clachan and up the hill.

VIII

It Was Not I

When Ellen came down Ardmory a pale gold mist hid everything before her, muffling the beat of the sea and the first sound of morning life astir in the clachan of Ballyrhinn. Ellen was angry, and she hurled an impatient curse at a tiny rabbit that leaped out of the dewy rushes by the burn and scuttled between her feet, almost tripping her. She hastened on, grinding her bare heels into the ferns and mosses as savagely as if they were at fault because she had had to stay alone all night at the shieling after being there all the previous day. Waited, she had, while the stars burned themselves away, but that worthless Lavan had never come to take her turn. Well, Ailis would be there in an hour or two. She'd go home now for a bit of bread and a cup of barley-bree. Then she'd go and rout out that idle strumpet, as sure as her name was Ellen Deveron. Putting on airs, Lavan thought she could, now that she was a married woman!

There had been some sort of outcry in the glen last night, about the time Lavan should have come to her work. Ellen had not paid much attention to it then, for Kenneth had just left her, and she had still lain soothed and sated with love in the nest of heather all warm from the two of them. What a lover Kenneth was! She could lie with him forever. Fire in his blood and marrow in his bones. Not like the cold-eyed American lad, unbending as a dry staff, for all the gold in his pocket. If there was, indeed, any gold there. Then the querulous suspicion went out of Ellen's mind. Everyone in Scotland knew that all Americans had money.

Well, thus she had lain up there, feeling herself almost ready to weep out of a fine sadness, thinking how the old proverb was true, that a man could woo where he would but must marry where his fate was. Kenneth would have his Margery, become the Laird of Rona when the old man died, for she had often heard there was no male kin close enough to stand heir. Kenneth expected that she, Ellen, would go on, living disgracefully on his bounty, perhaps as a servant in his wife's very hall. But

that, Ellen did not mean to do. She meant to be married herself and
away to America. Thinking these thoughts, it was no wonder that she
had not missed Lavan until it grew cold and very dark. Then she had
watched, and shivered, and finally warmed herself with rage. All night
Lavan had not come. Perhaps her husband was back from the fishing
and she was even now lying in bed with him. How strange and sweet it
must be, thought Ellen, to lie so with a man.

Now it was morning, and she was still alone, still thinking the same.
Why was this sweetness given to Lavan and not to her? Oh unfair
thing, most unfair! Envy and anger grew in Ellen's heart with every
step she took. She crossed the burn, ran through the mist to her mother's
house beside the invisible sea, flung open the mat and went in.

The first thing she noticed was the close smell of sickness, the smell
of blood. It often greeted her when she came home. The place was as
common to the villagers as the open street, and folk were always dragging themselves to its refuge for a death or a lying-in. Andra stooped
over the fire pit, settling an iron bake pot in the swirl of yellow peat
ashes. Staring past her mother, Ellen saw a slight form under the blankets
of the low bed.

"Who is it?" she asked impatiently, fetching herself a cup of ale from
the stone shelf near the door. "Who's taken now?"

"Lavan," answered Andra quietly. "She fell on the way up the glen
last night. She miscarried."

She pulled a lump of hot barley cake from the pot, slipped a wooden
plate under it and gave it to Ellen. "Don't burn your fingers, child," she
said.

Ellen began to devour the meager breakfast. "So that is where she
was," she replied, still aggrieved. "I should ha' thought somebody could
ha' come up there, and at the far least, told me."

"She was bad—and we were all afraid," said Andra, looking quickly
toward the pallet and then back to her daughter. "When she fell she
cried out, and kept crying till Ewen Gow heard her. He'd been fishing
for trout in the loch and was coming down the burn. He carried her
here. I doubted we could save her, and folk were distraught about it,
for they all love Lavan. I be sorry, Ellen, but no one thought of you at
all."

"Oh they're a fine kindly folk, and they all love Lavan," said Ellen
with bitter sarcasm. "Will she live, is it settled now? How long will she
cumber us here?"

"She will stay here till she can go forth well again," said Andra quietly.
"Yes, I think she will be healed in a week or two. It was the work of
the strange lad at Rhinn House. He is a doctor in his own country, Ellen,

and he came down here last night and saved her with such means as I never saw."

"He—was here?" asked Ellen, her voice sour with a new vexation. To think the American had been in her very house, and she had not known! Then a happier thought came.

"Is he coming back this morning? To see how she does? Do ye look for him soon?"

Andra smiled. "I doubt he will come at all unless I send for him," she said. "The crisis is past. Lavan only needs to gain strength and heal. I promised him I would let him know of anything untoward. He must be asleep by now. He is still young enough to need sleep."

Ellen knew what she meant. Too often she had seen the watchful, wakeful eyes of the old looking at death, lying and looking at it all night long. She sighed. Well, she had missed the one chance, but likely there would be another soon. She stood up and yawned, and was just going to the empty bed to lie down when a rough cheery voice called from outside.

"Ho, Andra! Be ye up and about? How's the lass? Is it decent I come in?"

Andra hurried to pull the mat aside and bid Rona a good morning and welcome to her poor home. He wore a tartan coat and a three-cornered hat, Ellen noticed, and carried a small chest under his arm. Not as if it were a gift, she thought, but as if he was prepared to travel somewhere. And so it turned out.

"I'm away to Glasgow, lass," he told the older woman. "Tam Mac-Vean brought me a word last night from my factor that's left me nothing to do but go. 'Tis these new laws about America that blast the tobacco trade. I do not know where the right lies. I canna' say, with Kenneth, that the King should call out the red Indians to help put the white rebels down. But 'tis not as if they were strong enough to wage war. Should we fear our own blood, these colonies of our own?"

"We have seen wars," said Andra soberly, "you and I. Seen our own blood fight against us before."

Rona shrugged. "I fought in one war I didna' want to—only to please a lass. But I was young then. Still, if she were alive and asked me, I'd do it over." His sharp brown eyes always misted, Ellen noticed, when he talked of his wife. He turned his head slightly.

"But how is Lavan?" he continued. "I came here to ask for her, that and to take leave as I go away."

"Lavan is sleeping," Andra told him. "He is skillful, the American doctor. She would have died without him, I fear. Did he tell you about her when he came home?"

"Too sleepy he was to tell me much, but well-pleased with himself, I thought him, when I asked what he had done. I am glad if he be able to help ye at such times. 'Twas for that I brought him here."

He watched Andra closely, and Ellen watched her too. She saw a faint color darken the cheekbones of the pale ivory face. "I am glad for the people," she replied evenly. "He tells me he has been in Edinburgh at the College and studied with all the great ones. He knows much that I do not know."

Comyn Rhinn flung his arm around her shoulders. "Ye're a good lass not to take it ill. I know there's no better heart than yours, and none more skillful in all the isles, when it comes to the old ways o' cure. But there be many new ways o' doing now, and so much new knowledge. It was against my conscience that the folk here should have no benefit therefrom."

Andra bowed her head. "Yes, there are new ways. Ways that are beyond me. I have been out in the world, and I know how much wiser the great doctors are. They had new skills twenty years ago, and they will have more now, for they always seek to experiment and learn. I am no wiser than the old women of the glens in my grandmother's time. I shall be glad to aid and follow this young man."

Rona smiled approval.

"So now, I go. A week, two weeks, no more. If Lavan needs aught—or any of the people—go to the house and ask Margery. Ye will find her there. Ye will find the doctor, the young man."

He stopped at the door. "Ellen, lass," he said kindly, "I thank ye for staying at your post last night. 'Twas brave in ye not to come wailing down. I spoke to Ailis Ogg and Janet Gillander as I came by. They will help ye all ye need till Lavan be about. Dinna' hurry the lass. Give her full time. Well—a good day to ye."

He left the mat askew behind him. Ellen could see the bright sunlight dancing on the water, the fishing boats putting to sea. The early morning fog was dissolved and gone. She stretched and yawned and turned toward the bed.

"I could sleep till Dunvegan Castle falls," she murmured. She gave Lavan one curious glance, but the girl slept on, unstirring, her face the color of the faded blankets around her. Ellen lay down and went to sleep.

She slept deeply at first, and then fitfully, dreaming. In her dreams she lay utterly contented, drugged with all the warm sweetness of love. Kenneth was hers, she thought; not with her, only gone from her for a little while. He would not have to marry Margery, and she would not have to struggle to charm the American lad. Leave them to themselves

and their money, that bleak, proper pair. She and Kenneth would have
enough without. She seemed to be lying on the heather, the full purple
heather of summertime, and she could see the white clouds drifting overhead and hear the curlews crying, hear them all so plain. Then in the
midst of their crying came another cry. It was near her, somewhere in
the low grasses; it was weak and plaintive, full of pain, but more full of
terror. She rolled over. Heavy—her body felt so heavy, and it took her
a long time. She was looking suddenly into the eyes of the rabbit that
had crossed her path that morning as she came down the glen. The rabbit was caught in a snare, she saw, a snare woven of horsehairs, sharp
hairs that hurt. The rabbit cried out again. Ellen had not known that a
rabbit could cry. The cry brought her broad awake.

She was not in the heather, she was in her own bed in her mother's
cottage, with the smoky thatch overhead instead of the blue sky. But
the crying still went on. She struggled up on one elbow. The sound
came from the other cot. Lavan! She remembered. Lavan was lying there,
and Lavan had miscarried, and she was crying now in terror and pain.
There was something about the cry that frightened Ellen.

"Mother!" she found herself wailing like a child, and then, "Mother!"
again.

No one answered. She glanced quickly round the cottage, rubbing
the sleep from her eyes. Andra was not there. She jumped from her bed
and ran to Lavan.

She was shocked at the pinched gray face on the pillow, the dark eyes
sunk deep in the head. Lavan was not crying now, only making a weak,
desperate noise like the rabbit caught in the snare. Then Ellen saw the
red stain. It had soaked all the bed around. Blood dripped on the stone
floor. On Lavan's wedding day she had hated Lavan, she remembered,
had hated her this morning, but she did not hate her now. There was
no feeling in her except fright, and only the one thing to be done.

"I'll find my mother, Lavan," she cried. "I'll find her. Lie still, and
I'll go."

Lavan croaked something, but what it meant she did not wait to see.
Out into the wide lane she ran, then along the row of houses, calling,
"Mother! Mother!" till her chest seemed to turn to iron and she thought
her breath would fail.

"Has hornets stung ye, lass? Has the French landed?"

Johnny Dweeney rambled toward her, his bagpipes under his arm, a
peace in his slack old face and faded eyes that somehow quieted Ellen
and eased the fear in her heart. People did take sick and die, she thought,
and the world ran on the same. Death was a thing Johnny Dweeney
would many times have seen. She had seen it herself, come to her

mother's house to the stricken souls lying there. But her mother had always been with her then. She had never seen it alone.

"Where is my mother?" she gasped. "Lavan's dying!"

In a second he had put the bagpipes to his mouth. Leaning against a driftwood hurdle stacked with herring spread to dry, Ellen heard the shrill, squeaky tones of the "Lament" lifted on the sunny air. Johnny only played the "Lament" when trouble was abroad, a storm coming, or a ship foundered on the reef in the outer sea. All down the lanes of the clachan, heads poked out of doorways inquiringly. Colin MacKay came leaping down from the roof of his cottage, where he had crouched unseen, mending thatch.

"What be wrong, Johnny?" he demanded.

Ellen cowered against the hurdle, too spent to notice Colin, for all he was sturdy, dark-haired, and young, and indeed a braw man.

"Ye seen Andra? She's needed bad. Her lass says Lavan's like to die."

Colin nodded, his black eyes grave. "I saw her," he said. "She went to Meg Munro's. They sent for her there. The daftie's had a fit again."

Ellen watched him as he ran, head down, elbows close to his sides, to the weathered cottage halfway up the hill where the young widow dwelt with her idiot boy. In a moment he came hurrying forth, her mother beside him, moving almost as quickly as he. Ellen's composure returned to her in a flash. She smoothed her rumpled hair and skirts and held her head high. Into that head ideas began to come. Her own weal was before her eyes again.

She caught Andra's sleeve as the midwife hastened past.

"Lavan's bleeding," she said. "The bed looks like Martinmas slaughter time. Shall I go to Rhinn House for the doctor lad?"

Andra nodded. "Aye," she said. "Aye, do that, Ellen. And Johnny, go and bestir your wife. There's none better than she at such a time."

Johnny pleaded that his Nan was turning to stone in her bed, and 'twould be the work of a regiment to move her, but he would try. Ellen turned her back on them and walked swiftly up the hill to Rhinn House.

On her way she suddenly realized how long she had slept. It was no more morning, nor noonday even. It was late afternoon, and far in the west beyond the red crags of Kindearg the sun was going down. The rambling stone house faced away from the clachan and Ellen approached it from the rear, coming on two broad wings with an unpaved courtyard between, where geese and hens roamed in the last warmth of the day, picking up scattered grain. She crossed the yard, with the granaries and kitchen on one side and the byre on the other. No one seemed to be about, and she slipped into the hall by a low door at the rear.

No one was there either, so she walked straight through, out at the front and around to the terrace. Then she stopped.

Kenneth and Margery stood near a bed of yellow primroses. He had gripped her by the shoulders and was staring unhappily into her eyes.

"How can ye say that, lass," he was pleading. "How can ye say ye'll have none of me any more, after all that's been between? Ye gave your word."

Ellen forgot her errand. She stood tense and still, feeling her face stiffen in an ugly mask, her fingers curl.

"Ah, well I know it, Kenneth," she heard Margery saying, her face white. " 'Tis a reproach to me, sure, to change. But should I bring you the curse of an unloving wife? Is there honor in that? Could you take any happiness there?"

"Ye will love me after," he insisted doggedly. "Ye will see then, Margery. Ye are mine and ye canna' choose. Ye know how it was before. Ye searched the courts and the cities, and ye came back. Ye came back to a Highland man. As ye always will. It's the MacNeill in ye, ye canna' help."

Margery stood there, swaying like a willow wand, and Ellen thought she saw defeat and acquiescence in the girl's eyes. Oh, she would lose him in the end, Ellen knew, but not so soon, not before one more summer of love in the heather on the hill, not before her own plans were complete. If she remembered Lavan now, it was not with compassion, only as an excuse for her own ends. She hurried forward.

"Oh Madge, Lavan's dying! Mother bade me come—"

The pair turned sharply. Kenneth let go of Margery and stood back, drawing his black brows fiercely down. He turned on Ellen, angered by the interruption.

"And if she be, there's no help in us. Get the doctor from his chamber above."

" 'Tis for Doctor I came," murmured Ellen smugly, well in control of herself now. "Will ye fetch him, Madge, or tell me where I'll find—"

"Randall!" called Margery, lifting her voice anxiously. "Randall!" She turned to Ellen and explained. "His room is just above." She pointed to an open casement, and soon enough a tousled head thrust forth.

"Oh Margery! You think I've slept long enough, and you're right. I'm a sluggard sure. I was just waking!"

"Randall! Ellen's come for you. Her mother sent her. Lavan's worse again."

"How?"

"She's bleeding, I think," said Ellen demurely, looking down.

"I'm coming. Tell Andra I'm coming," he said. He withdrew from the window. When Ellen turned back to Margery the girl stood alone. Kenneth was no longer there.

"Shall I go with you, Ellen?" Margery asked.

Ellen shrugged. She could not see what use Margery would be at the bedside, the tryst with Kenneth was broken and that purpose served. She shook her head.

"Oh the house will be full of women, I dinna' doubt, who know of themselves what's useful at such a time. If we need ye, we'll let ye know."

She lingered, thinking to walk back to the clachan with Randall, but she misjudged his swiftness. When she crossed the midden and started down the hill in the first long shadows of twilight, she saw him striding far ahead of her, too far to overtake. Since there was no need to hurry she walked slowly through the peace of the village. Most of the women were by the hearths cooking supper, and the men came straggling home now, in little groups, from the fields or the sea. Blue smoke drifted upward, and children played on the green turf in the pleasant evening light.

When she peered into her mother's house she did not find the turmoil she expected. Randall bent over the bed, his hair still tousled from sleep and the ruffled sleeves of his white cambric shirt rolled to the elbow. Old Nanny Dwecncy, her face like an oak gall left on the ground all winter, crouched in a corner grasping her staff and watching him with steady toadlike eyes. Andra stood close to the bed, too, soaking rags in a wooden bowl.

" 'Tis the coldest water," she was telling Randall, "and Colin has gone to the spring for more."

Ellen slipped in and stood silently watching them. The American looked calm and sure, she thought, even a little self-satisfied. He was proud of having saved Lavan last night, and he would now proceed to do it again, with no more trouble than taking his supper and a dràm. Even Rona, who trusted the old ways more than most, had let it be known this morning that she found them no longer good, that she preferred the skill of this young man.

"Cold water," said Randall, turning away, "and pillows to keep her feet high."

"I have done all that," said Andra. "She is bleeding still."

He moved to the table, opened a small chest and began reaching into it, taking certain vials out.

"These should help," he said, smiling confidently into Andra's eyes.

Ellen watched them as they stood, shoulder to shoulder at their work. Then time drew out, and Ellen forgot to watch them. She moved idly about the room, now crouching on a stool, now going to the door and gazing up the hill at Rhinn House and its lighted windows on the night sky, wondering if Margery lay in Kenneth's arms as last night she had lain.

"All that had been between them!" What had he meant by that? He had never spoken intimately of Margery, and she had never dared to question him. Was Miss Margery, for all her fine airs, only a common slut after all?

With one ear she listened to Randall and her mother. Lavan was still bleeding. They dosed her with powdered alum and honey. They steeped wads of linen in alum and tannin water to check the flow, and Lavan bled still. Finally she heard Randall say tensely, "She is going now, I think! Andra—I know of no other thing!"

"Nor I," said Andra slowly, standing by his side and looking down. Ellen let her eyes follow theirs. She had never known so much blood could flow or that it took anyone so long to die.

And then she became aware of a new presence in the room.

"I remembered something—and I brought it down," a low, faltering voice said.

Ellen turned, sensing that the others did the same. Margery Rhinn stood just inside the doorway. She had a velvet cloak over her flowered silk dress, and in her hand a small stone crock.

"Margery," she heard Randall say harshly, "go away. Your father would not want you here. It is no place."

Margery looked at them uncertainly. "Is Lavan—?"

"Lavan is dying," he rasped. "We cannot help Lavan any more."

"Not you nor Andra either?"

"No, neither of us."

"And it is sure Lavan will die?"

"Yes," he told her, half swallowing his words before he could get them out.

"Then—this I have brought—it would not be wicked to try it now."

He only stared at her. Andra stared. Margery went on, falteringly. "I went to the cellar for some wine or cordial—for something that might help. I was alone there in the house—not knowing—wishing there was something I could do."

For the first time she looked past them at Lavan, gray and shrunken in the stained bed. She caught her breath.

"And there, all in the cobwebs, I found it. It is old, and it is strong, and there is a curse on it. It can kill of itself. But I saw it save a man from death on Barra long ago. I will give it to Lavan, if there is no other way."

"There is no way at all," said Randall.

Then Andra spoke. "Is it heather ale, Miss Margery?"

Margery gave her a timid smile. "Yes," she said, "it is heather ale."

Randall looked at them questioningly, his back turned to the dying girl, for he could not bear to watch her any more.

"I have heard of it," Andra went on. "It is said to be half made of blessings and half of curses, and it was the drink of the little old dark men who held all Scotland long ago. It is said to be an uncertain risk always. But in the last extremity—one may try."

"If it was a thing you had heard of, why did you not send for some before?" asked Randall, reluctant to dose a patient, even a dying one, with the curses of little old dark men.

"I never saw any of it," Andra told him simply. "I did not know there was a drop of it left in the world any more. I do not know its action or its source. There's none alive knows the way for making it now."

"I know the way," said Margery steadily. "The MacNeills of Barra know. But I did not make this. I think it was from my grandmother's brewing."

She stepped forward and went down on her knees in all the blood and filth of sickness on the stone floor. She held up Lavan's head and hesitated, with the crock grasped in her other hand, looking for a cup.

No one brought it to her. Lavan gasped. Under the flickering lamp the gray shadows gathered in the hollows of her face.

"Ellen," said Margery imperiously, "fetch me a cup—or spoon."

Ellen wanted to resist the command, less to protect Lavan from the uncertain drink than to show the other girl who was mistress here. But there was a quiet strength in the voice of the laird's daughter that would bend iron and halt flame. Silently she brought a small earthen cup.

Margery filled it from the crock, held Lavan's head up again and set the cup to the drawn mouth. Lavan's head lolled back. She made no attempt to drink. After a moment Margery turned as if seeking help from them. Mutely they stood and watched her—Randall, and Ellen, and Andra, and old Nanny Dweeney, and the neighbor women. Randall slowly shook his head.

Margery's face hardened into a cold little smile, and Ellen suddenly hated the girl, that she had smiled instead of railing and cursing at them, as she herself would have done. Setting the cup down, the laird's daughter ripped a flounce from her silken skirt, soaked a bit of it in the dark purple liquid, and worked the rag between Lavan's chattering teeth. Then she held her hand across the sick girl's mouth so that she could not spew it forth, waiting there on her knees, paying no more at-

tention to the others than to the soft crackle of the fire, the thin smoke
drifting through the room.

Convinced now, that the magic fluid would seep down Lavan's throat
and save her life, Ellen waited for the miracle, but no miracle came.
Lavan still lay like a corpse in the reddened bed, and Margery still knelt,
and the others waited, tense and alert and looking down. Suddenly Ellen grew aware that it had been a long time. She looked at Randall
and followed his glance. He was watching the pulse in Lavan's throat,
that somehow kept beating on. She could not see Margery's face, only
her slim, defiant shoulders, and dark silky hair falling in ringlets on her
neck. Then it was swiftly all too much for Ellen, and she began to cry,
with ugly shuddering sobs that shook her as a wind shakes a thicket.
Hard old arms went round her, and she sensed it was Nanny Dweeney
bending down.

"Come outside, lass," she mumbled. "We seen too much, I think."

They stumbled from the house of sickness and went and sat on
Nanny's doorstep all alone in the black dark under the old stars wheel-
ing down the sky.

"We'd disturb Johnny, did we go in," explained the old woman, "and
he might take a taste for a bit o' the bagpipe music. 'Twill come on
him at any queer time."

Ellen did not want to risk that either, so they crouched there, shivering with a cold that did not come from the hills or the sea. She must
have slept, for the next thing she realized there was a faint light in the
sky over the Long Island, and Nanny was shaking her.

"Here comes Miss Margery," she said. " 'Twould seem she's going
home."

Margery walked slowly toward them, her dress all torn and stained
and her hair hanging down. Ellen jumped up and stood waiting, while
old Nanny dragged herself painfully to her feet.

Margery held her head up, pale and disheveled, but smiling still.

"Lavan is better," she said. "She is not bleeding any more. Andra
thinks she will live, and Randall himself is almost convinced of it."

"And it was all your doing, Miss Margery," cried Nanny, her wrinkled
brown face alight. "For all their wisdom, it was ye was the more wise."

"Oh no, Nanny," answered Margery soberly. "It was not I. I had nothing to do with it at all. It was only a thing I happened to remember.
It was all done by the little dark people a long time ago."

MacNeill of Barra

Between the day and the dark, in that slow hour of a warm June evening when the shuttle stands still till the lamp is lighted, Margery walked through the upper gallery of Rhinn House, under the black-framed pictures on the wall. There was little to choose among her ancestors, she thought wryly, for the brandy-faced old men looked much like one another, the same dull blue and green plaid cloaking all of them. There were not many portraits, for the line did not go back very far. The Rhinns were incomers to the Hebrides; Scottish, but no one knew from exactly where. One story had it that they went back to that exiled Earl Ruthven whose name was decreed to be forever dead in the land, but there were other stories as likely to be true.

Only two women had been allowed to leave something of their color and softness here on the hewn stone walls; red-gold Charlotte Stewart, whom her grandfather had wooed and wedded in the Lowlands, when he went south on his way to the court of Anna Regina before ever the Georges came to the throne, and Margery's own mother, Gillian Mac-Neill. Allan Ramsay, the poet's son, had painted Gillian in sea-green and silver with a scarf of silver gauze drawn over her hair and one or two dark curls showing through. Margery remembered the dress and the scarf and the long hot afternoons in Master Ramsay's studio where she waited with her mother while the sketches were made. She had been a tiny child then, who kept reaching in vain for a large golden pear in a dish on a corner shelf. The artist's face she could not remember, nor his voice, but she could remember the rank summer smell of Edinburgh streets, and the wonderful unattainable golden fruit, and her mother's warm hazel eyes smiling down.

She stood now under Gillian's picture, wanting to tap on Randall's door close to her elbow, not quite daring, quite sure that to do so would not be the proper thing. They were alone in the house save for the servants, since her father had not returned from Glasgow, and Kenneth had gone out after supper with a muttered excuse she had not even bothered to hear. Randall, she knew, had come up to his room to write. He had told her that he meant to keep a journal of all the cases he treated, so that he could send it piecemeal to his father, submitting himself to the older man's criticism or approval as he had always done. But he had been there for more than an hour now, and the house seemed lonely and so very still. She had read a page of Thomson's *Seasons,* and gone into the deserted kitchen and made herself a cup of tea. She had walked in the garden and played three tunes on the spinet. She would call him once, just once, she thought, and then if he did not answer, she would go down to the clachan and chat with the women there.

"Randall!" she called lightly. "Oh, Randall! How much longer will it take you? Is your writing not done?"

She heard his chair scrape back, then quick steps approaching the door. He flung it open and stood smiling into her eyes. His blond hair looked as if he had been running his hands through it, and there were ink stains on his chin.

"No, it is not done, and will not be until you help me, Madge. Come!"

He beckoned and she followed him inside, gazing around the pleasant chamber, at the gray wool carpet, the plaid bed curtains, the heavy chairs built in the woodyards of Edinburgh. The only really elegant piece, she thought, was the mahogany writing table. It hurt her to remember the graceful white and gold furniture her mother had brought back from France, warped past all usefulness now by the island damp that would dissolve sugar to a sticky paste and rust iron latches away. Candles burned on the table, and beyond the windows the sunset still flared in the endless summer dusk.

"I can help you?" she asked, smiling back at him. "I?"

"Yes."

He motioned for her to sit down at the table and stood there facing her, holding out a sheet of foolscap so that she could see the writing thereon.

She wrinkled her brows and bent forward in the flickering light and read. Then she sat back and asked, "But how can I help you?"

"You read it? You know what is written there?"

"Yes. You have written about Lavan. How she miscarried and was taken with a bleeding afterward; that you and Andra could not save her, but that I came and gave her heather ale; that you have examined her two weeks after, and she seemed healed and well."

"Yes, I have written that."

"And that was the way it was. The virtue was in the old drink, and I only put it to her mouth. What more would you say?"

"Margery," he explained patiently, "think of my father reading this. You do not need the second sight to know that he will ask about heather ale. What will he think of me when I tell him I do not know what it is and have not bothered to find out?"

She looked at him with dismay and apprehension in her eyes.

"You mean you want me to tell you how it is made—to prepare it—how—?"

"Yes. That is what I want. You said you knew."

She forced herself to look him squarely in the eye. "Yes, I know, but I cannot tell—not even you."

"Why not? From what you said, I thought it must be some family secret. You said, 'The MacNeills of Barra know!' Have you promised someone that you will not reveal it? Have you given your word?"

She sank into a low chair and gazed at him with troubled eyes.

"Even if you have," he told her, "you would be justified in breaking it for such a cause. It should be stabilized in the laboratory and added to the pharmacopoeia to advance human knowledge. It is your duty to science, Margery."

She clasped her hands in her lap and looked down. Whenever she was with Randall she felt a closeness and understanding between them, a companionship beyond the delicious excitement of being man and woman. Most of the time she felt that. But on the turn of a phrase or the lift of an eyebrow now and then, the understanding vanished, and he reminded her of a bright new coin, of good worth, but hard and shining, and so proud of being new.

The laboratory! The pharmacopoeia! Her duty to science!

She knew her duty, but how could she make him know? She could not put it into his language, and he could not understand hers—or perhaps he might, if she could only help him to find his own key.

"Randall," she said, "will you forgive me if I take the long way round, since there's no straight way there?"

"Take any way you please, Margery," he said, flinging himself into an oaken chair and leaning back, watching her face.

"It is all—" she groped for words, stumbled, and went on, "that some things are old and some are new—thoughts and ways, I mean."

He tried to help. "You mean that heather ale is an old medicine made by a people who used to live here, a people who have died out. I learned that much from what Andra said."

"Yes," she agreed. "It is that."

"Andra believed the secret lost, but you say it is still known in your family, that you know it yourself."

"Yes. I know it."

"Who told you?"

"My mother."

"Did she swear you not to tell?"

"No, she did not swear me. There was no need. She said, 'We know, and we tell it to our children. To none but they.' I heard her tell me that. She knew it would be enough."

"What others know?"

"I cannot say. It is not a thing we talk of. My cousin Helen, perhaps. I have many cousins more. Perhaps other families know. All I know is that my mother told it to me."

"And you will not tell?"

"I will tell my daughter or my son."

"And meanwhile folk may die for the need of it. I did not know any mixture of drugs held such power to restore. But you would withhold it from those to whom it would do good! Why, I do not see! Margery!" His face had a stony look, but there was a pleading light in his eyes. "Margery, can you not say something that will help me to understand you?"

"I—I was trying to," she faltered, "till you questioned me."

"What were you trying to say?"

She leaned toward him to make one more desperate try before she rose, and asked his forgiveness, and slipped away.

"You are from America," she began, "and that is a new country. What is there that seems old to you?"

"Old? Why a man past sixty's old. My father's house is old—"

His father's house? Here, she thought, was a place to begin.

"How old is that?"

"Oh, it's ol—l—d!" he answered, giving the word a long impressive sound. "My grandfather built it. Let me think. He came up from Beverly in 1720 and built the house the next year. Fifty-three years, that would make it."

She smiled faintly. "And you say he lived in Beverly—before that?"

"Yes. In Beverly."

"And where did his father live? And his father before?"

"Why, in Beverly. We always lived in Beverly."

"How long has Beverly been there?"

"How long has—?" He stared at her. "Why it's always been there. Ever since the coming over."

"When was the coming over?"

"About a hundred and fifty years ago," he told her solemnly, as if that ended the matter.

"And before that?"

He looked startled. "Why I think—I heard my grandmother say—the Woodburys came from a fishing town in Somerset. But it's never mattered, what's back that far."

"I am not boasting, Randall," she went on quietly. "Believe me, I am not boasting, only trying to make you understand me, when I say the MacNeills were kings in Scythia and were summoned into Egypt for their learning. They sailed west from there in the time of Moses, and to Ireland out of Spain. We were in Barra before the Norse came down."

"Do you believe that?" he asked her, his voice keen and his eyes narrowed, a scornful smile on his mouth.

She flung out her hands. "Why not believe? I cannot prove it is true, and you cannot prove it is a lie. If it helps—"

"How does it help?"

"It helps, somehow, when something happens that is hard to bear—when your mother dies—or your wife—" She paused and swallowed and turned her head away. "It helps to think back to all those other people all the ages down, people who have the same blood as you, and who faced such trouble and worse, and behaved themselves so that—so that there was no great stigma on the name. You want to be true to them and do as well as they. Do you see—Randall, do you see what I am trying to tell you? Everyone knows it here in Scotland—but in America, I think, it might be hard to make known."

"You are telling me that I am a new man from a new country," he replied slowly, choosing his words, "and a creature of yesterday. That I cannot understand the ways of people who know much of the past and think much of it, and feel that their roots go back through time."

"Yes. I am saying that. But I am not saying you are a worse man for being new. You may be better. I am only saying that we are different. That it is not strange you cannot understand me."

"And you understand me, of course?"

"No, Randall, I do not understand you. But I wish—I think we could both try."

A warm little wind blew in from the garden heavy with fragrance, stirred the curtains, and troubled the candle flame, and set Randall's pages swirling to the floor. He ignored them.

"You are right, Margery. We shall try. For tonight let us say that your duty to the dead MacNeills is greater than your duty to living men who may suffer because you feel as you do. I shall not trouble you any more about it—now."

Still he did not understand, she thought. Still he was impatient and angry. She stood up.

"I shall go down to the clachan, I think," she told him, "while you finish telling your father—what you have to say."

He brightened. "The clachan? Will you see Iver Gall?"

"I can see Iver. If you have a message for him, I can."

"Ask him if his arm has any soreness? If he is fevered or feels in other ways ill?"

She had gone as far as the doorway, but now she turned, wondering what these ominous questions meant.

"You think Iver may be unwell?"

Randall sighed. "No. I think he will not be, now. It has been a week since I inoculated him."

"Oh," she cried, reassured as soon as she understood. "You have begun the smallpox inoculations. I wondered when you would do so. Have you tried others? Father says you are to do all in Ballyrhinn who have not suffered the disease before."

"I'm afraid we'll have to wait, worse luck, until God knows when. I have plenty of dried lymph with me, but I fear the virtue has gone out of it. I tried it on Iver and it seems to have no effect. That means I must wait till I can draw matter from a fresh case."

"It means—?"

"I shall have to wait till someone nearby falls ill of it and I can draw from their infection. Once I am sure I have failed with Iver, I shall go to Stornaway—or perhaps to Skye."

"You cannot send to Edinburgh, then?"

He shook his head. "I am afraid it would be useless. They have none better than what I brought. I have never put much faith in the dried lymph. We do not use it much at home. Perhaps when your father comes back—"

"He may have heard of a case," said Margery as cheerfully as she could. "Tam MacVean will bring him, and Tam travels the islands and well could know." And then, "Randall—are you trying to understand?"

"Yes," he answered. "I am trying, Margery." But he did not look at her. He had turned to his papers again.

Outside Rhinn House, the evening light was like clear water flowing over the landscape. Margery walked slowly through the beds of king-cups and forget-me-nots beyond the east terrace—neatly laid-out, well-tended beds, that showed the careful touch of Sim's gardening. She wondered briefly how the old man could perform all his usual chores when he had to spend such long hours in the kitchen carrying out much of the work that had been done by his wife and his ailing sister. Tomorrow she would put on an old bodice and petticoat and go to Leitis and offer to help her, she thought. She had done it before, only to have her suggestion refused with excuses and embarrassment. It had been the fashion one winter for the young ladies of Edinburgh to attend cooking school, and Margery had gone with the rest. She could pickle anchovies and whip up French creams and jellies, but her attempts at simple Scottish cooking usually ended in a sodden gray-black mass at the bottom of the oven. She sighed ruefully as she thought of them.

Then her thoughts went back to Randall and stayed with him all the while she was walking down to the clachan. Would she ever be able to make him see? Would he ever trouble to try to explain himself to her?

It was a soft, starry night, with no moon and a white mist curling up from Glen Fruin and the burn beyond the village. Down on the sand the men were burning cow dung and barley straw and sea tangle for nourishing ash to spread on the fields tomorrow, and Margery wrinkled her nose at the rich familiar smell of it. In front of the first cottage she met Meg Munro, a pretty widow, red-haired and young, her face incredibly sad. The daftie followed her—a boy about eight, with a slack mouth and vague eyes, skipping along in time to a music no one else could hear. When he saw Margery he stumbled toward her, yammering and pointing to a cluster of paste jewels that fastened the collar of her dress. Margery spoke soothingly to him, took off the trinket, and dropped it into his hand. The daftie loved any bright shining thing.

Petting the child's head, Margery spoke to his mother. "It's a fine night, Meg."

"That it be," said Meg soberly. "Davy and I been up by the Cursing Stones. We went there to watch the sunset. But—but there was others there, and we came away."

Margery's eyes flashed. "I think you are not telling it quite as it was, Meggy. I think Colin followed you there and wanted to court you, and you would have none of him. It has happened so before. Why?"

Meg looked even sadder. The child made a little inarticulate croaking noise and sidled against her. She stroked his hair.

"Ye know, Miss Margery, why I canna' court with Colin or any man. That I couldna' wed and bring into the world another poor soul, maybe —another like this."

"Oh Meggy, it need not happen twice that way. Nellie Gow's first born was lame, but after that she had a healthy four. Every time I see Colin, he looks so sorrowful it near breaks my heart."

"He needna' look sorrowful. He could have Janet Gillander, for I know she wants him. She is bonny and fresh and young."

"Yes, Janet is bonny, but he does not want Janet, he wants you. Some day, Meggy, I hope you will change your mind."

Meg shook her head stubbornly, and they walked on in silence, the child ambling before.

"I wonder if Iver is down on the beach with the men?" asked Margery, as they passed Johnny Dweeney's cottage, lamplight streaming through the open doorway, the old couple moving about inside.

"Iver Gall? No, he is at Andra's, I think. He and Lavan were going there tonight to carry a present. He is so grateful to her for making his wife well that he brought her a fine pair of leather shoes from Stornaway."

They walked a few steps further and then Meggy said, "Ye know, Miss Margery, Iver is a stubborn man. He distrusts the strange lad in your house, and he is afraid of heather ale. He says it was Andra who saved his wife, and he is grateful only to her."

"But if he is ungrateful to Randall—if he distrusts him—why did he let himself be scratched for the smallpox?"

"He would not—at the first. But the doctor lad—Randall, ye call him —was canny in that as in all. He is canny, is he not, Margery?"

Margery noticed that Meg had forgotten the title before her name, and it pleased her. But she was more concerned for another thing.

"What do you mean?"

Meg regarded her steadily, in her eyes a veiled question.

"He told it all to Iver, what he meant to do, and why. That he was not sure his drugs had strength, being so long from their source, and wanted to try them on a young, strong, wholesome man; that they might do good, and could do no harm. He asked Iver to bare his flesh to the wee knife."

"And Iver would not?"

"Not at first. He muttered of warlocks and potions. He started to move away. It was at Andra's house. I had gone there for a poultice for Davy, for he cut his toe at the last full moon, and I feared lest when the month's time returned, he would bleed again. I saw Iver and the doctor there."

"What did the doctor say?"

"He put the vials back in his pocket, and his little knife, and smiled, and oh, but there was taunting in his smile, Miss Margery!"

Margery knew that taunting smile and was silent.

"He put his tools away, and he said, 'Very well, if ye are afraid, Iver, I will ask the next lass bairn I meet. It will not frighten her.'"

"Did he say 'lass bairn'?" asked Margery eagerly.

Meg looked as if she thought the laird's daughter was as daft as poor Davy.

"Yes, he said 'lass bairn.' What else would he say when he meant that?"

"Girl child" would have been the English thing, thought Margery, and the American words—there was no knowing what they might be! But he had spoken the proper Scots phrase to a Scotsman. Perhaps he would come to understanding after all.

"So of course Iver turned from that word 'afraid.' Your jo could have cut off his head after that. Is he really your jo, Margery? Some of the women say that he is. Some say it is Schoolmaster."

"I do not have a jo," said Margery with sudden formality. "Look, there is Andra, and Iver and Lavan nowhere about. You have told me wrong."

They had come almost to the end of the clachan and the white mist rising up from Fruin Burn. Behind them the men's voices echoed across the shingle, once a seal barked from the crags below Ardmory, and in the background was always the low murmur of the sea. Andra sat in her doorway in the midst of a group of children; fair-haired, dark-haired, pale-skinned, and brown. She had a tiny black lamb on her knees and was gently rubbing its eyelids with a white fluid. Two women, Nell Gow and Christie MacNayr, stood watching her, young wives and comely, in spite of the large broods around them. Margery called from the pathway.

"Whose is the lamb, Andra, and what ails it?"

Andra lifted her head, but Nell had the first answer.

"It is ours," she said. "Ewen brought it down from Caldune pasture when he came at suppertime. 'Twas born blind, and we fear there's little help. But if there be any, Andra will know."

"Sometimes powdered chalk," murmured Andra, bending again to the tiny creature in her hands.

"Andra surely will," agreed Margery. "But I came here looking for Iver. Has anyone seen him about?"

Nell and Christie shook their heads, and Andra replied, "He was here early, but he has gone up Ardmory to keep watch at the shieling with Lavan tonight. She felt sure she was well again and wanted to go back to her work. But the first time she tried it, he did not wish her to be alone. I think he was wise."

Margery shrugged. She certainly did not intend to go prowling alone up the misty glen to the dark moorlands above, no matter how Randall might chide her afterward. The colors of the sunset had faded, and the long soft gloaming was almost done. Soon it would be deep night. She would go home.

"Ah, well," she answered, "it will keep—the errand I had with him. Did he happen to say if he was feeling well?"

Andra, still busy with the lamb, did not seem to hear, but Christie spoke now, a troubled look in her warm brown eyes.

"Ye were thinking of his arm, Miss Margery, where the young doctor scratched it and put the pox seeds in? Iver says his arm feels as it always has, and the wound is healed and gone. He says Doctor means to scratch us all."

Both Nell and Christie looked so worried that Margery hastened to explain.

"It is nothing to be afraid of. I had it done myself years ago in London. The Queen ordered it for her two daughters, not far back. My father brought Dr. Woodbury here to inoculate everyone on Rona who has never had smallpox. It will give the disease in a light form to prevent the fatal one. He means it as a kindness for them."

The women stood silent, watching her, with wise, worried, mother eyes. It was not for themselves they were afraid, she well knew, only for the small heads all turned intently toward Andra and the lamb. She murmured a brief good night and walked homeward through the clachan, alone now, for Meg and the daftie had remained with the others.

But she was not alone for long. First she sensed the beat of purposeful steps behind her on the turf path. Then Kenneth's hand fell on her shoulder.

"A good evening, lass," he greeted her. " 'Tis well that I met ye away from the house, for I'd like a private word with ye."

Margery turned and stared at him.

"If ye've aught to say," she retorted, "that cannot be said in my father's house, I am not sure that I want to hear."

"Ye will want to hear this," he insisted, taking her by the arm. " 'Tis a bonny night. Come up to the Cursing Stones with me."

Margery glanced up the hill to Rhinn House. Randall's window looked to the west, and she could not see it. She wondered if the light still burned there. But even as she hesitated, Kenneth was pulling her along the narrow track that wound upward through grasses sweet with wild strawberries, flecked with young mushrooms showing whitely in the dark. She followed, half-willing, not having any reason to resist him, surely not fear. Whenever he caressed her it was more with possessiveness than ardor. Sometimes she wondered at that. But tonight there was a strange urgency about him, and she sensed it was not a matter of love-making, but of something he would say.

The sea lay behind them, and the lights of the clachan along the curving shore to the right. After a short climb, they came out on a long stretch of greensward, and enough light remained in the sky so that Margery could see the circle of upright stones, each one as tall as a man, several of them joined to each other with a slab laid from top to top. No one knew who had put the stones there, or when, only that it was very long ago, before ever the MacNeills had come to Barra, likely. If you walked about them sunwise, it was said, you could bring a blessing to your friends, and, conversely, if you walked widdershins, a curse to your enemies. Margery had never circled them either way. Everywhere else on Rona she felt free and self-confident, the way its laird's daughter should, but this was one legend she dared not try—not even the blessing. No one else alive had ever tried it, so far as she knew. And still, the place did not seem to strike awe into the people now, as it had done only a few years ago. It was a favorite trysting place for lovers, and she had doubted if she and Kenneth would be alone there. Yet strangely enough, they were.

When they reached a low clump of hazel bushes a little way from the stones, Kenneth drew her down on the grassy turf and sat silent, not touching her, staring downward at the fires on the shore of the clachan, and beyond them at the misty heaving grayness of the sea.

She waited for him to speak, waited a long time. Finally he said, "Lass, I had word from a friend o' mine in Skye."

"Did you?" she asked, trying not to seem curious. "How goes the weather there?"

"They say Kingsburgh and his wife are going to America."

"To America?" asked Margery blankly. "Flora MacDonald's going to America? Why?"

Her mother had once been well acquainted with the famous lass who helped Prince Charlie in his flight from the islands after the disaster at Culloden. She herself remembered Flora, married now to MacDonald of Kingsburgh, as a slight pretty woman whom she had met once at a ladies' tea-drinking in a London drawing room. Flora had lived quietly after the uprising fell apart, loyal as ever to the Stuarts, but making no move, so far as Margery knew, to stir forth into public life again. Why should Flora be going to America? Surely it was not for gold, the way so many went. She repeated her question.

The Highland man continued to look out over the water. There were deep shadows in his eyes and his heavy brows drew down.

" 'Tis noised abroad that there's to be a great upheaval in those regions. What does the American say?"

"He says little of it. My father says more. He begins to fear there will be war. I should think Flora would have seen enough of wars to last her for her time."

"She's going where there's rebellion raised up against England. Does that make better sense to ye?"

"What do you mean, Kenneth?" she faltered, her hand on his arm.

He turned to look at her. She remembered suddenly why it was she had promised to marry him a year ago, felt the old compulsion, the force of the old charm. Kenneth could have worn the white cockade and brandished a claymore in the streets of Edinburgh. He knew how to pass the wine glass above the water jug to drink to the king over the water. He could have lived in a byre on oat bread and brandy, as the Prince himself did after the fall. Kenneth came of the same earth as she, and shared her way of looking at life.

"There's talk," he said brusquely, "that the Prince himself will go over to take the lead there."

"Prince Charlie!" she breathed, with a little catch in her voice, the way she had heard her mother and their friends so often do. Then she checked herself and spoke sharply. "I thought—my father said—he was drinking himself to death in Rome."

Kenneth nodded. "Aye, that has been said. And this new report may be naught but clishmaclaver. But it has tongues all a-going like bell clappers in Skye. I will let ye know, lass, as I hear more. I thought 'twould be somewhat ye would care about."

"I cannot believe in it, Kenneth," she answered. "And yet—I wish I could. It was a thing my mother hoped for—that each new moon would bring the Stuarts back. My father—"

"Your father says Charlie is a done man," said Kenneth, smiling at her. "For all he was out in the Forty-five, he's no true to the Stuarts, and he was not convinced—then or after. He only went to please a lass, I heard him say."

"No," said Margery thoughtfully. "He was not convinced, when he went to that war. Few in the islands went. Few were free to go. The MacNeills were not. They were sworn to the MacDonald of Sleat, and he forbade his folk to rise. The Rhinns held Rona under Clanranald, and Clanranald was for Charlie. So my father could fight for the Prince, as her own father and brother could not, and that made him a hero to my mother and she married him after. But he was not convinced—only that he loved her. I do not think, if there was another rising now, he would so much as turn his head to look."

"But ye would turn—?"

"Kenneth," she said, rising to her feet, "we must go home while there is still light enough to see the way. What you have told me—it could be something too great and strange for us to see to the end of, kingdoms all changing about—or it could be no more than the rattle of dead haws when the winds come down in the fall. But for Scottish men to join with this uprising in America—with Flora already gone—!"

Kenneth, too, had risen, and they started slowly down the hill, away from the shadowy cluster of the Cursing Stones.

"She has not yet gone. I hear she will sail from Campbelltown at the end of summer. It could be as ye say, a great thing, but 'tis thus far only a bit of mist rising in the glen, where we thought naught could ever rise. But the American now? I wouldna' talk before him, but I would listen. Has he taken a side?"

"Hush," whispered Margery, catching Kenneth's arm. "'Tis he yonder. Be still!"

Kenneth looked where she pointed. Randall Woodbury stood on the grassy slope a little way from the path to the clachan. He stood very straight with his head lifted, staring into the night sky. He must have thought he was alone. Suddenly he flung out his arms and called aloud, in tones that seemed to Margery like those of a prayer sharp with anguish.

"Come back to me if you're coming, Sally Anne!"

She stopped and stood still for a moment. Then she began to run. Swift as a wind she went, leaping over hillocks and brambles, treading the path from memory, blinded by more than the misty dark. Kenneth did not catch her till she slowed her steps among the flower beds by Rhinn House. He was panting, but he managed to gasp out a question.

"Has he gone off his noggin, lass? Has he got a woman here? There be no one on Rona named Sally Anne."

"Sally Anne is his dead wife," said Margery tonelessly. "I did not know —that he still cared so much—for her."

Kenneth gave her an answer but she did not hear it. She went hurrying away from him, into the hall and up the wide stair. She knew that she was going to cry, and her tears would be just as salt, and her heart as full of hurt, as if no MacNeill of Barra had ever done the same.

X

The Darker Mystery

"Rocky ran afoul of a hedgehog in Ben Tilton's woods. Your mother and the girls have been plucking quills from her for near three days. By good luck, none were deep driven in. You need not worry now."

Randall frowned and looked up from his father's letter. Poor Rock! He hoped Sue and Betty had been gentle with her. They were kind, but impatient and young. She was an old dog. She might be dead before he could get home again. But maybe not. The way things were going there, it seemed as if he ought to start for home now.

He sat at his writing table, by the open window that looked out on a hot August morning, all white haze and lucid green sea. He had withdrawn here after breakfast, partly to reread his letter, partly to get away from John Riddoch, a Presbyterian minister from Harris who had been Rona's guest since his return from Scotland a week ago, and seemed likely to remain until forcibly driven away.

"While men of this province are slow to quarrel," his father had written, "once they have taken the cudgels up, be the cause good or bad, they are most ardent therein. Every day it seems that bad matters grow to worse here. At present there is a tea ship lying off New Castle. There is talk of boarding her and destroying her cargo as was done in Boston last winter, but Governor Wentworth has so far succeeded in restraining all, and 'tis rumored he thinks to reship the stuff to Halifax. Portsmouth profits much by the closing of Boston Harbor, but we had rather see it open and trade moving in its accustomed ways. Every ship from England brings word of some new act Parliament has taken to bedevil us, and humble as we are, we retaliate whenever we can. Your mother and I have signed a pledge to purchase no English goods, and so have most of the neighbors. The Governor has adjourned the Assembly because there is a rumor that the country will raise a general congress to protest our grievances to the King, and he does not wish that New Hampshire should send delegates thereto. I cannot say that I have great faith in any plan for all America to act as one country. There are too many differences among us. A Massachusetts man and a Virginia man are hardly the same species of life. Many say there will be war—"

Randall stopped reading and stared out into the sunlight, at the shimmering barley fields to the west of Rhinn House, all silvery green. War, his father had written, but how could there be a war between England and America? Where would they fight it, to begin with? Somewhere halfway between them, somewhere in mid-sea? No land battles, surely, for England had all the armies. His own colony had nothing but a few little trainbands meeting on muster day. No, he did not think there would be a war, but he had the vague uneasy feeling that trouble threatened those at home, and he wanted to be with them and share.

Margery's laughter rang through the garden below his window. He looked down and saw her standing with the white-haired clergyman beside the tawny orange curve of a marigold bed. John Riddoch lifted an admonishing forefinger and shook it under her nose.

"Hush, lass," he warned her gruffly. "'Tis the Sabbath Day!"

The word that leaped to Randall's mind was not a Sabbath word, but he left it unuttered. He could not hear Margery's reply, but he knew from her face and bearing that she made a demure apology. The pair strolled out of sight behind a glossy clump of rhododendron, and he returned to his letter.

"You will probably find that the woman who claims to have the second sight employs some form of trickery," John Woodbury had written. "We have no time for superstition here in America. We must get on with the business of the world. My grandmother came from Salem, and she has often told me how in her girlhood she witnessed a disgusting spectacle there. The witchcraft delusion, I am speaking of. Thank God, we are wiser now."

Were they really any wiser, Randall wondered. True, they had learned new things and laid old ones by, but was that always a better change? His father would not yet have received his account of the powers of heather ale, but he would probably scoff when he read it. Yet he remembered, that for all Dr. John's homely common sense, he had his own superstitions too, and was uneasy when he offended them. He turned the page over.

"We are making salt hay every morning, and yesterday I delivered Ruth Janvrin of twins; as you will recollect, her third set. The new church has no settled minister, and Mr. Thurston continues to supply. We are forced to do most of our buying in Newburyport because of high prices in Exeter. We hope you will soon return to your studies."

Randall put the letter down, stared out of the window again, and began to tap nervously with his fingers on the polished wood of the writing table. Again he was frowning. Late August had come; sheep-shearing was over and the harvest ready. He should be planning to go back to Edinburgh, but he did not want to go back, and he had a good excuse to stay where he was, because he had not even begun the inoculations. The dried lymph had proved useless, and so far he had been unable to find a single case of the disease from which he might draw fresh venom. The islands had been blessed with a healthy summer. Rona pleaded with him to stay till the work was accomplished. Margery did not plead. She did not have to. She smiled, and that was enough. He refused to examine his feelings toward Margery. If you could not pick the lilacs, at least it was sweet to linger where they grew. It was also tantalizing. He sighed, stood up and straightened his cravat, and started downstairs. It was Sunday morning and getting on towards meeting time.

When he first came to Rona, he had thought that religion sat lightly on the island people, but as he came to know them, he realized that hasty impression was not true. Kenneth preached often of a Sabbath; sometimes on the slope below Rhinn House, sometimes in the hall itself, if rain was coming down. They listened politely, but with neither transport nor rapture. In their daily lives they lived, it seemed to him, most clean and Christianly. But the savage and rigid insistencies of the Kirk, as he had observed them in Edinburgh, had not penetrated here. Slowly he was beginning to realize that their lives were dominated by a deep quiet faith in the unseen. They had a sort of weekday religion, made up of the thousand little superstitions his father was so scornful of, and a Sabbath Day religion that was pure love and reverence for God, undisciplined with theology. Rona had told him the Synod sent a minister to sojourn among them now and then, preach the Word, and investigate any irregularities of conduct. This was the first time such a visitation had taken place since his coming to the island, and he was not enjoying it, and neither, did he think, were the hapless people of Ballyrhinn. Rebellion troubled his heart as he went downstairs.

"And I tell ye, when I came to Taransay to hold Kirk Session and take cognizance o' scandals, I found there three contested bastard bairns—a thing unheard of in these isles since the Reformation!"

John Riddoch stood in the middle of the hall, a strutting little turkey cock of a man, haranguing his listeners. The laird and his daughter shifted uneasily in their high-backed chairs, on their faces something of the same distaste for the man's self-righteousness that Randall felt in his own heart. Margery's mother had been a Catholic, and the girl herself attended the English church in Edinburgh, as did Comyn, when he went at all. He was used to relying on his own strength, and it had always served him. Religion had given him but cold comfort when his wife died, and thereafter he did not turn to it. Kenneth, too, seemed uneasy, and that was harder to understand, for he should surely find himself in agreement with Master Riddoch if he still aspired to a living in the Kirk. Perhaps he was afraid the man would suddenly turn and upbraid him for the sins of his student days.

"Come, sir," protested Rona, drawing his brows together in a frown. "Be ye no accustomed to bastard bairns after forty years o' holding Kirk Session? 'Tis unlucky if the young folk make too free with each other, but no cause for a man to work up an apoplexy."

"I can see y're no troubled at the thought o' wickedness yourself," retorted the minister. "Ye think less o' religion than o' trade and manufacture. Ah, the love o' Mammon be greater than the love o' God nowadays. Little your ships and warehouses will boot ye on the Day o' Judgment!"

"Why, little will anything boot us then, Master Riddoch," said Margery, leaning forward. "Doesn't the Kirk tell us we are all saved or damned before we are born?"

"I will na' argue religion with a lass," said the old man, shaking his head stubbornly. "Let us go now, for I have a braw sermon in me that will take four hours for its preaching. Is the woman prepared for a'?"

Randall had joined the group in the center of the great hall and stood beside Kenneth, listening. He did not comprehend the last remark, and his face must have reflected the question in his mind, for Rona hastened to explain to him.

"He's meaning Andra, lad. 'Tis held by the Kirk that taischers can be relieved of the sight by the waters of Baptism at the pulpit side. Ofttimes when Parson's been here, he's deviled me to let him touch her for the cure, but I wouldna'—only if she herself be persuaded she should. Before sermon today he's determined to try, but I doubt—"

"Dinna' talk of cures, sir," interrupted John Riddoch truculently. "This woman has no disease or affliction. She commits her impostures out of self-seeking and vanity. I ha' seen many like her in my time. God's mercy, and what do they not claim to see! Black dogs, funerals, phantoms, corpse candles, ghosts carrying the very wood and nails to make their coffins of! And they swear later that it all came to pass just as they foresaw it, and a dozen ignorant cotters in the parish will swear the same! We touch them as for the Sacrament and bid them give over their lying practices, whereupon they generally do, claiming to see visions no more, not daring to persist further in sin. Folk were hanged or burned for it a hundred years gone. 'Twas a wise custom that should prevail with us still."

"Andra had a great-grandmother burned for it," said Margery. "Her name was Kate Manson of Cromarty. Andra said she was a good woman." The minister ignored her, speaking only to his host.

"How can ye believe in it when 'tis founded on no principles, and would be naught but a senseless deviation from the known laws o' nature if it were so?"

"Everyone believes in it in these islands except the clergy," said Rona shortly, climbing to his feet. "If ye've a four-hour sermon under your hatches, we'd best be awa'."

The little party walked out of Rhinn House, the laird, brave in blue bonnet and tartan, going ahead of them, and the old minister close behind him, like a shadow in his rusty black clothes. Margery followed with the young men.

"Where are we going?" asked Randall, as they crossed the slope where Kenneth usually held services and walked over the rough sweep of moorland just below the Cursing Stones.

"To the chapel," the girl replied. "It is hidden away in a curve of the hill, and we never go there except when the minister comes. 'Twas a church of the Old Faith, but when that faith died out on Rona it began to crumble away. Soon it will be gone."

"The faith of Rome!" muttered Kenneth, grinding a tuft of goldenrod under his boot heel.

"My mother was of the faith of Rome," said Margery steadily. Watching the other man, Randall saw his face soften and a wary look come to his eyes.

"I'm sorry, lass," he said awkwardly. " 'Twas the faith o' Barra, was it not, and ye were born to it? 'Twas the faith the Stuarts followed—whenever they dared."

Margery lifted her head quickly and put her hand on Kenneth's arm. She seemed to have forgotten that Randall was there, which did not much please him.

"Did you have aught to tell me of the Stuarts, Kenneth?" she said.

"Yes," he answered, his deep eyes gazing into hers and holding them. "Flora has gone."

"Oh?"

"Last week, from Campbelltown."

"For—where?"

Kenneth looked pointedly at Randall and did not answer her. He began to whistle, but was checked by a shout from John Riddoch, who halted abruptly in the path and turned on the tall Highlander.

"So ye go whistling to the Kirk o' Christ on the Lord's Day! If 'twas that they taught when ye studied Divinity in Glasgow, praise God I be Aberdeen bred!"

Kenneth yielded with a better grace than Randall felt he could have done.

"Pray for me, Master Riddoch! As I hope for mercy, I was looking at the bonny heather, and the occasion I quite forgot."

To Randall's surprise, he saw a smile come over the harsh old face.

"Well, for that I dinna' know that I can blame ye, lad!"

Randall did not think the reason Kenneth had given was the true one, but he could have understood if it had been. The way before them, more like a channel than a path, wound through a sea of tall spiky blooms, deep purple, pale rose, and lilac, fading to pure ivory. Wherever he looked, up and down the hills of Rona, from the cove of Ballyrhinn to the dark green reaches of the western ocean, the heather lay like a fragrant mist on all the land. One need not be a Scotsman to feel his blood quicken and respond to the beauty of it. He would remember the changing lights and shadows over this impossible landscape, Randall thought, when he was back in Hampton Falls where no heather grew. At the minister's insistence, Kenneth walked ahead with him, leaving Randall and Margery to follow, which they did, unhurriedly. For a moment or two they were almost alone.

"Who is Flora?" he asked her curiously. "You looked as if it mattered to you—that she was going—and where. I thought you were startled by it."

Margery did not try to evade. She looked him straight in the eye, and he knew she lied to him.

"Flora is a friend of my mother. She is sailing for France, Kenneth tells me."

"But he did not tell you. He only whistled a tune when you asked him where—and what had the Stuarts to do—?"

"Well, maybe she is sailing for Rome. It is one of the twain. Hurry now. If we are late, Master Riddoch will make us sit on the cutty stool for repentance, till his four-hours preaching be done."

They came suddenly out of the heather onto a grassy plain with a low wet bog at one side and half a dozen dwarf willow trees. All the clachan seemed to be there, crouching patiently on the hummocks or outcrops of stone. Most of the men were away at the Wick fishing, but all the old folk, the women and children, had come. At the far side of the glade Randall saw a small stone building, hardly bigger than a backwoods cabin at home, roofless, and all open to the sky. But its window openings were arched, and as he and Margery drew close to it, he noticed scrolls and swollen crosses delicately carved in the stone. Rona and

Kenneth sat on a small knoll, and Randall and Margery joined them. John Riddoch went to the crumbling steps of the chapel, stood forth and began to pray.

He prayed long and vehemently, so that Randall lost the thread of what he was saying. It was easier to listen to the gannets and kittiwakes that went screaming over in the blue air, easier to think his own thoughts, however troubling they might be.

Why had Margery lied to him, and why should it matter? What really mattered was not this unknown Flora; it was the fact that Kenneth and Margery seemed to draw close together at the mention of her, to retire into a secret fellowship of their own and shut him out. It was like being with two people who spoke in an unknown language; like being a child and hearing your elders discuss something you did not understand. He looked at Margery. She gave him a wicked grin, right in the middle of John Riddoch's calling hellfire down, and he felt better. But Riddoch went on praying, and he was soon so numb from the sound of the high-pitched singsong voice that he did not feel anything at all.

The minister prayed that this congregation might be saved from sensual appetites and random lusts, and told them that such abominations might seem to triumph, but that after this life there would be another state of things.

"The Children of the Kirk are indeed the excellent ones," droned the minister, in a thin voice that carried over the assembly like a searching wind, "while all other men be but the beastly slaves of Satan, and there is none whom he assaulteth not. Yea, the Great Deluder is strong in evil, having had these six thousand years to study on it, and to go from this life is to go from one hell into a worse!"

Meg Munro's daftie gave a shout of glee, and his mother put her hand tightly across his mouth. Somewhere another child began to cry. A light wind stirred in the dwarf willow trees.

"Creation is an old rotten house all dropping through and leaning to one side—"

Comyn bent forward and spoke to Randall. "He croaks like a raven, like flocks of ravens enough to cloud the sun over. They be blackbirds all, the corbies and the clergy!"

"Now I call ye to witness that there be fifty-two diseases for the sinful eye, one for every week in the year, but today we are no dealing with one o' these—"

A murmur went up from the congregation. Close to Margery's shoulder, Randall could feel her stiffen, and he looked around him for the cause.

"We are here to purge a sister of the lying way of the second sight.

Come forward, Andra Deveron, and stand before your God as ye will on the Judgment Day!"

It was not that the gulls burst forth in a shriller fury of sound, it only seemed that way because everything else was so still, and when the gulls flew over and their clamor ceased, Randall could hear the little waves that broke far down the shore. He looked up, somehow expecting the bright sun to darken, but above the burning summer mist, it still shone warm and clear. Then he saw Andra come from among a group of women and walk slowly forward. She held her shoulders high and proud, but she kept her eyes down, and her fingers plucked at the rough gray folds of her dress. Standing before the minister, she lifted her face up.

"Woman," he called out harshly, his eyes cold and his lips curling, "are ye ready to renounce this unhappy gift?"

"I will renounce it, if it pleases God," said Andra in a low voice.

The minister smiled coldly.

"Assist me, Mr. Crary," he said.

Kenneth strode forward with dignity and a sort of heavy grace Randall had never observed in him before. He was holding out a glass-stoppered bottle, and rainbows flashed from its prismed sides as it caught the sun. Mr. Riddoch cupped his left hand and Kenneth solemnly poured a few drops of clear fluid therein. Then he stepped back.

The minister moistened his right forefinger in his palm.

"With baptismal water I anoint ye," he announced harshly. "Stand closer, woman!"

Andra took a step forward. He leaned toward her and touched the holy moisture to her eyelids.

"Ye shall see visions no more," he declared. "It is the will of the Kirk."

Why did he not say, "It is the will of God"? thought Randall. Or did he assume that they would be always the same?

With a gesture as if he meant to hurry an unclean thing from his presence, Master Riddoch waved Andra back to her place in the congregation. Then he straightened his shoulders and threw his head back, and launched himself on his four-hour sermon, with no admonishing hourglass to tell him nay.

His hearers were exhausted at the end of it, children sobbing with weariness, and Nanny and Johnny Dweeney openly snoring, but the preacher himself seemed to wax stronger with every word he spoke. He finally ended with the Ten Commandments and a separate homily on each one. After the benediction folk dispersed quickly, disordered and hungry, and in no mood to stand about gossiping. Margery and Comyn collected a little party to take back to Rhinn House for dinner, and

Randall found himself bringing up the rear as they started homeward, John Riddoch at his side.

Looking ahead of him, he noticed Margery and Kenneth arm in arm, talking closely, their heads together. Comyn had been joined by two grizzled men in tartans, whom he introduced as James and Ranald MacKenzie, friends of his who owned estates in the south of Harris. They had come to fetch Master Riddoch away. The rest of the party were women—Andra and Ellen, of course, Widow Agnes Gillander and her Janet, Ailis Ogg and Lavan Gall.

"I hear ye're no cursed with the sight in America," said the minister, still drunk with the power of his own words and their fine sound on the air.

Randall was glad they were nearing the gardens of Rhinn House so this conversation could not be prolonged.

"No," he said. "I never heard of it till I came to Scotland. I understand it does not cross the sea. Andra says that in Ireland she was never troubled by it."

The crabbed old face darkened. "Ah, I hear there isna' much to be said for her life in Ireland. She should face Kirk Session, even at this late day."

"That was twenty years ago," said Randall coldly. "I consider Andra a good woman."

"Ha!" said Riddoch through his nose. "A sin after twenty years is still a sin—a stench in the nostrils of God."

Randall bit his lip and reminded himself that the man had been stirred by the beauty of the heather, and must have a gentler side, loath as he was to let it be seen.

A few minutes later they were all sitting around the long table in Rhinn House, eating sheep's head broth and boiled beef and greens, drinking dram after dram of whiskey. Not wholly by accident, Randall found himself between Janet and Ailis, pretty girls, slender and brown and ruddy, and he chatted and laughed with them, pretending, for the purpose of jest, that he knew less Gaelic than he did, and thus mistook them. Margery devoted herself severely to Kenneth, Andra ate little, and Ellen was sulking, Randall neither knew nor cared why. After the cheese and treacle pudding, Sim came round to fill the men's glasses, and Margery rose and withdrew with the women into the east parlor. Rona lit his pipe.

"Do ye think the lass is cured?" he asked the minister, who sat at the foot of the table. "That the sight willna' trouble her more?"

"Aye, she is rid o' the sight," answered the minister. "She will no persist in her vanity when the Kirk reproves her—no!"

The MacKenzies were shaking their heads. They were not so certain. "Why, there was a man in Barvas once, and he—"

Slowly everyone relaxed in his chair, full of hot food and old whiskey, and always sipping more. Randall pulled out his pipe too, and sat smoking and listening, not because he was loath to join in the conversation, but rather because he had nothing to add to it, and he was interested in what he heard.

He learned that some said St. Columba himself was a taischer, for did he not foresee the triumph of Christendom over the little dark picts (the heather-ale men)? He learned the customs of visions and the rules that governed them, while outside the late afternoon darkened over, and far off, thunder troubled the air.

Taischers were, for the most part, he discovered, sober and clean-living folk, not given to drink or madness or excess, but not godly. They seldom saw men who were already dead, but their function was to tell what death a man would die and when it was near. He might appear to them wrapped in a winding sheet, and the farther up on his body the sheet had moved, the sooner his death would fall. If he were to be drowned, he would appear with a dripping coat, or drenched in the phosphorescence that lights up the summer sea after dark. If he were to be hanged, the shadow of the gallows would fall across him. Each man had his double who dwelt in the old fairy country among the middle earth men, and when a seer saw a man's double walking behind him, it was a sign that he would soon be gone. Sometimes there was no indication what man would die, only of coming death. Glasses that were to be drunk from at funerals could be heard by the taischers to rattle loudly before, and so with the nails for a coffin, or the needles that would make a shroud. Not always did the vision presage death. It might warn of illness, or strangers coming, or some simple household event. A man might have a vision once in his life and never any more, or he might be a taischer all his days. His neighbors believed in his powers and respected him, but they were glad that they were not as he.

Now and then Randall peered into the lowering dark outside, but the storm did not break nor yet move away. Finally Rona knocked a last bowl of pipe ashes into an empty platter, leaned hard against the back of his chair, and confronted John Riddoch, who had taken drink for drink with them all afternoon.

"And ye still say, sir, there's no truth in it. That 'tis all a pretense, and that touching with the baptismal water will check it because it puts them in fear o' the Kirk?"

Riddoch nodded confidently. "Fear o' the Kirk," he said. "That is God's weapon in our hands. It is strong against all."

"Father! Randall! Andra is seeing before her again! She was never so shaken! I think she will die!"

Margery stood in the doorway of the east parlor, staring at them, her eyes gone dark in her white face.

All Randall heard was his own name. He did not know what the other men did. He supposed, later, that they must have followed him, but he shoved his chair back, flung down his smoking pipe, and ran toward the room where the women had withdrawn.

He had never been in that room before, and he saw nothing of it now, only a stretch of wall hung in gilt leather, lightning that flashed through an open window, but pale and far away, and Andra crouched on a sofa, the other women standing nearby. He strode forward.

"Do not touch her!" shrieked Ellen. "Wait till it is gone! Do not touch her! No!"

The shrillness of her voice stopped him.

He stood looking down at the pale tense figure with the disheveled hair and staring eyes. Then a tremor shook her. Then a mighty nerve storm seemed to convulse her whole body. Then she went limp, half falling from the cushioned seat, on her face a look of exaltation.

Ellen darted forward and pulled her eyelids down.

"You told me not to touch her," he accused the cattle maid sharply, "but you do it yourself, now."

"Because the taisch is gone," said Ellen. "It is always over when she falls sideways so. 'Tis said if ye try to wake them too soon they will die."

"Here's whiskey, lad," said Rona, panting at his elbow. "We'd drunk the sideboard dry, and I couldna' raise Sim. Give her a drap o' this. Kenneth's awa' to the cellar for more."

"I think she will want water," said Randall quietly. "She did that first night I was here."

"She always does," said Ellen, faint freckles standing out on her pale skin. "Lavan's gone to the well."

Gingerly Randall picked up the flaccid wrist, but even as he held it, he could feel the pulse slowly change from thin and fleeting to full and strong. Her eyelids flickered. Ivory color was returning to the chalk-white skin.

"She's coming out," murmured Ellen. "So bad—I never saw!"

Randall felt her eyes watching him as he bent solicitously over her mother. He twisted with the discomfort of it, and shot a swift glance at the girl's face. Yes, she was watching openly, and with a look he could not fathom. It suddenly came to him that he knew little enough of what went on inside men's bodies, but what happened in their minds was a darker mystery still.

Andra stirred and tried to sit up, so Randall lifted her and propped her among the cushions. She opened her eyes and looked around, first in confusion and bewilderment, then with a suddenness, as if all things had become clear. Then her mouth twisted. She gave a bitter little cry.

"Oh no!" she moaned, and buried her head in her hands.

"Here's water, Andra," said Randall, holding out the cup Lavan had just given him.

She shook her head and waved him away.

"Would you rather have whiskey?" he asked her.

"No. No. Nothing. In a moment I will go."

She still crouched there in their midst, her head bowed, hiding her face.

"Andra," said Comyn Rhinn sternly, "what did ye see?"

"I will not tell."

"Andra, I be your old friend and the Laird of Rona, and I asks ye, what did ye see?"

"If you were my own father and the King of Scotland too, I'd not tell you this time what I saw."

Rona bowed his head and was still.

"Andra," ventured Margery in very small tones, "will you come to my bed and lie down for a while. You're not fit to walk home."

Andra lifted her head then and faced them, calmly, but there was a dull heavy look of sorrow on her face.

"Yes, I will go to your bed, Miss Margery."

The laird's daughter beckoned to Ellen, and the two girls helped the taischer from the room.

Randall sighed and looked around him. The other women straggled mutely away without bidding good night. The MacKenzie brothers stood like statues. Kenneth hurried in, bearing a white glazed pitcher in his hand.

"Here be the whiskey, sir," he rumbled. "Be it in time? Is she—?"

"She's gone upstairs with Margery," said Rona, his shoulders sagging and a baffled look on his face. "But for us, ye're in time. We'll back to our glasses, lads."

As they gathered once more at the feasting table littered with greasy dishes and cold meats, Randall remembered John Riddoch.

"Where's the parson?" he asked.

It was Kenneth who told them. "I passed him when I went to the cellar. He was going to his room, he said, and read his Bible, and meditate on the ways of the Lord and the prevalence of sin."

Rona growled and splashed whiskey into his glass.

"He done his best for Andra, and ye see how she be cured! She's **no**

cured at all. There be some things outside the power o' Kirk Session,"
he muttered, "but Riddoch will no admit to that."

"No," said Randall. "He may be no wiser now, after what's gone on
here tonight, but perhaps the rest of us will."

But Rona shook his head. "I ha' always known there be things in this
world not understood, and ye might as well bolt your door with a boiled
carrot as stand forth against such as they."

XI

No Law of Nature

RANDALL was still musing over those words three weeks later as he sat one afternoon in a smoky little tavern in Stornaway, waiting for Comyn Rhinn. Summer had broken just the way it often did in New England about this time of year, with a cold beating rain that stripped the flower stalks and drenched the late hay, but the winds here blew higher and stronger, tearing slates from the rooftops and driving them along the street, together with bits of driftwood, hats, tiny furze bushes and anything else that was not nailed down.

John Riddoch had said that if the second sight were a true phenomenon and not a trick, it was a senseless deviation from the known laws of nature. He, Randall, had never met with any deviation from these laws before. He believed in them. He believed there was nothing they could not eventually explain. But Rona was a sensible man, a practical man, a keen trader in Glasgow, London and beyond. And Rona had said that there were things in this world, as well as the next, that had never been understood and were not likely to be.

He glanced through the one small leaded window and saw nothing but a liquid wall of rain, then moved his stool closer to the turf fire and called for the old woman who tended the whiskey keg to bring him another drink. The room was empty, save for the two of them. It smelled of herrings, and peat smoke, and lamp oil, and sour ale. He went back to his thoughts.

Very well, he told himself, suppose the sight was a true phenomenon, how would he go to work to explain it in terms of natural law? First, he would ask, did the vision come from without or within? Was it perceived by the eye and transmitted along the nerve paths to the brain, or did it arise, like imagination, from some inner source? And yet imagination itself was only decaying memory, Aristotle had said. The mind cannot create; it can only rearrange what the senses gather in. Then he would want to know—

The door creaked on its hinges and swung inward. The turf fire blazed up as the draft struck it. Randall turned and saw the Laird of Rona against a panel of thick gray rain. He came in, hastily closing the door behind him. Water poured from his brogues with every step, and dripped from the oiled linen cape he wore. Going straight to the fire, he wheezed and snorted until his pipes were clear, and then turned to the younger man.

"Devil a fine porpoise I make, do I not, lad? It's raining yet, but the sky's breaking clear in the west, and Tam MacVean is a'ready to go. Did ye visit the smallpox case we heard of?"

Randall drained his glass and smiled back ruefully.

"I visited the sick man. But it turned out to be spotted fever he had."

"So he was no good to ye?"

"None at all, but I hope I was some to him. I gave him bark and a purge, and told him to drink brandy till the spots appeared. He should recover well, if he keeps himself warm and dry."

Rona shook his head. "That be none so easy to do in weather like this," he said. "I thought to toast myself here for a bit, but now it comes over me that I'd rather do it at home by my own fireside, drinking my own whiskey. Let us go!"

Together they stepped out into the street. The rain was indeed slacking off, but the wind that drove from the eastward out of Scotland was still damp and raw. Randall shivered as they walked in silence down the terraced slope of the little fishing town, noted, Rona had told him, for drinking and piety. The mist had cleared away from the black boggy moorlands to the westward, but wisps of it still lingered about the Castle, gutted by Cromwell's soldiery a hundred years before. Few people were abroad in the narrow streets, and the only sound was the wail of the curlews and the unending complaint of the sea.

Rona led the way past a pile of lobster traps to the crazy wooden wharf where Tam waited for them, a young man with thick shoulders, a leather-brown face, and smiling blue eyes. He murmured a greeting in Gaelic, leaped into his boat and offered a hand to help them down. In a few minutes they were tacking out of Stornaway Harbor, round the low headland to the north. From there on, the wind was behind them, and they drove steadily over the sullen gray sea.

Tam had come on an errand to Rona the day before, and the laird had decided to return with him to meet the weekly packet from Dunvegan that should be bringing them goods he had sent into Scotland for. Randall went along because of the rumor of the smallpox case. He, too, had been eagerly awaiting the packet. He had sent for drugs—opium, Plumer's Pills, calomel, ginger, rhubarb, and aconite—and also for Dr. Cadogan's book on the gout. He had been treating Johnny Dweeney for rheumatic feet and was doing him no good at all. The symptoms of the two diseases could be much the same. It seemed unlikely that the old piper could have the gout, since it was a trouble that came of living too rich and high. Still, Randall wanted to know what Dr. Cadogan would say.

Crouched under heavy rugs in a sort of roofless gallery midway of the small craft, the two men made little conversation. Randall kept his head down, and Rona watched a streak of sunset flaring raggedly ahead of them. Finally he spoke.

"Last time I went yonder, I thought I'd found a lad for Ellen. But I was talking wi' his father again today, and he's gone sour of the bargain. He'll hear no word o' her at all."

Randall turned to him in surprise. "I did not think that was how courting was done here," he said. "I'd thought the girls were most free and forward to look to it themselves—not in any harmful way, I mean —only that they are not so coy—" He floundered in his own rush of words and broke off.

Rona smiled somewhat grimly with his brows drawn down.

"Aye, I take your meaning, lad, and ye are right. But Ellen is an uncou' case. Ellen spoiled her market years ago."

Randall shifted about uncomfortably. "Was that what you tried to tell me about on Ardmory that first day?"

"Aye, and was balked by my own child therein. But it be none so much to tell. It seems in the afternoon when the schooltime was over, Ellen would go up to the Cursing Stones with the young lads, and show them how they were made different than she. Their mothers came at me for it, and I turned them off and told them 'twas summat all lads must learn. But I called Miss Ellen to me then, and I told her did I hear any more such talk, I would send her to the country workhouse in Dingwall or elsewhere beyond the sea. If I hadna' so valued her mother, I would ha' sent her then."

"She was young," said Randall thoughtfully, "and she has surely learned better now. How has she borne herself since?"

"Well enough, for all I hear. But when the lads are choosing wives, the old tale is remembered, and they'll no choose Ellen. I thought perhaps in Stornaway—but the word has gone even there. Folk here in the islands do not give money with their daughters—two cows is considered enough—but I would offer gold. 'Tis for her mother's sake I do."

If he would take so much trouble in the interests of his cattle maid, Randall thought, what must he have in mind for his own daughter? Something, surely. A marriage to someone high-placed in Edinburgh or

among the loyal Stuart families abroad. He tried to think of a way to
ask, but could find no words and his throat felt dry. Rona changed the
subject.

"Well, I hear everybody be off for America, and no doubt Dunvegan
Castle be going next. Three months back there was a Philadelphia captain a-stealing away of immigrants, the colonies be that eager for indentured help. And now I hear even Flora MacDonald has gone."

Flora! That was the name Kenneth had whispered to Margery. The
Flora who was going somewhere. Flora MacDonald? He had heard that
name often in Edinburgh, where she was still the toast of many in town,
almost thirty years after her heroic adventures that saved Prince Charlie.
But he had not known it was she of whom Kenneth spoke. Perhaps it
was not she. And in any case, why should Margery's face turn so strange
at the news, half-happy, half-troubled, wholly upset? Suddenly he felt
baffled and impatient because there were so many questions in his mind
he had no answer to. He was sick of these misty islands. He longed for
the clear-cut look of a winter landscape at home, all white fields and
black branches, every twig standing out against the sky's iron gray.

Then he felt the boat nose against the barnacled wooden piling of
the wharf. They were back at Rona. It would be good to be in a warm
house with hot food on the table, to hear Margery's laughter once more.

The clachan seemed even more deserted than Stornaway had been.
It was almost dark, and lights shone through the cottage windows and
around the door mattings. As he and Rona left the shore and started
homeward, carrying their bundles, he glanced toward Andra's house.
The matting had been pulled aside, and Ellen stood in the open doorway. The wind whipped her skirt and tossed her pale hair. She was
looking at him, Randall knew, but she gave no sign and neither did he.
He followed his host along the muddy cart track winding up the hill.

Margery met them in the doorway. She wore a dress of soft yellow
wool with buttons of carved ivory, her cheeks were flushed and her eyes
bright.

"I watched you all across the cove," she told them. "I knew the boat
for Tam's."

"Have ye been painting your face, lass?" asked her father critically.

Margery smiled and shook her head.

"Oh, no," she answered, "I've been sitting too close to the fire. I told
Leitis to lay supper in the east parlor. It will be ready by now, I think.
What did the packet bring?"

Once in the warm pleasant room, all flickering hearth fire and candlelight, the men spread out their purchases on an oak bench for Margery to took at, while Leitis moved to and fro, bringing covered dishes

to the table. Randall's drugs and his book on gout occupied little space, but Rona's goods were more varied: a pruning hook for Sim, a keg of nails, pickled limes and Lisbon sweet oil; coffee, raisins, chocolate, and a packet of bright sewing silks for his daughter. Finally, with a smile of triumph, he stripped open a thin wooden box and pulled out a huge Cheshire cheese, smelling, Randall thought, as though it had died and been buried and dug up again.

"There, lad," he said, crossing over to set it among the steaming platters on the table, "is a cheese with a soul in it!"

Kenneth strolled in just then, and the diversion saved Randall from having to make any reply.

They seated themselves around the table and gave their fullest attention to the tender young woodcocks, that Leitis, under Margery's prompting, had stewed delectably in wine in the French way. Rona did most of the talking, chiefly about the horse races to be run on North Uist on Michaelmas Day.

"We always had horse races at Michaelmas on Barra," said Margery dreamily. "I was born on a Michaelmas night. My mother said she sat at the window and watched them lead out the horses while she waited for me. Do you have horse racing in America, Randall?"

"Yes," he answered. "I hear they've had them sometimes at Narragansett. Myself, I've never seen—"

He was interrupted by the sound of the hall door opening. Ellen Deveron came in. She had a dark shawl over her olive-green dress and carried a stone crock in her hand.

Margery jumped to her feet.

"Oh Ellen, you did not need to come here tonight. She is quieter now, and Leitis could leave her long enough to get supper for us." She turned to explain to the men. "Caitlin had an ill turn this afternoon. I hated to tell you till you had eaten and rested a little, but she was so bad we sent for Andra, and Andra said we should try oil—from a solan goose."

Randall frowned. Caitlin had never allowed him to come to her bedside, but Andra had told him what little she knew about the case, and he was as baffled as she. She had told him many of her remedies too, and he knew that the oil of the small, black and white, yellow-pated solan goose was said to have specific powers against cancer. All other diseases struck outward, only the cancer buried itself and struck in. His own favorite medicine for such cases was a paste of bloodroot and caustic —not that he had ever had much success with it, but after all, a man had to try. He thought he would send for some by the next packet boat. Ellen was speaking.

"Yes, it is the goose oil. Mother thought she should have some tonight. She couldna' come herself, for Meg's daftie is bad with the chin cough, and she went there. Shall I take this up now?"

"I'll go with you," said Margery quickly, "and we'll stop in my room on the way. I was cleaning the chests today, and I found a length of blue—"

The two girls left the parlor together.

"Michaelmas next week," said Kenneth slowly, "and the black rains o' autumn already begun, and winter will be on us soon."

He turned sharply to Randall. "Ye'll be late for Edinburgh and the beginning o' term."

Rona was silently pouring whiskey and watching the two young men. Randall felt his face grow hot. There was no reason for it, no reason at all.

"I'm not going back to Edinburgh," he said as casually as he could. "Not now, anyway. There's been no chance to do the inoculation."

The Highlander's face turned dark, and a quick light smoldered in his eyes, then died away.

" 'Twould be no great harm were the folk to bide forever without the inoculation," he retorted. "There's a feeling against it in the Kirk."

"There was many against it in past time when it was a new thing," said Randall lightly. "When Cotton Mather came out for it in Boston, he near had his house blown up for his trouble. But most folk now have got better sense. Why is the Kirk against—?"

"Because it takes the power out o' the hands o' God Almighty," said Kenneth, his voice still sharp-edged with anger. "Dragging men back from the grave when the Lord has ordered them into it!"

"Why you could say that of all medicine," answered Randall, trying to hide his own irritation. "Would you leave sick folk to die with no remedy, outlaw our whole profession, sir, and have all doctors turn to mechanics and laborers?"

Kenneth shrugged his shoulders and reached for the whiskey bottle. "If they did, I'd no object to it," he answered, filling his glass and drinking deeply.

Rona gave a loud laugh, and Randall turned his head. The laird sat in his high-backed chair with his hat still on, his face flushed with drink and good cheer.

"Go to, lads! Make a cock pit o' my parlor, if ye've got your spurs by ye. I'm o'erfond o' the sport, to stop it. But dinna' ye break the furnishings or scatter the fire about—"

"Hush!" said Randall, putting his hand up. He was sure he heard it, or almost heard it, louder than the fall wind tearing at the slates of

Rhinn House, a woman's scream. He listened, but it did not repeat itself. Kenneth and Rona were staring at him.

"I thought I heard—" he was about to explain, when the door burst open. Margery stood there with a look of horror on her face.

"Oh come!" she cried. "Please come! Ellen is seeing before her!"

Rona swore an oath in Gaelic that Randall did not know the meaning of, and lumbered to his feet, heavy with food and drink, weary from battling the wet day.

"Where is she, lass?" he demanded.

"In my room. We were sitting there, and she was looking into the fire—and suddenly I saw her face turn strange. She looked as her mother looks when—"

"Come, lads," interrupted Rona.

The men went out of the parlor, through the great hall, and up the stairs. Margery crept after.

Randall had never been in Margery's room before, but he did not stop to gaze tenderly around it, as he would have liked to do. He knew there were blue and white hangings of some sort, pictures on the walls, a thick carpet, furniture of dark, polished wood. Ellen was crouching, tense and rigid, on a heap of cushions before the small brass grate. She gazed steadily into the fire with eyes that did not seem to see. Randall stood still and watched her, not knowing what else to do. Kenneth and Rona stood and stared.

"She never had it before," whispered Margery, "but she well could have it. They say 'tis in every red-haired daughter."

Yes, Ellen's hair could be called red, he thought, as he studied her vacant eyes and clenched hands, the pattern of violets and green leaves on a cushion at her side. He turned to Rona.

"Is there something we can do, sir?"

Rona shook his head and answered roughly. "No, there is naught we can do but wait. But did I think the wench were a-bamboozling o' me—"

"Oh no, Father," pleaded Margery. " 'Tis no trick. You can see it is not. She has the sight just as her mother has."

Kenneth made a hoarse sound in his throat that drew Randall's attention. The lowering Highlander looked even more distraught than Margery. It seemed strange that he should be troubled so. He must have seen taischers a-plenty, too many to be unnerved by one more. But he stared with stricken eyes almost as blank as Ellen's. Here, thought Randall, was another question he had no answer to. Suddenly he remembered his thoughts in the tavern that afternoon. He strode forward and waved his hand with a downward motion before Ellen's face. The girl gave a scream and tumbled sideways among the vivid silk cushions.

In an instant they were all about her, Rona holding her head up; Randall on his knees taking her pulse—for no good reason he could think of, except that he was used to taking pulses; Margery bringing water; only Kenneth standing back.

"What did ye see, lass?" asked Rona impatiently. "Did ye see a taisch before ye, like your mother'd do?"

Ellen lay back against him with the air of a tired child. She put her hands to her face.

"We went to Caitlin's room," she said vaguely, as if reaching back beyond the vision to the old security that had been there, "and Caitlin was asleep, so we left the oil with Leitis and came here. We were looking into the fire, and suddenly—and then—"

"Go on, Ellen," said Randall gently. "What happened then?"

"Why then it seemed that the fire grew till I could see nothing but fire, and then the fire faded out, and I saw the road that goes through the clachan and across the burn—I saw it all so plain. I saw Caitlin coming toward me. But when she came near me, she stood still. She began to dwindle away. She dwindled down till she was no higher than the hem of my skirt. And then she grew tall. That must mean—it must mean—"

It seemed to Randall that some frightful significance now became clear to her, but none was clear to him. He bent closer to catch what she said, and found he was still holding her hand.

"Caitlin will die soon," she whispered.

"Aye," said Rona gruffly. "That's nigh the commonest taisch o' all. To see a body dwindle and then resume forbodes its death. Poor Caitlin! For a long time I ha' thought she could no last."

Margery held a cup of water for Ellen to drink.

"Has the like ever happened to ye before, lass?" Rona wanted to know.

Ellen shook her head. "No, and I care not if it never happens again," she murmured weakly, beginning to cry.

"You must stay here tonight, Ellen," said Margery kindly. "I'll make a milk posset and—"

Kenneth interrupted, speaking for the first time since he had entered the room.

"She'll fare best with her mother who understands such," he rumbled. "I'll take her home."

Rona approved the idea at once. "Aye, Andra should know of what's come about," he said, "and the lass will be better there. 'Tis no matter for Madge and me, or our doctor of medicine."

Watching Kenneth help Ellen from the room, Randall became aware that the rain was beating again on the slates above, the wind lashing the breakers into new fury along the dark shore. Could Ellen have been tricking them, he wondered. After all, Caitlin's death was probably a safe enough prediction to make. But suppose she was not—they had been truly, terribly convincing, the glazed eyes and stiffened body. Suppose it was not a trick but an actual phenomenon—like electricity—like magnetism! Was it really a deviation from all natural law, or the workings of a natural law he did not understand the principles of? Well, he would certainly talk to the girl when she was over the first shock of discovering her affliction; search her with questions and see if he could glean enough facts to build an hypothesis on. Rona had said it was not a matter for a doctor of medicine, but how did Rona know? He, Randall, was not so sure. He found himself following the others downstairs, watching Kenneth and Ellen disappear into the black rain as if they, too, had been part of a vision irrevocably gone. And then he was sharply aware of Margery standing beside him, close, and warm, and sweet-scented, in her golden dress. All the rest of the world could leave him and go its way, he thought, if only Margery would not go.

XII

Two and the Fire

Two NIGHTS after Kenneth had taken her home from Rhinn House, Ellen stood in the twilight by the curving stones of the beehive hut and chatted with Rob MacNayr. Rob had a small mouse-colored pony harnessed to a crude sledge for dragging burdens over rough ground where wheels could not go. A thick-set, brown-faced man, he was loading the sledge with leather buckets full of new milk, fastening a lid tightly on each one.

"There be no more here, lass, than folk is needing," he said dubiously.

Ellen gave him an indifferent stare. "Cows always give less milk when the wind's north," she answered. "Ye can no blame me." Then, mellowing her speech a little, she asked, "Did ye hear what went on at the laird's o' Wednesday eve?"

It was in her mind to know whether the gossip had run through the clachan yet that she, like her mother, had the sight.

Rob shook his head. "I heard naught. I been for birds to the Flannans. A good year for fulmar, though gannets be scarce—"

"Didna' Christie have any news when ye got home?"

"Christie? Where would she get news from?" he asked, strapping the last bucket in place so it could not shift and spill over when he was leading the pony down the glen. "She's near her time and keeps to the house, sewing for the new bairn and caring for those already by. But if something happened at the laird's, I'd say 'twas likely Miss Margery's banns be posted. Did she plight her troth now, whilst I was away?"

Ellen stiffened. "Who would she plight it with?" she demanded.

He smiled widely and picked up the reins at the pony's head.

"Why, with any one that pleased her. Could be Schoolmaster or the doctor lad. Some rich man's son from the cities. I wouldna' know."

He moved away, apparently not much interested in gossip, and for Ellen, too, the talk had lost its savor. She turned and went into the hut where Janet Gillander was scouring milk pails with a heather brush.

"Be off with ye, Janet," she said. "Would ye work all night after working all day? Have ye naught better to do?"

Janet put the brush down and gazed back, a wistful look on her pretty face flushed with the heat of the turf fire.

"Oh Ellen, ye know well what I wish I could be doing," she said.

Ellen smiled coldly. "Why it wouldna' matter what ye were doing, so long as Colin MacKay were by. But ye canna' have him, Janet. Meggy's in his heart, and he wants none but she."

"I know," sighed Janet. "But I'm told Meggy keeps giving him nay."

Ellen shrugged. "When the daftie dies, 'twill be a different story. If ye'd mend your market, ye'd best go to Portree or Stornaway."

Janet's eyes snapped, and she spoke tartly. "There be others could use the same advice," she said. She pulled a tartan shawl around her, stepped out, and vanished in the purple dark.

Ellen stirred the fire and stacked the clean wooden pails at the back of the hut. Then she went to the doorway and stood there, gazing down the hill. Tall clumps of prickly furze and reaches of drying heather showed all pale in the light of the harvest moon. She heard the belling of the red deer from the uplands, and on the crags below, the endless trouble of the sea. Smoke from the kilns drifted by, stinging in her nostrils. She was waiting for her lover, Kenneth, but it was Randall Woodbury who came.

"Did I startle you, Ellen?" he asked, stepping out of the darkness suddenly, just at her shoulder. "If I did, I am sorry. I mean you no harm. It was only to talk with you in private that I came here, but if you wish, I will go away."

Ellen stood still for a moment watching him, trying to keep her face from showing the triumph in her heart. She had felt he would seek her out soon, but she had not known just when or where it would be. "Lord Jesus," she prayed inwardly, "make Kenneth be late tonight. Oh, make Kenneth be late."

Aloud she said, looking down, smoothing the skirt of her dark dress, minding the proper English speech, "Oh I am not afraid. Not of you, sir. I could not be. But I was startled, I own, for I had been watching the path, and I saw no one approach by that way."

She lifted her eyes to his and let her smile widen. Yes, he was handsome, she thought, with his wispy yellow hair blowing in the night wind, his friendly gray eyes and persuading smile, for he stood just in front of the door where the firelight shone out and she could see him very plain. Not so handsome as Kenneth. Thinner and finer-cut, without the ruddy earthiness of the Highland man. But he was an American, and she reminded herself that in America there were gowpins of gold—whole handfuls of it.

He sighed lightly and shook his head, as if amused by his own blunder.

"And I did not come by the path, for I could not find it in the night. 'Twould be more fitting if I came to your mother's house, I know—"

Ellen felt her heart stir with surprise and delight. Did he mean to ask for her hand already, with no courting at all? When they had not even kissed? When they had not—?

"But what I have to say cannot be said there."

"Oh?" murmured Ellen, in her voice all the flatness of her disappointment.

"I waited for you to come to Rhinn House, for I knew Rona would let me take you aside and speak with you alone. He does not feel as I do in the matter. Still, he would let me try—"

Ellen kept her eyes cast down.

"It was in my mind to come to you," she told him very low. "But my mother has kept me a-spinning and gathering dye herbs. She was not pleased when Schoolmaster brought me home that night and I told her what had happened to me. She would keep the sight all to herself, that one. She would not have even her own daughter share it, no."

He was regarding her steadily. His look made her feel confused inside, and she knew that she must keep her outward manner direct and simple, keep her two halves separate, with a brazen wall between.

"Why did you think of coming to me, Ellen?" he asked her gently.

This was the moment, she thought. She let herself shiver in the chill wind blowing down from the dark purple uplands under the waning moon. The deer were still belling far away.

"Come in," she invited. "It is a poor place—but there is a fire—and all—" She let her voice trail into silence without finishing her speech.

When they were both inside the hut, she pulled the mat across the door. Kenneth was almost sure to come, and if Kenneth came—ah Lord—but she would have to take that chance.

"Not even a stool," she cried, flinging her hands out in a gesture of apology. "Only the blanket here—"

Randall looked at the strip of gray wool laid close to the small seething pit of fire. Then he went to the heap of milk pails, placed one of them bottom-up a little way off, and sat down upon it.

"I'd be back out of the smoke," he said.

Ellen sat down on the blanket, arranging her skirts carefully about her.

"I was coming," she said, "oh, I was coming—" She looked up at him with obvious distress, her eyes dark in her thin face.

"Tell me," he said, leaning toward her. "You need not be afraid."

"Well I thought I would come, because of that night in August— when my mother was churched for the sight and then stricken after—"

He interrupted her. "Did she ever tell what she saw that night?"

"No, she has never told, and she shudders and turns ill when I ask her. But from the way you looked at her and tended her that night, I thought, ''Tis not the Kirk can help this affliction, 'tis the doctors, maybe. Perhaps she needs not prayer, but medicine.' I meant to tell her that I thought so. But then—when it happened next—it was not to her."

His face had lighted. "I am glad you feel that way. The same thought must have been drifting in the air that night, and went into your head as well as into mine. I have wondered ever since if the sight is not a problem that could be explained and treated by medicine. We do not have it in America. It was not lectured upon in Edinburgh, and I heard it mentioned there only once. That was when Margery spoke of your mother."

"Aye," answered Ellen, feeling, in spite of herself, a lift of pride in her mother's powers. "Miss Margery could scarce speak of the sight and not mention her. Her skill be well known."

"So its manifestations were new to me when I came here. I watched your mother, and I thought I would like to study her case. But then I grew to know her and work by her side—as with Lavan—and I saw that I never could study her. Can you understand why?"

Ellen looked thoughtful. "My mother keeps a wall around her," she said.

He nodded, his face clearing. "How well you put it! She does exactly that. Without meaning to do it, she makes me feel like a greenhorn and a fool. I honor your mother. There is a great goodness in her. She is strong and wise, and gifted beyond the common run. But I could not ask her what she eats for supper, as I mean to ask you. Can you see that, Ellen? Can you see?"

She looked into his eyes, honest and gray and open. Not even the flickering firelight of the hut could raise any shadows of false purpose there. It would be a slow path, she thought, but she would tread it, straight to all those gowpins of gold. She let herself smile, and tossed back her hair with just a touch of provocativeness in the gesture. "Do you mean to ask me what I eat for supper?"

"Yes, as any doctor might, if you had a sick stomach or an aching head. Ellen, I do not know that I can cure you of the sight. I do not even know that you want to be cured of it. But I want to find out more about it, to study it, and see if it be a matter for doctors to cure. Will you help me in this—to increase the sum of human learning—?"

Now there was a light in his eyes she did not like, she thought; the same light that shone on the faces of earnest young ministers too deeply devoted to the Kirk.

"Yes, I will help you," she told him. "But how am I who have no learning, to help increase it? That I do not see."

"You may not have learning, but you have knowledge," he replied, "a special knowledge." He drew the improvised stool closer and sat there, looking at her intently.

"First," he said slowly and carefully, as Kenneth talked to the children at school in the byre, "I would know whether it comes to you from within or without. Is it seen by the eye or the brain?"

Ellen replied as slow as he, cautious, venturing every word forth as if ready in an instant to draw it back.

"I do not know. It is like something seen in a dream."

"You say you saw Caitlin walking toward you on the village street. Was it summer or wintertime? Was it a bright day?"

"It was all gray about her. It might have been in time of autumn rain. I cannot tell."

"Were there other people on the street?"

"No. But there were little green lights like butterflies hovering along the way she came."

"She dwindled then?"

"To the hem of my skirt, as I said that night."

"And then she grew to her proper size, but she did not speak to you? She made no cry?"

"No."

"How did the vision end?"

Ellen wet her lips and darted a swift glance about the hut.

"Why, it was as if—as if a black lightning flash came and swallowed all."

"You are sure of that?"

"Yes."

"Do you know what it was?"

"No."

"It was my arm descending. I swept it before your eyes. I wanted to know if the vision was coming to you from within or without. Suddenly, in that moment, I wanted to know."

He stopped, looked puzzled and dismayed, then he went on.

"I had been sure it came from within the mind. But if my arm fell across the vision and destroyed it, it must have come to you through the visual senses."

"I do not know," said Ellen simply, shaking her head and drawing a long breath.

In a moment he had another question.

"Have blind folk ever been known to possess the sight?"

Ellen pondered. She might as well tell him. She could see no harm.

"Oh yes, there was an aunt of Tam MacVean's at Stornaway. She is dead now, and I cannot remember her name. But she had the sight, and she was blind all her last days as any newborn thing. Once Tam had a passenger fall overside and drown, and just before it happened, both she and my mother saw him with his clothes shining like the skins of fishes, and the hairs of his periwig all wet. Folk can also see taisches in the dark."

His face showed an even greater bewilderment and dismay.

"Why then, if it can be seen by those whose natural sight is clouded or destroyed, it must come from within, as I thought at first. Ellen, you are telling me yes and no all in one breath."

"I am sorry. I told you I had no learning," she said. Long before this, she thought, Kenneth should have been tearing away the mat at the door.

"Do not ask pardon. 'Twas no fault of yours. This is only the beginning, and it will take a long time to get things clear. Do you wish me to cure you, if I can ever find a way?"

"Yes."

"But do you think of it as a sin upon you?"

"How can I, when it came to me through no wish of mine?"

"I thought it was according to the teachings of your Kirk that very deep sin came about so. But I am not interested in that. Have you suffered any illnesses? Do you ail in any way?"

She shook her head. "Nothing worse than a chill when the wind blows east in winter, and for more than two years, I have not ailed at all."

"Did anything uncommon happen that day?"

"Nothing. I slept till noon, having watched by the cattle all night. After the rain stopped, my mother sent me to gather sea herbs along the shore."

He smiled. "And for supper—?"

She allowed herself to smile back. "Potatoes, and herrings, and wild carrot wine."

"And after?"

"My mother gave me the goose oil in a little crock and told me to take it to Caitlin."

"Did she say what it was for? What illness she thought Caitlin had?"

"No."

"Do you know the uses of oil from the solan goose?"

"I thought it was used for healing green wounds," she said innocently.

"And for no other thing?"

She looked him in the eye and lied boldly. "It may be," she said. "I do not know."

"Had she or anyone ever told you Caitlin would die?"

"No. No one had told me. We are all afraid lest she might, but no one is sure of her death."

He stood up. Ellen rose quickly and moved toward the door. This first meeting had passed well, but if it kept on much longer, the interruption she feared was sure to come.

"I am afraid," she murmured plaintively, "I have not helped you. But I will try again, if you wish it, Randall. I hope you will try to help me."

He stared at her long and reflectively. He wore a different countenance now, she thought, than he had worn that first night when they exchanged their wordless speech across the laird's table. He was drawn to her now, not in the way she wished, but she was content for the moment that it should be accomplished in any way.

"I shall talk to you again, Ellen, surely," he said, a sober note in his voice and a sober look in his gray eyes. "I shall want to ask you more. And if you have another taisch, as soon as you awaken—please send for me."

"I promise," she murmured, smiling a little, wishing he would be gone.

"Good night," he said, "and thank you. What you have told me confuses me only the more. But the beginning of any new thing must always be that way."

For a moment they stood looking at each other. Then without another word he strode out into the dark.

Scarcely had his footfalls lost themselves in the silence of the heath before Kenneth thrust through the doorway. A flush burned high on his cheekbones, and his eyelids looked hot and inflamed like those of a man in drink, but he did not smell of whiskey. He lunged past her and flung himself down on the blanket Randall had ignored. Ellen stood perfectly still, staring down at him.

"What Hell's broth are ye brewing, lass?" he demanded, not letting his eyes meet hers, peering into the fire as if he expected to find his answer there. "What do ye mean by it? Setting up for a taischer! And the whole of it a lie!"

Ellen sighed with relief. So he had known! Known that she only pretended to see. They had not met since he had taken her home to Rhinn House that night. He had walked silently then, holding her arm, letting her lean on him. But he had not gone into the house to confront Andra. He had left her at the door, muttering that she would do well enough, now she was at home. Well, she was glad he knew for he would not betray her, and she liked to have as little pretense as possible between them. It interfered with another thing. She had not dared to reveal the truth to her mother, only to tell her that she had seen a taisch and hoped it would not happen to her again. Andra had believed. She talked of sending to Ireland for holy water from the Roman church. Perhaps, because she had been in a nunnery once, she believed it would be a more powerful fluid than the common Scottish kind. But Ellen did not need holy water. She was not ready yet to be cured of such sight as she had. It was a comfort to know that with Kenneth she need not lie, at least, about this, so she spoke out, blunt and forthright as he.

"And why should I not set up for a taischer, if I choose? I seen my mother do it enough times, so I ken well the way. I could think of naught else to make the lad notice me."

"So it was for that. I should ha' known. I seen ye give him that slanty look o' yours. But why did ye think he would notice ye for that? 'Twould scarce drawn a Highland man on."

Ellen explained with more patience than was usual to her.

"Why I watched him tend my mother the night Master Riddoch was here. He thinks he is wiser than the law and fifteen lords of Edinburgh; that he can find the right pill for anything whatsoever that is crosswise or untoward. I thought I would set him to curing me."

Kenneth laughed harshly. "He is uncou' well begun! For I watched him at it! Through a crack where the mortar is cleft from the stones, I watched him."

"I thought ye must ha' done that," said Ellen, "when ye rushed in the moment he was gone. I feared lest ye would come before and ruin all. I feared on 't."

Under the dark bush of his eyebrows he stared up at her for the first time that night.

"No, ye needna' ha' feared, lass. I hate your game, but I wouldna' spoil it, since it furthers my own so well."

Ellen spoke slowly, her greenish eyes narrowing, the right one more than the left.

"What do ye mean by that?" She sank down on the blanket beside him.

"When he's with ye, he's not with her," said Kenneth, his anger smoothing itself away. "I tell her lies of a rising for Charlie Stuart, and it draws her to me for a while because the poor lass loved her mother so. But it doesna' last, and I canna' always think of lies. Arrhh Ellen!" and he caught her by both wrists pulling her close to him, "ye know 'tis my plan to wed with Margery and keep ye for my lass, in your own little house, with silk gowns and a'. And I ha' tried. But she has smiled o'er-much of late on the outlander, and if she were wed with him and I lost her portion, I might lose what's more to me than her. Every time I see them together, I feel my purse grow a guinea light. But every time I see him with ye, I want to cut his throat."

Ellen considered slowly what she had just heard, like trying to unwind one thread from a tangled skein. Kenneth feared that Randall was finding favor with Margery, so he was willing that she, Ellen, should try to divert the other lad. If he did not win Margery and the portion, he feared that Ellen, too, would go. What would he say if he knew she had plans of her own in which he had no part?

He was still holding her wrists, drawing her ever more close.

"Awww, lass," he was pleading, "say ye are only after him in sport— to while away the time that I must tend so close to her! Say 'tis for me ye care—!"

She looked into his stern dark face and troubled eyes. Then she bent forward yieldingly. He dropped her wrists and caught her in his arms.

Ellen felt as if the fire in the earth pit was rising and surging through the hut, enveloping both of them. A short while before she had sat with a lad before this fire—two people and the fire there once before, tonight— but it had been a different two. Even she herself had been different then. But now, but now—oh, there was never such a pair as Kenneth and she —together—for one time more. Ellen gave herself up to the living wonder of the flame.

XIII

No Death in Scotland

GOING to the window to draw the curtains against the wild black storm roaring up from Ireland, Margery remembered that much rain in autumn was supposed to be a sign of the Lord's displeasure upon the land. She stood there in the circle of casements that formed the bay, gazing out into the late October night. Far down the wind-racked seas, she thought, were the towering cliffs of Barra Head, the walls of Kismull Castle where she had done much of her growing up. The seasons returned as regularly to Barra as to other places she had known, but in her heart it was always summer there, in that island lying like a dark green shadow on a peacock-colored sea. She thought of the scarred hillsides and white sand beaches and little, crooked apple trees where such sweet fruit grew. She could taste those apples, almost, and smell the pink, trumpet-shaped flowers said to come down from seeds Prince Charlie had scattered out of his pocket, just north of there, on Eriskay where he had come ashore. There had been an eagle flying over that day, her mother had told her. Everyone thought it boded well for the Stuart cause. And now most of those who had seen the eagle were dead, and the bonny young prince a beaten old man, destroying himself in Rome.

Or was he destroying himself? He had taken a young wife, and now there were rumors of a son. At least, Kenneth had said there were such rumors. Almost every day Kenneth leaned to her ear to whisper some new tale about another uprising to try to put the Georges off the throne again, but when she asked him where he got the news from, he would only say that he heard it in the cry of a passing bird. She wondered what her cousins on Barra would say. If any such matters were afoot, they would be sure to know. It seemed fantastic to think such a thing could happen after all the years since the Forty-five. But "The Stuarts will come again," her mother had said, said it in her last hour, looking on death.

And then, Kenneth himself puzzled her even more than his stories.

Always at her side when he was not in the schoolroom, yet seeming to
get no pleasure from being there. He said little to her himself, but if
Randall or any chance guest of her father's tried to engage her in speech,
he would scowl, and mutter, and show plainly by his manner that he
wished they would sail north into utter darkness and never return. He
kept referring to their marriage, but he never asked her to set a day.
Well, if this was Highland courting, she thought, she was ready to take
herself to Paris again. And still worse, if he had been more ardent—
but that she could not have borne. Sometimes after supper he would
disappear in the direction of the clachan, saying he needed a walk in
the fresh air because his throat and eyes were dusty, the schoolroom
being just over the threshing floor. She had no idea where he went. Perhaps to meet some boat bringing the rumors he would whisper to her at
breakfast next day. While Kenneth was out on his walks, she would chat
or play chess with Randall. Thinking about Randall hurt her. She could
hear voices now, crying alone in the wind outside, and they made her
remember that night in the dusk below the Cursing Stones when she
had heard him call out to his dead wife, Sally Anne. She drew the cur-
tain quickly across the small thick panes, shutting out the night. She
crossed the room and flung herself into a low cushioned chair by the fire.

Now that she was withdrawn a little from the clamor of the storm,
she could hear Caitlin's moans coming from the far end of the servants'
wing. Caitlin had been crying out at intervals all day. Rona had left in
the early morning, taking Kenneth and Sim, and gone to Stornaway to
meet the wood boats from Mull that were bringing timber, and blue
stones of Talisker to mend the terrace pave. Leitis had not once left
the sick woman, so Randall and Margery had been alone. They ate cold
chicken and cockle pie on the kitchen table, and sang together at the
spinet, and played chess until darkness fell. Then he had gone to his
room to answer his father's last letter. It had been a happy day. Margery felt conscious-stricken now that she had been so happy, with Caitlin
lying only a little way off in such pain. Twice Randall sent her to rap
on the door and call to Leitis, offering his aid, but both times she had
been forced to carry back the woman's stubborn no.

Now she stirred uneasily in her chair, shivered and leaned to the sea-
coal fire. In a moment she would go downstairs, she thought, calling
to Randall on her way, and set out some spice cakes and a cordial. Suddenly Caitlin's wails rose loudly and were muffled again by the closing
of a door. Margery ran out into the narrow wooden corridor that led to
the back of the house where the servants slept.

"Leitis," she called softly. "I heard you coming out, Leitis, and I
wanted to ask— Is there anything—? Will she let Randall come in now?"

Leitis was twisting her apron in her gnarled fingers, and tears ran down the grooves of her brown old face.

"Oh, Miss Margery," she choked, "she is that bad I never saw. I wish Sim were here. He shouldna' ha' gone. I shouldna' ha' let him go. I wish your father were at home."

"Please let Randall go to her, Leitis. And I will fetch Andra. Together they might—"

Margery broke off. She had a feeling there was nothing anyone could do.

Leitis' hands fell limply at her sides. "He may go to her if he will—the doctor lad. She will not know. She knows nothing now but the pain."

Margery clasped her hands and her eyes lighted. Quickly as they had come, all her doubts were gone. Randall was going to treat Caitlin at last, and now, miraculously, she would soon be well.

"Go back to her, Leitis," she cried. "I will tell him at once. In a moment he will be there."

The old servant wiped her eyes and shuffled away, her horsehide slippers scraping a little on the timber floor. Margery ran out to the gallery in the center of the house where the portraits hung, coming around a corner quickly. After a step or two, she halted and stood still.

Randall and Ellen were sitting on the narrow stone bench just under the picture of Charlotte Rhinn in the green brocade she had worn at the court of Queen Anne. Ellen's wet shawl lay at her side, and there were raindrops on her hair. Randall was looking earnestly into her face, and she gazed raptly back.

"Do you see what is past?" Margery heard him say, as she waited, so surprised at the little scene she was uncertain for a moment what to do.

"No," said Ellen gravely, but with an air of quiet pride. "We see the future, and what is happening in the present, but far off. The past we do not see."

"Do you ever—" his voice broke off and resumed on a slightly higher note, "—ever see the dead?"

Sally Anne! thought Margery, a quick pang leaping in her heart. He wants to use Ellen's power to reach Sally Anne!

"No," continued Ellen, "we do not see the dead. We see the deaths men will die."

Just then Caitlin wailed at the far end of the house. Ellen half turned and lifted her head quickly. Margery remembered her errand and hurried forward.

"Oh, Randall, you can go to her now. Leitis says you can go."

Randall stood up. "I'll get my chest," he answered. Then he turned

to Ellen. "Thank you for coming. You have told me much that I wanted
to know, but there is still more."

Ellen smiled at him, stood smiling after he had disappeared into his
own room.

"I'd ask you to have a cup of hot tea, Ellen," said Margery evenly,
"except that we need your mother. Would you mind giving her a message to come?"

Ellen shook her head. "Ye'll no get her up here this night," she replied, "Christie MacNayr's in labor and making an ill piece o' work."

Without stopping to consider her motive, Margery suddenly found she
had another errand ready.

"Well, you can at least stop by Colin MacKay's and tell him to go to
Stornaway for my father as soon as it's fit to put a boat in the sea."

Ellen picked up her wet shawl with reluctance. "Let me dry myself
a bit, Madge," she protested. " 'Tis raining a flood, and the wind's enough
to take the tails off horses. Dinna' send me forth in it."

"Ye got up here," said Margery, with a tartness she was quickly
ashamed of, "and ye can get back."

She turned and went down the corridor to Caitlin's room, left Ellen
standing there.

Why—why, I'm jealous of Ellen, she thought.

Just as she reached Caitlin's door Randall overtook her. He rapped
gently, and they stood looking at each other, listening to Leitis fumble
with the bar. For the moment Caitlin was still.

"Margery," he said, looking down at her soberly, "I wish—I don't know
—but I wish you wouldn't go in there. Go back and have tea with Ellen,
or go to your room and read a book, but please—"

"But you may need help," said Margery simply. "Andra cannot come
because Christie is in labor, and she must bide there. And Leitis is nearly
worn out. You must let me stay."

Leitis opened the door then, and they stepped into the room.

Margery had not been allowed here since midsummer, and she was
unprepared for the fetid odor of the place, an odor like decaying rushes,
gray-green fungus, and creeping slime. Impulsively she covered her
mouth and nostrils and looked at Randall. She saw recognition flash in
his eyes and then grim lines appear in his face. Andra had told her once
that every disease had its own unmistakable smell that can never be confused or forgotten once it is known. Randall must know what Caitlin
ailed of now, but he did not look as if the knowledge cheered his heart.

"Margery," he said harshly, "will you please go away."

"No," said Margery.

She turned stubbornly and looked past Leitis toward the figure on the high wooden bed.

Caitlin was a good twenty years younger than her brother Sim. She had been a quiet woman always, Margery remembered, tall and graceful, with dark eyes and hair and a very pale skin; pale lips, too. Perhaps the reason no lad had ever been drawn her way was because there was no warm color about her anywhere. But now her face was a waxy yellow-gray, and her nose hooked downward like the beak of a bird. Her eyes were fixed and staring as if they looked out on a world full of darkness and fright. One clawlike hand lay outside the counterpane. As Margery watched, the sick woman's mouth sagged open and a rusty-looking fluid seeped out and drooled over her chin and wasted neck. She uttered a croaking moan. Leitis hastened to her with a towel of clean linen. Sick and horrified, Margery could not take her eyes away, but stood there looking on.

Then Randall touched her arm.

"Margery," he spoke gently now, "will you go and make me a pot of hot tea."

"I want to stay here," she choked. "I want to help Caitlin."

He continued patiently as if he were explaining something to a child.

"I know you do, and you can help by bringing the tea quickly. I have a tincture here that may ease her pain, but fear her stomach will reject it, and hot tea makes it easier for her to take. You will get the tea— unless," he looked at her searchingly, "you think it is a time for heather ale."

"She has had heather ale," said Margery. "Leitis gave it to her a month back, but it only made her sick, it did not restore. I will get the tea."

Caitlin's moans rose to a shriek, and she rocked to and fro in the bed, clutching both hands to her bosom.

"Go quickly," said Randall.

Margery fled to the doorway and turned back just in time to see him lean over the sick woman and strip the covers off. Then she ran toward the gallery and the wide stair.

Only one of the small iron wall lamps was lit, and she paused to make sure of her footing before she started down. In that moment of pause she heard a slight sound. She lifted her head. The door of Randall's room stood halfway open, and candlelight flickered inside. Was someone there? Who could be there? There was no one in the house except for the three in the sick room and herself. Had the men arrived home unexpectedly? Had one of the crofters come to fetch the doctor lad. Maybe

Christie was worse and Andra had sent. Curious, and not in the least afraid, Margery stepped to the door and peered in.

Ellen Deveron stood by the table reading a letter.

"Ellen!" exclaimed Margery.

Ellen turned swiftly around. Panic flashed in her eyes one moment, and then a cool, self-possessed smile spread over the thin face.

"I stepped in to warm myself," she explained. "It was cold in the hall, and drafty, but 'tis scarce better here. This had blown to the floor, and I but picked it up." She tossed the letter on the table. "Well, I'll be going now, if ye'll no offer me a cup of tea or a drap."

"Good night, Ellen," said Margery as calmly as she could, watching the other girl until she was well out of sight on the dark stair. Then she picked up the letter herself. It was no longer a private thing. Ellen had read it. It now belonged to the whole world.

"Dear Son," John Woodbury had written, "While your account of the heather ale cure was interesting, I am not so impressed as you seem to be. I feel that a noggin of Newburyport rum would have served as well. Still, I should like to test and observe the workings of it. Can you not cozen the lass to give you the recipe? Sally Anne's mother has closed her house and taken lodgings in Portsmouth for the winter, she being all alone now. We had a wind storm last week that scattered the green nuts and ruined all unpicked fruit. Most folk lost some of their trees, but we was lucky. Ours were spared to us. Your mother and the girls are well. Rocky is too sluggish to chase crickets, so I dosed her with buckthorn last night. We are going to drive to Kingston for the preaching next Sunday.

"The affairs of the country worsen every day. The Assembly met to choose delegates to the great Congress to be held in Philadelphia, but the Governor ordered Sheriff Packer to disperse them, and they repaired to a tavern. Later they met in Exeter and chose Nat Folsom and John Sullivan, a lawyer from Durham. I believe the province is finally aroused. Before this, we have been but a poor ground for agitators. Many are still weak-noddled and distracted, and I confess I have not been in haste myself to take a side. But when the King's governor disperses the people's lawfully chosen assembly, I think it is time to cease this endless choosing of committees and prepare for a more active part. I look for war, red and bloody war, to break out between Great Britain and these American colonies. When this happens, every man of us will be needed, and you will want to come home. Governor Wentworth tries to flatter and appease all, but I met him in the street yesterday as he was coming out of the taproom of the Earl of Halifax, and I said to him, 'Sir, fair words butter no parsnips'—"

Suddenly she remembered Caitlin. She flung the letter down and hurried to the stairway.

Moving about the shadowy kitchen with only the firelight to see by, she got out the little earthen box of dried tea leaves and set the kettle on the trivet. Herring, carefully wrapped in rushes to preserve them in drying, hung from the beams overhead. An old crested targe served as a lid for a flour barrel, and a rusty, two-edged sword propped open the low wooden door that led to the dairy. It was a homely, familiar room. Margery could remember being little and crawling on the floor of it. Caitlin had picked her up often then, when she cried, and soothed her. Caitlin, having no children of her own, had always been gentle with children.

When she carried the tray into the sick room, both Leitis and Randall were too busy to notice her. They bent over Caitlin, whose moans had grown weaker and hoarser but more insistent, longer in dying away.

"Andra never told me of this," Randall was saying. "She told me that nowhere on the flesh was there any mark, that it was all within."

"True that was, yesterday," declared Leitis. "She was shriveled there, and gray, but that was all. She would never let me touch it, and hardly let me see. This morning it burst through in the open sore. She has not spoken today."

"I do not think she will speak again," said Randall. "I can do nothing except try to ease her pain. If Margery would come back—"

"I have come," said Margery stepping forward, her hands shaking so that she almost dropped the tea.

Caitlin died a little after one o'clock, when the tide had turned and the storm blown itself away. Randall's tinctures had not quieted her pain, and God had granted her no easy way to die. Margery worked as hard as the others, trying to keep the sick woman dry and clean, to stanch an occasional welling of blood from the ulcered, decaying breast. Once when Caitlin was quiet for a few moments, she looked across the bed at Randall and smiled weakly. He smiled back.

"Could you have helped her," she asked anxiously, "if she had let you treat her when you first came here? Could you have saved her then?"

He shook his head. "I do not think so. But I could have made it easier for her. She took the hard way."

"She was a maid," said Leitis defensively. "She would not lay her bosom bare before any man."

"Maids should be schooled differently," he answered with some bitterness. "They set knowledge back a hundred years with such modesty. Sometimes it is no shame to lay the bosom bare."

His eyes met Margery's. She flushed and turned away, then when he

was once more busy with Caitlin, touching her own breasts to be sure
they were still sound and well.

The poor woman went peacefully at the end of it, the yellow ebbing
out of her face, leaving only the gray. Her whole body seemed to shrivel,
and her hands turned cold. The moan became a little fluttering cough
high in the throat.

"I think she is bleeding from a deep vein within," Randall said, feeling the pulse, and then a moment later, "she seems to be going now."

Tears ran down Leitis' face as she mumbled a little Gaelic prayer.
Margery went to the narrow window and stood there, tearless, gazing
out into the dark. She did not know how long it was before Randall
came to her and put his arm around her.

"It is over, Margery," he said. "Let me take you back to your room.
You must sleep now."

"No," said Margery, "I must help Leitis to wash her and make things
fitting in a house of death."

» » » « « «

Two days later they buried Caitlin, the maid, on a day of windy sunshine when clouds drove across the sharp blue sky, and their shadows
followed them, across the heathery moorlands far below. The crofters
and fishermen and their families stood awkwardly around the great hall
at Rhinn House, but there was tea going like chaff, and whiskey like
well water, and it soon proved to be true, what Margery heard her father telling Randall, that a Scotch funeral was merrier than an English
wedding.

"Do not look so shocked, Randall," pleaded Margery, as they stood
together in the midst of all, "by our ways of doing things. I know you
find us outlandish—"

He turned to her and smiled ruefully. "I apologize," he said, "for
showing it so plain. It is only that death—well, it seems there should
be some respect for it."

Margery looked thoughtful. "I think we behave this way," she said,
"because there is no death in Scotland."

He looked at her disbelievingly. "What do you mean?" he demanded.

"It is only that the two worlds seem so close to us here—the shadow
and substance, the flesh and the spirit. It is no very dreadful thing to go
from one world into the other. The wall between the two is no thicker
than the mist on a hilltop. Caitlin has only gone a little ahead of the
rest of us, that is all."

"Aye," muttered Rona, dipping a ladle into an iron-rimmed wooden tub full of usquebaugh and filling his glass, "that's well put, Madge—no thicker than mist on a hilltop. King and pawn go into the same bag when the play's done."

Then he prayed loudly for God's peace to descend on the departed spirit and on all of them, and the men formed in a double line for the march to the little graveyard beyond the Cursing Stones. Randall paired himself with Colin MacKay, just behind Rona and Kenneth; and Sim, the chief mourner, preceded all, his gray head bowed, awkward in a long black coat, walking alone. Johnny Dweeney limped ahead of the coffin and its strong young bearers, squeezing now and then a blast from the bagpipes and calling solemnly as the procession wound along over the dead grass.

"All brethren and sisteren, I let ye to know and wot that there is a sister departed out of this present world, according to the will of Almighty God!"

When the sight and sound of them died away below the hill, Margery turned from the doorway where she had stood to watch, and started for the kitchen to see that Nellie Gow and her helpers were preparing the baked meats and pastries to be served at the mourners' return. She stopped to give Janet and Ailis a hand in upending a small cask to replenish the whiskey barrel. Both girls were laughing and rosy, panting from their exertion.

"I came to ask you, Miss Margery," said a low voice beside her. It was Andra Deveron.

Margery smiled into Andra's troubled eyes.

"To ask what, Andra?" she inquired.

Andra repeated the familiar question. "Could he not—could not Randall have saved her if he had seen her before?"

"He says no."

The voices of the island women swirled around them in many small eddying pools of sound. The red light of the dying sun shone through the long windows, and on the black, old hearth, large as a small chamber itself, Ellen was helping Leitis to light a fire.

Andra went on, her voice very low. "I am sad for Caitlin," she said, "more than common sad. Not that she is dead, but that she had not lived at all when she came to die."

"I think I understand," murmured Margery, and Andra continued as if she had not spoken.

"When I came here, near twenty years ago," she said, "Caitlin was a young woman, past her girlhood, but still young. She had grown up in the kitchen where she always served, been born in the little chamber where she was to die. She never went further than Stornaway. She never had a lad. She loved children, but had never one of her own. She had nothing women prize."

"She had the sunlight on the heather," said Margery. "She loved that, for I have heard her say so; and the stars at night, and old songs in her head, and turf fires to keep warm by—such things as that. Perhaps they were enough for her."

"Would they be enough for you?" asked Andra bluntly.

"No," said Margery. "They would not be enough for me."

XIV

What's between Taischers

THE ISLAND AUTUMN, Randall thought, as he walked down to the clachan through the November afternoon, was much like other autumns he had known in his home beyond the sea, and yet there was a difference on it. Here as there, the cold came down the moment the summer broke, followed by sharp days, and days of clinging fog, frosty mornings, and nights of wild rain. It was mainly the colors that were different. A month ago, in New England, the maple-covered hillsides would have burned in gold and scarlet almost too vivid for the eyes to bear. Now there would be only the yellowish gray of dying grasses and the dark gray of bare boughs against the sky; stripped fields running back to evergreen forests hardly less austere. Here the moorlands had darkened slowly in a rich pattern of dun and brown and russet, and an occasional patch of spring-fed rushes still flaunted its May-time green.

It was a chilly afternoon of thin pale sunlight with no warmth to it, and he shivered inside his velvet coat and thought he would have to provide himself with a heavier one. There was plenty of good thick wool being woven in every cottage, but he could not remember that he had ever seen a tailor shop in Stornaway. He let his mind play with inconsequential things, like the thought of buying a new coat.

His heart lifted within him as he walked along, almost as if he had taken one of those eastern drugs Rona sometimes talked about, that heightened a man's sense of physical well-being and his capacity for pleasure. It was a little like having a fever, like having drunk too much wine. He had been feeling that way ever since the night of Caitlin's funeral, when he had gone to his room early and sat there alone, not reading or sleeping, but gazing out of the window at a world that seemed to hold nothing in it but stars and darkness and the sea. Not that he had seen the island midnight, or anything at all except Margery: Margery in a brocade dress with jewels in her hair, as he remembered her from the dances in Edinburgh; Margery in brogues and a short plaid petticoat, climbing up the rocks where the sea birds nested, to gather eggs and wild flowers; Margery as she had knelt by the death-bed, her fashionable gown all stained with blood and illness and her curls awry. A man who had Margery would have so many women, all in the one.

At least, he was sure in her case it would not be as some said, that silks and satins put out the kitchen fire. From the way she had helped with Caitlin, he knew she would not think herself too fine for anything she wanted to put her hand to. But would she, a MacNeill of Barra, want to put her hand to being the wife of a country doctor in Hampton Falls? It wasn't likely. And then he remembered how her soft eyes would light when he met her in a corridor unexpectedly. No, he had thought after Caitlin's funeral, he was glad he didn't have to settle it that night.

And ever since then he had refused even to attempt to settle it, re-fused to subject his own actions to any logical scrutiny at all. He had gone on living joyfully and irresponsibly in her company as much as he could. He was acting like a green, sick girl, he knew, and part of him was ashamed of it, but with a good-humored, tolerant shame.

This was Saturday afternoon, and Margery had gone with Kenneth and her father to do the weekly shopping in Stornaway. Randall had expected until the last moment to go himself, but then Colin had come knocking on the kitchen door with a message that he had almost given up hoping to hear. An Irish trading vessel on its way north to the Ork-neys had stopped to put a sailor ashore because he was suffering with painful loins and a high fever, and Colin had taken him in. Now the man's illness was increasing, coming out in dark red spots that began to fester. Andra said it was the smallpox. She had said Randall would want to know.

So he was on his way to treat this unknown sailor and see if the diseased body would provide the venom he had been seeking in order to secure folk from its very sting. He had some oil of Riga balsam, too, for Christie's young child whose navel was slow to heal. He would spend the afternoon in the clachan, doing the work he had chosen to do, so much more satisfying to him than living the student's life of book and bell in Edinburgh. And tonight he would be again with Margery, smiling at her across the wide table, sitting by the fire with her while her father told old stories, or turning her music at the spinet. They would not be alone; there would be others there, but the others did not matter. No one mattered, in that mellow golden dream of his life at Rhinn House, except Margery and he.

He was shaken out of his pleasant reverie by the voice of Johnny

Dweeney calling to him as he passed the blackened stone cottage where the old couple dwelt. Johnny sat on the doorstone braiding a heather rope, his bagpipes leaning against the house wall, where they would be ready if he should on a sudden find himself taken with a piping mood.

"Aww, Doctor," he called, high and quavering, as if he himself were an old shrunken set of pipes. "Did ye find any new cure in the book, or aught for my sorry feet?"

"Keep on taking the meadow saffron, Johnny," Randall called back. "I know nothing better yet. But I pray every night God will make me wiser than I am."

"He's favored ye over most, lad—he's favored ye," croaked the old man.

Randall grinned, shook his head and strode on. He hesitated a moment in front of the narrow hut close to the waterside where Colin the bachelor dwelt all alone. Its wooden door was shut tight, and smoke pouring from a hole in the thatch above, probably the result of Colin's vigorous attempts to keep the sick man warm. He made up his mind not to stop there now, excited as he was at the idea of a smallpox case. It would be better, he thought, to go to Christie's house first. He would be less likely to carry the pox to her child if he proceeded in that way.

As he walked along the unpaved street between the wharves and cottages, he cast a glance now and then up the hillside, behind the town, where all the little crooked garden patches were. Stripped clean of potatoes and turnips, they looked almost as barren as the rock they were cleft from. Harvest must be over, too, in the oat and barley fields to the west. Men should be settling in for their fireside tasks to await the winter it would seem, but no, there was another chore to finish first, and every man-jack of them had taken to the rooftops that autumn afternoon.

Some of the houses were laid bare to the very rafters, and crews of stout lads struggled to hoist up new sods of turf and woven mats of heather and rushes. Widow Gillander and her daughter Janet, having no man to do for them, got on with the work themselves, spreading fish nets over the old thatch, and Iver Gall was weighting his roof with stones. Such winds blew here in winter, Margery had told him, as troubled no other place on earth, and the island people were readying themselves for the onslaught, as a thousand years of experience had taught them they must do.

Rob MacNayr's house was deserted, except for two little boys who crouched on the wide doorstone beside a mangy, sad-eyed greyhound, all three trying to crowd into one narrow space of sun. Randall bent to pat the dog, thinking of Rocky, and how if he were at home he would be prowling the woodlands with her, this time of year, far afield in the pines beyond Pickpocket Mill, looking for partridge, rabbit, a young

buck, or anything he could bring down. The greyhound lifted itself under his hand and then sank back, head on its paws and yellow eyes
closed. Randall saw that it was an old dog, like his own. Then he turned
and spoke to the children.

"What's his name, laddie?" he asked, pointing to the limp, rusty
shape stretched on the gray stone.

"Brian," said the taller child stolidly.

"Is he named for something or somebody?" Randall stood smiling
down, wanting to talk to the small pair, not knowing how, thinking of
a certain blue-green cedar tree. "Why is he called Brian?"

"Because that is his name," said the boy, with the irrefutable logic
of childhood. And then as Randall, crestfallen, was about to ask for his
mother, he lifted his head and smiled himself, and his eyes flashed wide
and sharply blue.

"I'm Donny and he's Jamie," he said, pointing to his companion. "Ye
want to see what I found?" He held out a small reddish stone, shale-
like and thin.

"But I found it first," piped Jamie, the plumper, darker lad. "It was
I gave it to him."

Randall took the proffered stone and weighed it in his fingers.

"Do you want to see your stone fly?" he asked them soberly.

"Yes! Yes!" they chorused.

"But if it flies, it will not come back. Does that matter to you?"

"No, oh no! We can find another! We want to see it fly!"

"Then come," he strode the few yards to the water's edge and stood
there poised, the flat stone in his hand.

"Come see!" Donny was calling at his elbow. "See our stone fly!"

Half a dozen other children, all boys except for one tawny-haired little girl, came running from behind the pile of peats cut for winter fuel
and stacked at the house end. They clustered round Randall where he
stood on the narrow strip of beach, smiling at them, wanting to make
friends and hoping this was the right way, holding the stone.

"I will make it fly over the water," he said. "You can wish on it, if
you like."

"But will the wish come true?" asked the girl child, looking at him
appraisingly.

"It will if you believe that it will," he answered lightly. "Now watch!
Just there!"

He pointed to the dark blue water beyond the shore, and all eyes followed his lifted finger; all the laughing chatter grew still. Expertly he
scaled the stone. It drove away from him in a straight line, hit the water
with a smart slapping sound, darted ahead like a swift bird in flight and

hit the water again, and then a third time. It did indeed seem to be flying over the surface of the sea. Randall cocked his head on one side and smiled quizzically at the children.

"It flew! My stone flew!" cried Donny, dancing all about.

"Let us find another," said practical Jamie. "Sir, can ye make another stone fly?"

Randall nodded. "Yes, but not today. You are Christie's sons, are you not? I came to see your mother."

"She's gone to the waulking," said Donny, and he scuffed the sea-washed pebbles at his feet, no longer interested in Randall or what he had to say.

"She's at Nell Gow's," piped Jamie helpfully. "Do ye know where Nellie lives? Over there." He pointed to a long low cottage of weathered stone, next to Andra's, almost at the edge of Fruin Burn.

"Good-by, lads," said Randall. "Save any flat stones you find. We'll scale more of them some day."

He walked along the hard turf path to Nellie's house and knocked on the door.

No one answered him at first, but this was no great wonder because of the continuous sound that came from the other side of the crude wooden panels, the sound of women's voices that blended and merged in a low, monotonous singing. Not so loud as the song, but steadier and even more monotonous, was a sort of rhythmic beating that accompanied it; not a drum, he thought, nor any known instrument. Curious, he knocked again and waited briefly, then a third time. Then he heard footsteps coming toward him, and the door swung open. Nellie Gow's pleasant brown face looked out.

"Come in for a drap o' barley bree, sir. We're a-waulking o' the cloth, and there's oat cakes and herrings for all. Ye're welcome, whatever's your errand."

Gazing past her into the low smoky room, he saw two lines of women facing each other, a long table between them. On the table lay a strip of gray woolen cloth, and the women were thumping it with their hands in time to their singing, a sort of four-beat time.

Ellen was there, he noticed, and Lavan, and Ailis Ogg, but he missed Andra. He looked around for Christie and saw her coming from the fire with a plate of crisply browned cakes in her hand. He stepped into the room. It had a turf floor, and a fireplace and chimney hung about with iron cooking ware.

"Thank you, Nell," he said easily, secure in the knowledge that he had been a favorite with the island women ever since Lavan's terrible illness in the spring, "but I can stay only a moment. There's a sick lad at Colin's, you know. I came to see Christie, if you'll bid her step here to me."

Christie was looking his way, he knew, and he could have caught her eye himself, but he was too busy watching Ellen. He had not spoken to the girl since that night Margery had interrupted them as they sat under the portraits in Rhinn House gallery, but he had thought much about her. Not about her, so much, as about her strange affliction—if it was an affliction. He was scientist enough to believe there could not be a physical manifestation without a physical cause, but the sharp edge of his skepticism grew more and more tempered the more he talked with Margery. Once he had teased her about believing in some popular superstition, he could not now remember what—not the fairies or the middle earth men; something about the stars or the weather, maybe—and she had tossed her head and hardened her sweet mouth and retorted, "We do not believe. We know."

He looked at Ellen, but he thought of Margery. And that was wrong of him, because Ellen was his patient. She had given him her confidence and put herself in his hands, hoping for a cure. Now as he watched her, he was suddenly aware that just as there were many Margerys, so there were many Ellens, too. Bold and easy, she had seemed to him that first night, seated by her mother at the laird's table, a woman made up of odds and ends, and not worth a second look. Rona, he knew, held her in little esteem. But ever since she experienced the taisch, there had been a difference in her. She had seemed chastened and unsure, appealing to him for help with quiet looks and tremulous pleadings. Well, maybe he was a fool to be flattered by her trust, but there were times when a man could not help being a fool. As if in answer to his gaze, she lifted her gray-green eyes that flashed with the light of the open fire, then blushed—but maybe that, too, was the work of the fire—and looked quickly down, her hands faltering a little in their beat, her lips ceasing to move in the rhythm of the song. She wore a dress of dull green wool, and he noticed the delicate curve of the bodice, wondering that he had ever thought her flat and thin. Smaller than Margery, she was, but quite as provocatively feminine, quite as well put together. Well, she was not for him, that he was sure of, but he had a duty to her and a duty to his profession, to study her trouble and look for the cause and the cure of it.

Christie stood beside him now, and he was about to give her the ointment and leave, but Lavan came running forward, caught his arm, and drew him to the center of the room. She insisted that he must take a cup of ale with them to bring good luck to the waulking, and while he ate and drank and chatted and examined their work, he learned that a waulking was a sort of cross between a quilting bee and a fulling mill at home.

They showed him how they soaked the woven fabric in urine to set the threads and tighten the color, and then beat it with their hands to a texture considered worthy of their famous island wool that would bring such good prices in London. Ailis displayed the crimson dye she made from lichens, and Nellie brought out little jars of yellow dye made from bog myrtle and bracken. Only Ellen said no word to him, and he did not approach her, for this was not the time, not now.

The early twilight had fallen before he was able to take his leave of the women and make his way through the cold gray sunset to Colin's hut. When he rapped on the door the young man came quickly to open it and usher him inside. Colin was handsome, he thought fleetingly, able, no doubt, to have his pick of the unwed girls and young widows, but tonight he looked worried and tense, half sick himself. Randall eyed him sharply and put the question.

Colin shook his head. "Awww, no, Doctor, I be in health, only revolted like at the smell o' him, and he canna' help that, poor lad."

Randall nodded, for the foul air of the place was already causing qualms in his own stomach. He went to the rope pallet before the fire and stripped back the blankets from the huddled form of the sick man. He was a burly fellow, twenty-five, perhaps, with great shoulders and thick black hair, his face reddened with fever, covered with the oozing pustules of the disease. It was indeed smallpox, and by questioning the man he learned that it had been three days since the eruptions first appeared. Only the fourth day mattered for his purpose, since that was considered the best for drawing lymph from the sores. Yes, the sailor had heard of the inoculation. Yes, he willingly agreed that Randall should take pus from him to introduce into the blood of others to protect them from the disease. He had, after all, a light case. It would run its course, no doubt, alleviated by bark and plenty of brandy.

A few moments later in the light of the turf fire Randall was instructing Colin about the medicines.

"And this," he said, holding out a small sack of powders, "I will leave with you for tonight, should he have any trouble in sleeping. Give it with water. Tomorrow I shall come to draw the pus and begin the inoculations. Do you think you could have four or five lads about for me to start on? Some prepare folk with a course of antimony and mercury, but I do not hold it essential, and find it scares many away in itself."

Colin nodded soberly. "I can see that. I ha' had mercury myself once, and well would think it might. But I'll have the five lads for ye. There's me for the one, and I'll speak to Iver. Gavin Gray, too, and Tam Darran, and Alan—"

"Colin! Colin, lad!" It was a woman's voice calling from the dusk out-

side, high, and excited, and thin. "Is the doctor there? It's a taisch has
come on Ellen. She wants the doctor by."

He couldn't have run quicker out of Colin's house and down the turf
path, Randall thought, if they'd called for him because someone was
bleeding to death, and maybe Ellen was bleeding through a spiritual
artery, bleeding out her sense and reason and personality till they would
all go away from her, like the gray mist drifting over the sheep pastures
of Caldune. He only knew as he ran that he was afraid of the sight.

In Nellie's house the women had all left the waulking table and stood
together before the fireplace, not so much frightened as withdrawn and
silently watching. Nellie spoke to him as he came through the doorway.
In contrast to the voice of Ailis, who had run to call him, her tones
were quiet and there was a soothing quality to her speech that is common to the voices of women who spend much of their time with young
children.

"We shouldna' ha' called ye, sir. 'Tis only the sight, and I ha' seen it
happen on Lewis where I grew up, to other folk than she, and they
never took hurt from it. But she is a young lass and not accustomed like
her mother."

"She began to stiffen," panted Ailis at his elbow, "and her face took
on that blind look, and she called for ye in the last moment before the
taisch came."

"I cannot help her," Randall muttered. "Would to God I might."

He glanced at the women by the fireside, but they stared back at him,
expressionless as a wall. Then he stepped forward, reluctantly, for all
the haste he had shown a moment before.

Ellen had not moved from her place at the table. She still sat there,
her head lifted and her face tilted upward, her shoulders tense, her gray-
green eyes fixed on something he could not see.

"I see war—red war!" said Ellen shrilly. "War between England and
America! War, red war—and wounds—and blood! There is a tall man,
a fair man. He is carrying a chest of cures into battle where other men
carry swords. But it will do him no good there. He will be—"

Randall felt his breath catch in his throat and his veins run ice water.
War between England and America, just as his father had told him
was like to happen. And here in this far island this ignorant cattle maid
with no knowledge of affairs in the world was predicting the same. Was
she predicting—his own death? He sought desperately to find some other
meaning for her words.

"War—red war!" Ellen kept mumbling.

And then there came a little stir behind him and a startled exclamation.
Unwillingly he took his eyes from the young taischer. Andra stood in

the doorway, her red hair escaped from its linen cap and hanging like a young girl's, all wind-tossed on her shoulders. She must have come from the moorlands behind the town, for she had a small willow basket full of herbs hooked over her arm. She stood there watching her daughter, her eyes blazing and her mouth twisted. He could not read her expression. Could it—it could not—be scorn?

One moment Andra stood there. Then she moved swiftly forward, stepped up to Ellen, and struck the girl a ringing blow across the mouth. Ellen's head jerked back and she gave a cry of surprise and pain. Andra stood looking down, her face livid with anger. Then she struck again.

Randall strode forward, moved by instinct rather than reason, and put a restraining hand on her arm, but she shook him off. Her eyes still burned in her cold white face and she muttered harshly in Gaelic, phrases he could not understand. He caught only the one word "lie." Then she rubbed her hands together as if to cleanse them and walked out of Nellie Gow's house into the night.

Ellen had put her head down on the table, shaken all over with fitful sobbing. He should comfort her, he thought. Her mother's action had been inexcusable, and he could not understand it, unless Andra was suddenly consumed with jealousy and wrath at this proof that her daughter had the sight as well as she. But no, he told himself, his bewilderment increasing, Andra was not a jealous and wrathful person. Andra was wise and calm and honest, as any woman he had ever known. He found that he did not go forward. He stood there, feeling like a fool, staring at Ellen.

Then he heard the low voice of Nellie Gow. "Ye'd best go, lad," she said. "Ye may be a doctor, but 'tis not a matter for doctors, what we ha' seen. Ye be an incomer, and 'tis no matter for such. Ye'd best go back to your books and your potions, and leave us to our own." Then her voice softened. "'Tis no unkindly meant, sir, but ye canna' settle what's between that lass and her mother. None of us can. They be taischers, and not such as we."

His pride began to recover, and he drew himself back from the woman's fingers that lay on his sleeve.

"Indeed I will go, if I cannot be of help here," he said stiffly.

Silently Nellie bowed her head. He turned on his heel and followed Andra into the night.

XV

If Ye Wait at the Ferry

"I NEVER THOUGHT my own daughter would make a mock of me," said Andra, with the cold bitterness that had replaced her wrath. " 'Tis true, I've been sinful and unholy myself in my time. There's a puddle at every door, and before some there's two, but I have been honest with the taisch as I fear God, and never lied and tricked and pretended it for ends of mine."

She was kneeling by the fire pit in her cottage, rubbing the carcass of a fowl with seaware ashes to salt it away. Ellen sat on the edge of the bed, silently watching her mother.

"When Schoolmaster brought you home from the laird's that night," continued Andra, "and I first heard of the thing, I was troubled, for I believed in it. I thought you were having the sight come on you in your girlhood, just as I. But when I saw you at Nellie's two nights back, I knew the truth, and you cannot bamboozle me. How did you dare pretend to a taisch in front of one who has it true? How did you dare?"

"How did I know ye meant to come running in?" said Ellen coldly. "I thought ye was away on Caldune, like ye said." She smiled, and stood up, and shook out her skirts. "And as for that, how can ye be sure I did not see before me. There's others besides ye has the sight."

"A dozen ways I could tell," said Andra, also standing up and staring at her daughter across the ruddy turf pit. "And if you were a true taischer, you'd know them as well as I. What do you mean by it? What do you hope to get yourself?"

"Why, I hope to get myself a husband," said Ellen, staring cruelly back, "which is more than ye've ever done."

"I'll expose you."

"Do it. I wish ye would. 'Twill only make him believe the more and feel sorry for me." She took down her plaid shawl and draped it around her shoulders. "I'm going out," she said, "on affairs of mine."

She walked out of the cottage and along the turf street of the clachan in the late afternoon. It was a mellow golden day, too warm by far for this season of December, with the seas round Rona almost a summer blue, and a shining mist on the horizon that left no sharp lines anywhere. Children played outside the doorways, for no matter how bad the fishing or the harvest might be, the island always had a fine crop of children. Most of the women were inside getting supper now, and the men away at the seal hunting.

Ellen soon left the clustered cottages and took the steep path that plunged upward through the heath just above Ewen Gow's turnip patch. The cattle were all home from Ardmory now, and she would no longer be sitting up there the whole night long, not again until spring. It would be hard to contrive to see Kenneth, soon it might be impossible, and Ellen sighed a little at the need for change. Well, she must get on in the world. A few moments of swift climbing brought her to the very top of the island, all wild shrubs, dead heather, and the sheepwalks, almost deserted now, since many of the crofters took their flocks as well as their cattle down to the byres in the late fall. To her right, the crags of Ardmory raised up bluntly against the sea, and on the left the land fell away to the green fields of the machair and the white sandy beaches all along the west. Hastily, because she wanted to arrive at the trysting place first, she skirted the little dark loch that fed the burn. Swans drifted along its surface, white silken birds that came in the fall and stayed all winter, stretching their necks and preening their feathers, enjoying the last warmth of the autumn sun.

That morning she had sent a note to Randall asking him to meet her at sunset in Puffin Town. Donny MacNayr had carried the folded scrap of paper to Colin's, where she knew the doctor would be busy inoculating the volunteers. She had watched Donny all the way to be sure there was no mistake, and he had come back with the one word, "Yes," on his grubby little mouth. Oh, she might not achieve her destiny today, but she was going to try!

The northern shore of the island, looking out to the windy sea that went, Ellen had heard, straight from there to the top of the world, was all high tumbled cliffs stretched between the two points of Kindearg and the Mull. Nobody went there except to kill wild fowl or search for eggs and downy feathers among the rocks, and that meant dangerous climbing, nothing folk would be likely to do with night coming on. She felt sure that they would be alone. On the top of the cliffs the grass was still vivid green, furrowed all over with the long burrows where the puffins lived and hatched their eggs, giving the place its name. She picked her way among the burrows and finally selected a little lichened cleft

in an outcrop of stone, sheltered from the wind, catching the last light
of the sun. Spreading her shawl beneath her, Ellen sat down.

Gulls screamed overhead in the waning light. The puffins, black and
white birds with long orange-rosy beaks, waddled unhurriedly by, staring
at her out of solemn dark eyes. Ellen shied a small stone at their leader,
and uttering hoarse croaks, they tumbled through narrow openings into
the earth and out of sight. Then, except for herself and the gulls, the
land was all alone.

She waited restlessly. Maybe he was not coming. Maybe she had come
on a fool's errand up here. Maybe the daftie had fallen in a fit and
needed his services. Maybe Margery had sent for him, and he had gone.
Ellen hated Margery intensely for a minute or two. Then far down the
path she saw the tall slim shoulders swinging along, the sunlight on his
bare blond head. Oh I shall have, thought Ellen, to be so careful now!

In a moment he was beside her, standing there, looking down and
smiling, then dropping to a place by her side.

"Ellen," he said, "I've been worried. I keep remembering how your
mother struck you. Why was she angered so?"

Ellen looked at him, a sad little smile on her mouth and lighting the
depths of her greenish eyes.

"Do not blame her too much," she said, affecting the careful English
speech. "She has been the only taischer among us for so long. It is hard
for her to find that another has the power. She will be happier if I go
away, I think. I wanted to talk with you, to ask you if I should go."

He did not meet her eyes. He was studying the toes of the boots he
had purchased in Edinburgh.

"Do you want to go away?" he asked. "Where do you want to go?"

"I thought—I thought I would go first to Skye," said Ellen falteringly.
"To Portree. And indenture with a sea captain for America. I have heard
that anyone who is strong and willing to work can engage their passage
so."

"Why do you want to go to America?"

"Why, to get rid of the sight," she answered simply. "It is said to be
taken from those who cross the seas away from their home. All the time
my mother was in Ireland, she saw no visions there."

"It is the wrong way," he muttered. "To cure an affliction, by running
from it. I wish you would give me longer, Ellen. Give me a little more
time to study its workings in you."

"I will give you anything you want," she answered steadily. "You have
been so good to me. No one was ever so good to me before."

The long light of the sky to the westward was fading out now, the
gold draining from the landscape, leaving only the gray, and the blue

shadows gathered round them. The gulls were not screaming any more. He looked up then and gazed into her eyes, and Ellen saw in his face what she wanted to see. She looked demurely down.

"I will stay, if you wish it," she said. "It will be hard—with my mother's hand against me in the house all day long. But I will stay."

"I have no right to ask it of you, Ellen," he said unhappily.

"It is not a matter of right," she answered. "If it is something you want, I will do it."

For a moment they were both still. Then she moved imperceptibly closer to him. She looked at his hands lying on his knees, at the little gold hairs on the backs of them, and she could see that the skin beneath was drawn hard and taut and brown.

"I thought," she said hesitantly, "if you could be with me when a taisch comes, from its very start, and I could tell you all the way how it was—"

With the swiftness of a cloud moving away from the sun, his attitude changed. He flung back his head, eager and excited at her suggestion. The shadows that had been drawing round them almost seemed to move aside.

"What a wonderful idea, Ellen! It could surely be studied in no better way! But how are we to know when the taisch will afflict you?"

Ellen cursed herself for a fool; cursed his inquiring mind that seemed likely now to free him from the demands of the flesh that she had counted on to help her.

"I thought—'tis known taischers cannot make them come at will. But they are encouraged sometimes by long gazing into water—into a mirror —or across a fire."

"You thought we might—?"

He was still the doctor, the scientist, the Edinburgh scholar. Ellen sighed and kept on. "I thought—if you have the time now—we are alone. No one will trouble what we do. We could build a little fire here between us, and I could gaze into it—and try."

He jumped to his feet. "I'll gather some bracken," he said, "and I have flints with me. 'Twill take but a moment or two."

Ellen rearranged her shawl, spreading it wide enough for both of them to sit on, and watched him build the fire. The stars were beginning to prick out, but no moon shone overhead. It was very dark in Puffin Town.

When he had a good sized heap of dried heather and bracken blazing, he dropped to her side again and sat there expectantly, watching her. Ellen gazed into the fire.

At first they were both silent, and then she began to talk in a low sweet voice that surprised her, it was so unlike her usual sharp tone. It was a good omen, she thought, and her luck was running well. She told him stories of taischers she had heard about, great seers who predicted the downfall at Culloden and simple folk who saw only boats drive on shore or cattle go astray. Sometimes she let her voice sink in her throat and did not talk at all. Beyond the reach of the fire, the chill winds of late autumn were stirring, and now and then a flight of small birds rushed past them down the night. But within the circle of firelight, all was warm and close and still, except for Ellen's voice and the soft murmur of the flame.

Suddenly she broke off in the middle of an old tale of Inverness and rose unsteadily to her feet, drawing a hand across her eyes. He stood up too, leaning toward her.

"Randall, I do not know—there is a mist—but as yet nothing comes quite clear. Randall, I have heard that when one of us sees before her, if she places her foot on another's foot, and her hand upon his shoulder, that he too will see—"

She turned toward him and took a step or two forward, her eyes wide open, staring straight into his face, fearing to see the keenly observant scholar, but she did not see the scholar. She saw only a man's face, bright and sharp with desire. She lifted one white arched foot, for she had long since kicked her brogues away, and placed it lightly on the toe of his Edinburgh boot. Then she leaned against him, placing her hand on his shoulder.

"Oh, Randall," she cried, "the taisch! Do you see it as I?"

He swept her into his arms. "No!" he muttered against her neck. "And I do not want to see it! I want—!"

But he did not say what he wanted. He only thrust upon her and took. For one swift moment as she lay there, borne down by his caresses on the hard green turf of Puffin Town, she felt a cold triumph soar up in her, higher than any carnal flame. She remembered Comyn Rhinn and how he had taunted her with still being unchosen. "Ah well, if ye wait at the ferry ye'll get across sometime." And she had waited, Ellen thought, long, almost too long, but now—! Ellen forgot Comyn Rhinn. Whatever the craft that bore her, she was swimming in a sea of light—across—across—across! Ellen reached out. She touched the other shore.

XVI

A Fair-haired Man
to a Dark-haired Woman

"Wait a little, lad," said Comyn Rhinn, jabbing away with a quill pen at an ink-stained paper spread in front of him. "Sit ye down. I'll no be long. Ye've business wi' me, I take it?"

"I came on business, yes," said Randall. He looked at the bent sandy head of the older man and noticed that along the center part the hair was beginning to wear thin. Then he looked around the little low room just off the passageway to the byre, where the laird kept his books and did his reckoning.

It was the last night of the old year, "Hogmanay," they called it in this strange world's-end country, and the folk of the island had been making merry all day long. He had watched the grown lads and married men out on the beach, playing with shinty sticks like children, and the children themselves had trooped from door to door in sheepskin masks, asking for sweetmeats and leaving twigs of rowan. But to him it had not seemed like holiday. It had seemed like the time to make an end and a beginning. That was what he had come after supper to the laird's study to do. He was here to ask for Margery, without confessing his guilt with Ellen, as he no doubt should have done, but he was learning more and more every day how a man does not always do the thing he should. He had seen what happened when a man denied himself beyond his strength, and he would do all he could to keep himself from being laid open again to those consequences.

"I'll no be long," repeated Rona, frowning at the littered desk before him. "Take a book there, if ye've a mind." He shook his quill toward a hanging shelf on the wall between the two diamond-paned windows, his gesture making a draft that set the candles flaring and smoking.

Randall looked at the shelf and let his eyes run idly over the titles, with dates inked blackly on the spines beneath them: *Husbandry Anatomized, 1697; John Reid's Scot's Gardener, 1693; Observations on Growing Wool in Scotland, 1765; Life of Sir William Wallace; Jocky and Meggy's Courtship.* He did not take down any of the books. Instead he seated himself in a heavy timber chair and studied the engravings on the opposite wall, that portrayed the Rake's Progress from Fleet Prison to Bedlam Madhouse. He felt sorry now for the Rake. Once he would have scorned him for a fool.

In the five weeks since his adventure with Ellen, winter had come to the island, frosty mornings, rain, and wind, and quick melting snows. There had been winter in his heart, too. But he felt now that it was a winter which pointed toward spring. He felt now a little the way he had that time under the cedar tree when he had been happy because he expected to have a child by Sally Anne—weak and strong at the same time; the most doomed and exalted and precarious thing there can ever be on this earth, a man alone. He did not need books at a time like this. He stared through the tiny window at one small star swung over the sea, somewhere in the way America must lie.

Suddenly Rona muttered a syllable in Gaelic that could only be a curse and swept his papers to the floor.

"What's the matter, sir?" asked Randall.

The laird did not answer at once, but sat staring ahead of him, tapping with the end of the quill on the pages of the ledger that had resisted his attack.

"Year's end, and rents owing, and not a ha'pence amongst them," he said. "If the land gets any poorer, the whole of Scotland had best be off for America. There's not a man on the policy has more than a coat full o' holes and a handful o' boiled beef to take to the field with him."

Randall shook his head. "They're poor, but not that poor. You're making the worst of it."

Rona nodded gloomily. "Aye, and ye wonder at it. 'Tis because I must do again as I have these three years, and forgive every man his rent instead of gouging it from him. Never become a landholder in Scotland, lad. Ye'd do better to go beg in the streets o' London."

"I may come to it," said Randall with a smile. "It seems unlikely, but a man never knows what's ahead."

"Never unless he has the sight," agreed Rona. "What did ye come about?" And then as the younger man hesitated, "If 'tis to offer your own account for the doctoring ye've done here, I'd say I'm well-pleased, and ye can name the fee."

"It has gone well, hasn't it?" said Randall, feeling satisfied, and then admonishing himself inwardly. "I've done like you said, inoculated every man-jack and woman-jill. Never a one has died, and only a few will have bad scars to show."

"Aye, I'll admit 'twas a fearsome sight to me when I watched ye prick the sores with your wee penknife and scratch the pus into the veins of a healthy man. But ye knew what ye was about, it seems. What do ye want in pounds and shillings, lad?"

"Why, I don't know. I hadn't thought," said Randall, glancing about the room and shifting a little in the chair, trying to hide his embarrassment.

"Ye hadna' thought? Then 'twas no about money ye came here?"

"Not about money. No."

"Another matter then?"

"Yes," said Randall, and fell silent.

Rona picked up his pipe, went to the small grate and lit it with a twist of paper and a live coal. Then he returned to his chair.

Randall did not feel like taking tobacco. Beyond the heavy oak door he could hear the voices of Margery and Leitis as they chatted together in the hall, preparing for the crofters who would be sure to come up and pay their respects tonight, since that was all they could pay. Finally he said, "Sir, I should like leave to court your daughter Margery."

Rona looked at him blankly.

"Ye want to court my lass?" he asked, not meeting Randall's eye, drumming again with the quill on the back of the ledger. "Court her to marriage?"

"To marriage, yes—if she will have me," said Randall a little grimly.

"If she will have ye—why there's a thought indeed," muttered Rona. "Sir, I ha' always said when it came to marriage my lass should choose and do what her heart bade her. I promised her mother it should be so. But to go overseas amongst the red Indians—that, unless she be much set on it, I canna' let her do. Ha' ye spoken to her o' the matter?"

"No, I have not. I want your leave to do so."

Rona looked full at him now, and there was a smile in the deep eyes under his heavy brows.

"And suppose I forbid ye?"

"I was afraid you might," said Randall thoughtfully. "She could get herself a richer husband with no trouble. Get herself a better one. But not one who'd care for her more. She's used to London and Paris and the ordering of servants. At home we live by doctoring folk in a country town, my father and I. We've help in the fields when there's need, but my mother tends her own house, unless she is sick and cannot. Likely my wife would do the same. You've a right to ask better for your daughter. You've a right to refuse me."

"But I ha' no refused ye yet. I only asked what ye would do."

"Why I would pack my chest and go down and get Colin to take me to Stornaway and stay there till the next boat for Edinburgh comes by.

But first," and he lifted his jaw stubbornly and looked straight at Rona, "I would tell her how I feel, before I go."

Rona nodded, still tapping the quill. "Aye, a man could do no less than that. I hate to lose ye, lad, but it seems to me best that's what ye do."

Randall felt as if cold winds were blowing on him and he were falling through space. Somehow he had not really expected a blunt refusal, though of course he should have been prepared for it. He scarcely heard, but Rona kept on speaking.

"My lass is used to servants, true, and silks and satins and the life that goes with such. I do not think she could be happy in the frozen bogs of North America."

"She's seen frozen bogs before," retorted Randall, feeling his courage coming back, and underneath it a thrust or two of anger. "She can see them from the windows of her father's own house when she looks out in the morning. Our fields are stony, but no worse than in Scotland, though our towns be not so fine. She wouldn't want there. Maybe now and then I could buy her a satin gown."

Rona went on as if Randall had not spoken. "Furthermore, I hear 'tis a cold grim life ye lead in New England, such as our Kirk enforces among its people. My lass has a liking to be gay. No, lad, it wouldna' do. It would end in tears for both of ye. Unless—I like ye well for a son. Could ye no stay here? I could set ye forth in the world."

"No. My father expects me at home—to take up his work when he is through."

Both men stared silently at each other.

Finally Rona stood up, went over and prodded the fire. "Aye," he said, "a father has a right to expect that of a son. So let it be as ye said. Tell her tonight, and be off tomorrow. I'm sorry to see the last of ye, but 'tis the only way."

"I'm sorry you feel that," said Randall, still not quite believing in the other's no. "Of course—I shall respect your decision, sir."

"Aye, ye're a good lad, not one to come at the thing behind my back, as ye could ha' done. Into the hall with ye now, for the whole clachan will be there to drink with us this night. Tell Margery I'll be amongst them as soon as I put my books away."

The hall of Rhinn House was still decked with the green boughs that Rona had ordered from the glens of Inverness at Christmastime. Sim had put out kegs of whiskey and claret, and Leitis had covered the long table with trays of cold food. Half a dozen of the villagers stood near it, helping themselves with their fingers, and Randall joined them. He watched Colin swallow pickled herrings, but he did not ask Colin to take him to Stornaway. Instead he waited till Leitis went by carrying a tray of roasted oysters, and then he asked her where Margery was.

"She's at the front door to welcome folk," Leitis told him.

That would be a poor time to catch her alone, but he wanted to settle the matter, so he started that way. In the shadowy corridor he felt insistent fingers pluck at his sleeve. It was Ellen.

"Randall," she whined, "why ha' ye kept from me?"

He had not been alone with her since that night in Puffin Town; made sure, in the shame and revulsion that filled him whenever he thought of that night, that he had not been alone with her. Early the next morning he had moved his medicines and clean linen into Colin's house which he had used for his hospital, inoculating the crofters one by one as they came to him there. Ellen could not ask for the inoculation since she had had the disease in her childhood, but she had come to the door twice and he had sent her away. Only two days ago he had finished the work, and tired out, come back to Rhinn House to sleep the clock round. Waking from that sleep, he had known what he must do. No man who has had a wife should go without one, he told himself, and he was ready now to give another woman the name and the love that could be claimed no longer by Sally Anne. He wished desperately that he had done so before—before his own flesh had betrayed him, and in his fall he had taken with him another human soul. That unhappy creature now stood before him, and he would make the inevitable ending as gentle as he might.

"Ellen," he said, "I shall tell you why. Come with me here."

He drew her into the small parlor, warm and lighted like all the rest of the house on that festive night. He stood before the hearth and she sank down in a blue brocaded chair.

"I think I kept from you because of shame, Ellen," he began. "I should not have used you so, and I am sorry for it. It will not happen again. We shall have always Margery or your mother by, when I am trying to treat you for the sight." He had forgotten for the moment that he must go away.

Ellen stared at him, her eyes cold and her cheeks flaming. "Ye mean then, that I am naught to you at all? That ye have no more use for me?"

"Not in that way, no," he muttered, not meeting her eyes.

She was silent for a moment and then burst out, " 'Tis wonderful, past all whooping, how a man can tire so quick of what he wanted!"

"But I never wanted it, Ellen," he answered wretchedly. "You know there is no love between us. 'Twas only that I—that it had been so long, I tell you over and over, I am sorry."

"Am I to eat and drink your sorrow then, and warm myself with it in the night?"

He threw back his head and thrust his hands into the pockets of his claret-colored breeches. "Are you asking me for money?"

"No, no!" cried Ellen hastily, tears welling in her eyes and beginning to run down her face. "There is nothing ye can do, if ye do not care for me. I would not have let ye if I thought ye did not care."

"Ellen," he said, "I shall suffer for this all the days of my life. If there is anything I can do—"

"Why, ye can take me away," she said, dashing the tears from her eyes and looking fixedly at him. "Ye can take me to America. Ye need not marry me. I can shift for myself, if ye will take me there."

"No," he said stubbornly, feeling a small-boy petulance rising up in him, feeling himself caught deeper and deeper in the net the more he struggled to get away. "I have harmed you, Ellen, but after all, I have not harmed you that much. You were not a maid when I came to you. You had been with others before."

She bit her lip and looked down at the thick carpet under her feet. At that moment Margery walked in. Her dark hair was swept upward in a crown of curls, and she wore a white wool dress embroidered with gold threadflowers, the bodice cut very low. She was smiling at them. "I hunted everywhere for you, Randall, and Kenneth said he saw you and Ellen come this way. He's outside, looking as black as a three-days' storm out of Ireland. What did you do to him?"

Ellen kept gazing at the floor, and her hand played nervously with the fold of her dress.

"Must be Ellen has injured him," said Randall lightly. "For in truth, I have not. I've scarce seen the lad since I got back from the inoculations. What did you want me for?"

"Why there's as many folk in the hall now as there's like to be at any one time, and Nanny's going to tell stories of the old days. I thought you would like to hear."

"Of course I would," said Randall, taking her arm, not looking at Ellen, but Margery held out her hand to the other girl.

"Come! 'Tis ill luck on Hogmanay to sit alone," she said.

So the three of them went back to the hall, now nearly half full of villagers, the men in dark wool coats and the women in plaid shawls, everyone a little threadbare, but nobody looking pinched or ill-fed. Randall noticed that most of the cold victuals were gone from the table, the kegs half empty, and Sim bringing out more, leaving a trail of cellar cobwebs behind him.

Nanny sat in a high-backed chair by the fire, and everyone drew toward her, the men pulling up benches for the women, then settling themselves on the stone floor. Kenneth brought a chair for Margery and did not go, but stood like a towering hawk, just behind her. Randall sat down on the floor a little way off and near the fire, watched Ellen find herself a place on the bench beside Ailis Ogg. Ailis smiled happily, and well she might, for her banns to marry Tam Darran had gone up the week before. Beside her, Ellen looked pale and thin and sour as unripe fruit. That was a lying look, he thought, as he remembered the ripeness of her and wished that he had left it untasted and unknown. He looked for Rona and saw him talking with Andra on the far side of the hearth, a half-eaten leg of turkey in his hand, and his whiskey glass on the mantel shelf above him.

Then a hush settled over the benches. The talking and laughing stopped. Everybody turned to Nanny and waited for her to begin. Randall had never been so close to the old woman before, for she was not one of his patients, trusting rather to Andra whenever pain visited her shrunken bones. Now he noticed every detail of her as he sat waiting, from the worn slippers on the small, sturdy feet, to the neat white cap and kerchief. Nanny's face was seamed and lined like a brown land riven with water courses, and her brown eyes stared unblinkingly before her. Her hands gripped the carven arms of the chair. There was acceptance in her face, and patience, and wisdom, the kind of wisdom never yet put down in printed words. He remembered hearing Rona say that the lords of Edinburgh made the laws, but the people made the proverbs, and that was, after all, the better thing. Then Nanny began to talk in a low voice, but strong and steady.

"I remember how it was when I was a girl on South Uist before ever Dweeney came piping there, and wed me, and took me away with him. We would gather by the widest hearth in Garnan—Ian MacCrae's, it were, till Jock Campbell built a better one—the young to dance at the feasting, and the old to tell the tales. And in those days, I was for the dancing. Sometimes, on such nights, the sea seemed to creep nearer the house, and the wind kept all the time trying to come in, and there was an eldritch moan to it."

Randall shivered, for there was something about Nanny's face and the tone of her voice that made him hear the sea and the winds of sixty years ago. Against the eerie background that she had somehow evoked for them, Nanny went on to tell one story after another. Maybe it would be a plaintive little tale of a human child carried off by elves, or maybe grim and savage, like the story of the old woman in Stornaway who held the lamp while the island men cut the throats of the Fife Adventurers; or the legend of the Norse invaders with greenish blue hair. The Hebrides lay in old waters that had seen the prows of the Vikings, the battered hulks of the Spanish Armada, and the British men-of-war hunting Prince Charlie. Nanny Dweeney had heard of all of them.

Margery asked for a story of her favorite hero, and Nanny smiled far back in her deep old eyes and told how she herself had seen the Prince drinking with his fellows till all the other men lay prone on the castle floor. Then he had spread their tartans over them and stood up in the midst, singing De Profundis, pious as any bishop, and all alone.

Half a dozen voices called for the tale of the Brahan Seer, and Nanny told of the woman who was herding cows near a graveyard, and when the graves opened at midnight and the ghosts flew away, she placed her spindle across one grave so its occupant could not return there. In order to get back to its resting place, the poor ghost had to promise her that her son should have the sight, and sure enough, he had it, but little good it did him, for the use he put it to caused him to be burned in a barrel of tar.

After that Nanny said her throat was dry and she wanted a drap of whiskey; that she was through with tale-telling. So everybody had a drap, and it was time to dance.

Randall had just stopped whirling round and round in a boisterous jig with Lavan, when he saw the watchful Leitis at his side, holding out a straw-jacketed bottle of foreign wine. The screech of Johnny's bagpipes filled all the room, and he had to put his head down to listen to her.

"Ye've no wintered here, sir," Leitis was saying apologetically, "and how should ye know what's fit for the keeping of Hogmanay?"

"Have I done something wrong, Leitis?" he asked quickly.

"No. Oh, no, sir. 'Tis only something ye might do if ye choose. The midnight will strike in a moment now, and they will all watch for the first-footer to come through the door."

"First-footer?"

"Yes. The first to cross the threshold after the break of the New Year. He should bring a present with him. If he be a fair-haired man, then 'tis a dark-haired woman he should give it to. We think it brings the house luck that way."

She held out the bottle. "For your gift," she said.

He grasped it, closing his fingers in a warm grip round hers for a moment before she could draw back her hand.

"Thank you, Leitis," he whispered. "It shall go to the dark-haired woman. Where else would my gifts go?"

She gave him a quick smile and slipped away through the crowd.

Tucking the bottle inside his coat, he crossed the room and went down the corridor to the front door.

Once outside, he stood there in the cold starlight, trying to order his thoughts. Seaward lay the black crags and the black water beyond, but a light snow had fallen in the afternoon, clinging to the furze bushes on the hillside and the thatched roofs in the village below. Suddenly he caught the faint far-off ringing of the church bells on the Long Island, borne by some trick of the wind over many miles of sea. Year of our Lord, 1775, those bells were ringing in, and he wondered what that year would mean to him, would he hear the bells that rang out the end of it. "War, red war," Ellen had said with the vision before her. She had said that his medicine would do him no good there. Then his thoughts went to Margery, and he tried to make himself believe that he might not see her again after tonight.

He was going in to Margery now, and bring her luck for the New Year, and he was going to tell her he loved her, but if she wanted him to, he would go away. Somehow he did not believe she would tell him that. And suddenly, there alone with the stars and the snowy hills and the night wind off the sea, he knew that it was time to say good-by forever to Sally Anne. They had not really parted in that little bedroom under the eaves in his father's house, where she had drawn her last choking breath. She had not left him there, and she had said she never would, but she had no choice now, because there was another so deeply in his heart.

"Good-by, Sally Anne," he whispered gently to the night wind. "You were good and sweet, and we were happy. But you are in one world and I am in another. We must each go our own ways now, Sally Anne."

He listened, but there was no articulate voice in the wind, and no star changed its place in the dark sky. Then he thought for a moment of that other one, who had never lived at all.

In the silence he could hear the bells still ringing beyond the narrow sea. Inside Rhinn House laughter and gay voices rang, and Johnny Dweeney's bagpipes shrilled as loudly as if the Stuart troops were on the march again. He had better hurry, he thought, or another first-footer would come sliding through the night and beat him to the door. He lifted the heavy iron rod kept there for knocking, and hammered loud enough to beat the oak panels in.

As he knocked the piping died away, voices lifted excitedly, and then they, too, were still. In a moment the laird himself threw open the door. "Welcome, First-footer," he said, bowing as formally as if he had never seen Randall before.

Randall bowed and pulled the bottle from his coat. "I come seeking a dark-haired woman. I have a gift for her," he said.

Rona motioned toward the hall. "Go in, First-footer. There are many dark-haired women there. Thank ye for bringing luck to my household."

Striding along the corridor, he could hear the footsteps of his host as they followed him over the stone floor. All eyes were upon him, he found, as he entered the hall.

"Welcome, First-footer!" shrilled Johnny, and blew a tremendous blast on the bagpipes. "Whom amongst us do ye seek?"

"I seek a dark-haired woman," said Randall easily.

He looked around for Margery and felt a little crestfallen to find her whispering in a corner with Kenneth, but he stepped toward her all the same, holding out the bottle.

"From a fair-haired man to a dark-haired woman," he said, "and good luck to her house for the New Year."

Margery bent forward, gracious and smiling, to receive his gift.

"I thank you, First-footer," she said, taking the bottle in one hand, and his hand in the other. "Come and have a bit and drap."

He let her lead him toward the table and pour him a glass of claret, waited for her to choose some refreshment for herself, which she did not do.

"Margery," he said after a moment, as she stood there smiling at him, "I want to talk to you. Let us be by ourselves somewhere."

She put her head a little on one side and looked doubtful. "Can you not wait, Randall? Tomorrow there will be time. You can talk to me from breakfast to sunset, if you wish. But tonight—if I steal away from our guests, and my father notices me—"

"I may not be here by sunset tomorrow," said Randall calmly. "It all depends on what you say tonight."

A startled look came into her hazel eyes. "Why—wherever will you be? Are you going to Stornaway?"

"Maybe. Maybe further than that. Come with me, Margery, where we can talk."

"Very well."

She walked ahead of him, through the crowd of merrymakers in the hall, and opened the door of the small parlor where he had been with Ellen earlier that night. Then, instead of stepping inside, she hastily closed it and withdrew. He looked at her, a question in his eyes.

"Meggy and Colin are there," she said. "They have quarreled, I think, because she is crying, and he looks so stern. It makes me sad whenever I see them together. He loves her so much, and she will have none of him because she has borne a daft child."

"I know," said Randall soberly. "I have tried to talk with her; tell her it need not happen again. But she will not listen to me."

"We can go up to the gallery," said Margery, leading him to the wide stair.

At the gallery's western end, beyond the last of the portraits, a broad bay window with a cushioned bench looked to the dark sea. She sat down, leaning against one of the angles, and motioned Randall to a place beside her, which he hastily took.

"Margery," he said. Then he paused, uncertain how to begin. All his haste and urgency had left him. He felt tremulous, unsure.

For a moment her face wore a puzzled frown, then it smoothed itself out. She saw he was in difficulty and began to make small talk to steady him—at least, that was how Randall interpreted her action.

"Randall," she said, "I should have asked before, for I've often been wondering. How do things go in your country, and do they still think there will be a war there?"

That was an easy question to find an answer to, if a hard question to answer. He had only to quote his father's latest news. "It would seem that things are drifting that way. They have closed Boston Port, and Portsmouth has sent help to the amount of two hundred pounds, more than four times the province tax. Other towns have done their share— Chester, Candia, Dunbarton, Newmarket–Concord gave dried pease—"

It steadied him to say the old names over. "There has been a great meeting of the leaders of all America."

He cleared his throat and began again, "Margery—" but she interrupted him.

"Do you know where North Carolina is? Is it far from Hampton?"

He frowned, wishing he could tell her she need not dally any longer. He was ready now.

"It is almost at the other end of the country," he said stiffly. "I have never been there, nor am likely to go."

"I thought you might know it. Kenneth told me tonight that was where Flora MacDonald had gone. Are they for or against the King, do you think? Will there be a rising there?"

His face cleared, and he smiled suddenly. "Was that what you and Kenneth were talking about tonight? Flora MacDonald and uprisings against the King?"

Margery looked startled. She replied cautiously, "We were talking of Flora. Randall—what did you want to say to me?"

"I wanted to tell you this, Margery," he answered, looking into her eyes. At first she veiled them, then opened them very wide as he went on. "I went to your father tonight and asked him if I could court you to marriage. He did not approve. He did not think you could be happy in the frozen bogs of North America with the red Indians and me. I promised him that I would go away, but first I would tell you how I felt."

He paused, and she waited until she saw that he was not going to say any more. Then she lifted her head, and smiled at him and said, "Well, tell me, Randall."

"But I told you. I want to marry you."

Her face wore a rapt look but her voice was steady.

"There are many reasons why a man could want to marry a woman."

"I know there are. But not for me any more. I married one woman because she wanted me to. Our life together was good, and I am not sorry. But this time it is the other way. I love you, Margery, and I want to marry you, and if you are willing, I will do it, if it has to be against the drawn sword of every laird in Scotland."

"Then—then—" her voice quivered, but her face was slowly brightening, "you can love me, and you will not sorrow for her any more. I thought you would never love anyone else. I heard you calling in the night—for your Sally Anne—one night by the Cursing Stones."

"I have told Sally Anne good-by," he answered steadily, still uncertain how Margery would finally answer him.

"Then—if you love me—and you will never lie by my side and be lonely for her—why then—" and a light woke in her eyes and seemed to shine from her whole face, "why then, of course I will marry you, Randall."

His arms started to lift, but he forced them close to his sides one moment longer.

"You will leave your father and your friends—all the gay times you have known—and go to America with me?"

"Yes. I will go to America with you, or anywhere." She lifted her face to his, and he did not hold himself back any more.

Later they stood together halfway down the stairs, hand-in-hand, while the Hogmanay guests filed below them, singing, and cheering them, bidding their farewells to Rona at the doorway. It was Lavan who had let the secret out before it was more than a few minutes old. She had come upstairs on an errand for Leitis, caught them kissing; in her young wifely wisdom immediately known what it meant, kissed Margery herself, and then run to tell all.

Rona's face had turned dark purple at first, and he choked back anger in his throat, but it was really more sorrow than rage, as he thought ahead to his own loss. In the end he shook his head ruefully and bade Kenneth to announce the banns of Randall John Woodbury and Margery May Rhinn. This Kenneth had done with a bitter ill grace, almost refused to do.

"We are Queen Mary's men," sang the crofters, outside the house now, going down the hillside in the night.

Randall pulled his thoughts away from his own happiness long enough to wonder if they meant the Queen of Heaven or the old Scottish Queen. He would have to think more of such things if he was to be a proper husband for Margery, who loved tradition and old time, and knew the secret of heather ale. Crushing her hand in his for the soft roseleaf feel of it, he stood proudly beside her and gazed down at the empty hall. Rona was now speeding his last guests at the doorway, Andra and her daughter. As Randall looked at Ellen he felt himself all burning inside with shame. She lifted her eyes and gazed upward defiantly. Margery's eyes were so misted with happiness that she misinterpreted the look.

"The luck of the New Year to you, Ellen," she called merrily. "May it bring a dark-haired man to your door!"

Ellen drew up her thin shoulders and tossed her head. "Ye'd never think, Miss Margery," she said, "what the New Year will bring!"

XVII

Brittle Bail

IF WEEPING endures but a night, and joy cometh in the morning, that joy is scarce like to last past noontime before sorrow clouds the sky again. Randall found this bleak thought coming often to his mind in a month that followed his betrothal, for he and Margery were never happy again, quite as they had been when they stood hand-in-hand on the stairs that night at the ending of Hogmanay.

It began the next morning, for he could hardly greet her across the breakfast table before he was called down to the clachan to comfort Ellen who was troubled with a vision. And almost every day thereafter she was troubled so. He had lost much of his scientific curiosity in the matter and was heartily sick of it, for the sight of the cattle maid was a constant reproach to him. True, she had tempted him, been quick to participate in what was for her no new game. But she was woman, and therefore the weaker vessel. He should have withstood the dangerous emotions rising in both of them. Oh God, he thought, he had been a fool all the way. He had not realized his own weakness. He had tried himself too far. He had loved Margery for a long time. Why had he distrusted that love, felt so unsure of himself, unsure of her? If he had told her how he felt three months ago, they would have been safely married now; he would not have been driven to make free with the first girl who flicked a petticoat at him. Yes, it had been his fault.

He was sorry for Ellen, distasteful as he found her. She was an unhappy person, perhaps a mad one. As the frequency of her visions increased, he found himself more and more considering that possibility. So he went to her whenever she sent for him, hating to go, but feeling he could do nothing less, not entering the cottage unless Andra was there, sometimes taking Leitis with him on one pretext or another.

And as for Margery, a mist seemed to settle over her like the mist that hung perpetually round her native islands. She laughed less often, the warm light of happiness no longer shone in her eyes, and her face wore a hurt, bewildered look, she who had always been so proud and sure. Was it because she sensed the confusion and unhappiness in himself, or had Ellen confided in her? Did she know what had happened that December night in Puffin Town? He could not ask her, and she never spoke of such a thing.

He spent most of his days in the clachan, for winter was an unhealthy season, full of colds and rheum. The women were busy in their kitchens with wheel and distaff, and the men repaired their boats, made shoes and tanned leather, and fished sometimes for ling, which great storms drove in from the deep sea. There was not the intense cold and drifting snow he had been used to in New England, but there was freezing rain, and winds such as he had never known could blow. Like all the island folk, he soon found himself walking crabwise in order to move at all or to keep from being thrown to the frozen turf.

At the end of each day, when the bracken on the hillside seemed all ablaze in the winter sunset, he would go back to Rhinn House to eat supper and spend the evening by the fire with Margery and her father, talking over their affairs. They would be married in Edinburgh, she said, on Midsummer Day, in the Church of England Chapel in Carruber's Close. Her linens and finery could be readied no sooner, and she wanted all her mother's people who were scattered far and wide to have time to receive their invitations and be there.

"Aye," Comyn had growled, "there be few enough of us Rhinns left alive, but ye might as well try to take the census o' a hornets' nest as to count the MacNeills o' Barra. It will take time, lass, to assemble them all."

Comyn was not overpleased at the match, but he had yielded with what grace he could. There was no talk now of going to America. It would have to be, some day, but it need not be yet. Randall was to continue his studies at the College, and they would take a flat there for the next season. Margery's face lighted when she spoke about the life they would lead in Edinburgh, when she could have all her accustomed parties and friends, and move about with the innocent freedom of a married woman.

Besides the underlying sadness in Margery, there was another thing about her he could not understand. That was the matter of Kenneth. Often he came upon them talking together, ceasing the conversation with guilty looks the moment he appeared. He knew, of course, that Kenneth had expected to marry her, and certainly the Highlander had every right to show savage disappointment. Randall would not have been surprised at that. He would not have been surprised at physical challenge of some sort. But Kenneth had shown no anger. He had continued quiet and sullen as a storm cloud that hovers, but moves no nearer on the sky.

Once Randall met him in the corridor and caught him whistling, a light, gay-hearted tune that MacCrimmon had used to sing in Edinburgh. But the whistling had died away when Kenneth saw he was not alone, and his handsome face had gone back into its usual dour lines. He had turned swiftly and walked away.

Not that his betrothal was all sorrow. Whenever he and Margery were alone together, the skies seemed to clear. They went for long walks over the wild moorland when the wind drove the spindrift till it fell like snowflakes about them, far from the sea. They sat together in the east parlor with the lamps turned low and nobody by, as it was proper for any courting couple to do. He had known there was sweetness in Margery, and gentleness, and warm, understanding love. He had not known there was fire, too, but he was glad to find it there. Remembering the adroitness of Ellen, Margery seemed awkward and ardent, and he loved her all the more. She would not shrink from him on their wedding night, he knew, she would look forward as much as he, find it as long till Midsummer. And still, when he held her close and kissed her, there was always a shadow between. He suspected it was because deep within each of them there was something held back from the other, but he could not know.

Leitis had told him when he was preparing tinctures once in her kitchen that February would come in with the head of a serpent and go out with a peacock's tail, like the saw they had at home about March coming in like a lion and going out like a lamb. But in February the snow would still be piled to the eaves in New Hampshire, while here, she said, he would see the first green stirrings of spring. The old woman had been devoted to him ever since the night of Caitlin's death, and she spoke of Caitlin now, the thing that worried her.

"It is an old belief among us, sir," she told him soberly, "that the last to die must always keep watch in the graveyard and canna' pass on to the other world until the next funeral appears. There has none died this winter in all Rona. I couldna' pray for any soul's death, but Caitlin has lain there three months past. She must be uneasy to go."

"I do not think there is any truth in the belief, Leitis," he assured her. "God knows I'm not learned in the ways of the church and the ministers, but I feel certain she was at peace the moment her eyes closed."

Leitis tightened her lips and went back to her spinning. As it happened, she need not have worried. Caitlin was to be relieved of her vigil very soon.

As Leitis said, February did bring a change in the season, and if green shoots did not spring forth overnight from the dead wastes of brown moorland, at least the air softened and the winds grew more gentle.

One day he went to the rocks below Ardmory where the men were cutting seaware to spread out in a slowly rotting mass on the long fields to the westward; not so good a fertilizer as cattle dung, but sure, and plenty, and cheap. He spent all afternoon among them, toiling with a saw-toothed sickle, for the good-fellowship of it, and came home up the cliff path among the lichened rocks all red with frost, past the shieling hut, and into the clachan through the burn valley. By the wharves he met Margery and fell into step beside her.

"Randall, I've a letter," she said. He could tell from the slight tremor in her voice that the letter was important to her.

"What was in it?" he asked warily. "Who was it from? If you want to tell me—"

She gave a nervous laugh.

"Do not sound so stern. It is not so serious as that. The letter is from Mairi, my cousin Roderick's wife. They live on Barra, you know."

"I remember you have spoken of them. What does she say?"

"She says they are happy to hear of our wedding plans, and they will be in Edinburgh at Midsummer. But she also says—"

He suddenly realized Margery was trying to tell him some simple thing in some devious way. He trudged along patiently at her side, and let her reveal the matter as she chose. She pulled a paper from the pocket of her heavily flounced skirt and unfolded it.

"Tam MacVean just brought the mail, and when I saw his boat making harbor, I ran down. There was nothing for you or Father. Only this for me. It is from Mairi—"

She broke off and walked slowly beside him, not looking at him. He felt uneasy. He had a terrible thought. Suppose in some way these Mac-Neill kindred could prevent the marriage! But no, she had said they would be happy to be there.

"She says, 'We heard your footsteps on the parapet of the west tower, last night, dear Margery. Roderick says they were yours, and so does Agnes, the cook—you remember her? Tappingly they went, with your high heels on. When a distant person longs to be at home, you know, his footsteps can be heard there by his near kin—' "

She paused. Randall wondered if his near kin had been hearing his footsteps lately in the snowy dooryard at Hampton Falls. He thought it quite likely that they had. He questioned her gently.

"Did you long to be at home?"

"I have often longed to, Randall, in the last month. When a lass is to be married, she must change all her ways of things—even herself, it may be."

Sally Anne, he thought, had made few changes when they carried her trunk and bandbox through the gap in the stone wall between her mother's hayfield and his own. Margery would, of course, have to make more.

"I thought I would like to go back to Barra again, to my mother's home. There are still things of ours in Kismull Castle that I will want to have sent on to Edinburgh. Oh Randall, you will not mind if I go there—only for a visit—only for a week or two?"

"No," said Randall carefully. She had not told him all the truth, and he knew it, but he would not question her. "I do not mind. Your father is going to Greenock next week. No doubt he can leave you at Barra on the way."

"You are angry?" she said tremulously.

"No," he said. "Of course I am not angry." He gave her a formal kiss on the mouth, hated himself for doing it, but found he could behave in no other way. So then between them there was not only the old shadow, but the new formality, risen because she had lied to him and he knew it.

Nor did her going improve things. Rona agreed to the plan without comment, except to figure how he could change his route in order to touch at Barra. He finally decided to hire Tam, a crew, and a stout Norwegian boat to take him all the way down the gulf, touch at the south islands, and then across to Oban where the packets put in. They left on a foggy morning when the hills and the sea were washed in gray rain. Margery clung to him at the last, and he thought she was going to tell him, but she did not. He kissed her and waved good-by as the boat pulled out on the tide; then he went back to Rhinn House, all along in the bleak, dripping day.

It rained hard for a week after that. Ellen ailed constantly and saw men carrying coffins whenever she turned her head too quickly about. He was tired and sick of the sight of her, but he did not doubt the genuineness of her torment and sought desperately to assuage it, partly, perhaps, because the matter was his first professional experiment, and he felt loath to give it up. Andra sat, grim-faced, while the girl described her visions, and Randall tried to understand how a woman so generous and kindly could have so little sympathy for her own flesh and blood. Then Johnny Dweeney's old legs became so painful that he had to be treated every day with soporifics, and Nanny complained of weakness and could hardly hobble from her chair to prepare their barley broth. Tam Darran and Ailis, newly married, had moved into the empty cottage next door, and did what they could for the old couple, but it was an ill season for everybody in the clachan; cold sodden bodies, not always enough fire, and too little food in the pot when suppertime came.

Once in a dank twilight as he started home, he saw a tiny elfin-faced girl hungrily gnawing a bit of frozen turnip that had been flung out for the cattle. He shivered inside his thick jacket and put down the impulse to take her on his shoulder and carry her up to Leitis for dry clothes and a hot meal. All that stopped him was the knowledge that he could not do as much for whatever brothers and sisters she might happen to have. He was particularly concerned for the children and had been for the last few days, for in nearly every house one or more of them was ailing. A slight cold, a low fever, vague pains darting here and there, trouble in swallowing—nothing he could diagnose or give a name to. He asked Andra if it was some Scottish disease he had never heard of, but she, too, admitted she had never seen the like. Poor food and exposure to the damp and cold was most likely the cause of it. He dosed them with Peruvian bark and sent down cordials from the laird's own cellar, but he knew in his heart that he was only doing it because he could think of nothing better to do. Fortunately nobody seemed to be very sick, except for Nellie's youngest boy who had a stiff neck and was inclined to tumble about when he tried to walk. On the other hand, the victims all lay listless on their pallets or piles of rags, and none of them got well.

Once inside the warm and quiet comfort of Rhinn House he went directly to the kitchen. He had been eating there with Sim and Leitis since their master's departure, and they made no pretense of serving meals in the hall any more. Leitis hastened to him as soon as he came in, coaxed him out of his wet coat, and began ladling up bowls of savory stew. Sitting between the old couple and spooning down the hot food, he told them of his worry over the children, told them of the hungry little girl.

Both of them shook their heads at the mention of the disease. "We can do no good there," said Leitis regretfully, "but if they are hungry, as ye say, I will go to Master Crary tomorrow. He has the steward's keys, and in the far cellar there is barley meal and bacon and dried pease kept there for such use. Sim shall go down and give it out tomorrow amongst those who have most need."

"Where is the schoolmaster?" asked Randall, feeling relieved at the solution of one problem; better, probably, because he was now warm and dry and well-fed. Then his horizon clouded over and he realized that tonight he must write to his father to tell him of his approaching marriage. He could no longer put it off. It must be done tonight.

Sim answered, drying the ragged ends of his beard on a homespun napkin.

"As ye know, he seldom eats with us, and when he doesna', 'tis a tray in his room he would have, and me that must climb the stair! Naught but the laird's best whiskey, too! There's none for whiskey like a Highland man."

"I think he has a lass in the clachan," said Leitis, "now that he can no more court with Miss Margery," and she smiled at Randall. "He took tea with me just before candlelighting and went out then, and I ha' no seen him since. He's says he's told the bairns to stay at home tomorrow, and all the days till he sends for them to come back; that he'll keep no more school whilst so many is ailing and canna' attend. Ewen Gow's Jessie was taken over her book and couldna' bend her head, and fell down when she meant to be walking. Her brothers carried her home. There is a trouble amongst the children, Doctor, lad, that I fear we canna' cure by feeding them."

"You may be right," sighed Randall. He helped himself to a bottle from the dresser, bade his good nights, and said that he meant to work in his room for the rest of the evening.

The room, when he reached it, was warm and bright, with the lamps and the fire already going. He sat idly at the writing table for a few minutes, listening to the rain on the roof and the sighing of a low wind in the eaves, thinking how much he missed Margery. Then he poured himself a glass of whiskey, straight and undiluted, after the Scottish fashion. He tossed down a deep draught of it and pushed the glass aside. He took writing materials and began the letter to his father.

He wrote quickly with blunt jabs of the pen into the leaf torn from his journal, choosing this as he usually did, instead of a smoother, more formal paper. He minced no words and he spared no feelings. He wrote that he was marrying the Laird of Rona's daughter, that she was a woman of beauty and fashion, for which, he hoped, they would forgive him. He wrote that he was not yet ready to bring her home. He meant to return to his studies at the College. If they continued to send him the usual bills of credit, it would be enough, he needed no further money. His winter's stay on the island had cost him nothing, and he had been paid handsomely for his professional services there. He hoped they would be pleased with Margery. She sent her love. He sealed the letter and laid it aside. Then he took another swallow of whiskey. Then he got up, glass in hand, and went to the deep armchair in the bay window, flung himself down, and lay back there, listening to the rain.

Slowly his taut nerves relaxed, and the sense of well-being that he had felt at the supper table returned to him. True, there was plenty of sickness about, especially amongst the children, but it seemed like no killing complaint. Given a little sunlight and some good food, and he felt they would all be well. True, Margery had gone from him for a time, but she had promised to come back before the month's end. When he held her in his arms again, he would not be the fool he had been when she went away. He would bring out into the open the thing between them that was keeping them apart. After all, there had been shadows in the old days between him and Sally Anne, but love and understanding had always cleared them away.

He heard Kenneth's steps in the corridor, going toward his room a little unsteadily. Then he heard the shuffle of Leitis' slippered feet and the sound of her voice asking for the key to the far cellar.

Kenneth muttered angrily, and his talk broke off with a ringing sound that puzzled Randall for a moment. Then he knew what it was. The schoolmaster had flung the key on the stone floor. His steps moved off then, lumbering and unsteady. Kenneth was apparently drunk. Well, Randall did not know that he could blame him. A door slammed at the back of the house and Leitis shuffled away. There was silence in the corridor.

Glancing at the pile of books on a small table near his elbow, he noticed that the one on top was Dr. Cullen's textbook on the practice of physic. He picked it up and began turning the pages guiltily. He had unpacked it to see what the master himself would advise in the treatment of nervous cases, if there was any suggestion there that would help him in dealing with Ellen.

In a few moments he was interested in spite of himself, settled even deeper in the chair, and pulled the iron lamp close, so it was easier to see.

"Imagination rising in the brain, presenting objects that are not actually present," Dr. Cullen had written. That surely described the sight as he had seen it in Ellen and her mother before.

"Derangement of the nervous power, a subtle moveable fluid present in every part of the medullary substance, of the brain and nerves—" Well, what to do? He read on impatiently, "Madness is false perceptions, false associations, and false judgments. In every case we may expect organic lesions of the brain. Keep them always in fear. Put in a straightwaistcoat if necessary—"

He muttered profanely at the idea of putting Andra, with all her dignity and calm wisdom, in a straightwaistcoat. "Shave and blister and purge with soluble tartar—snow packs, clay caps—ducking—"

God help the man who went mad, thought Randall. And then, "The cures are found in the causes." That he stopped to think about.

The visions had first come to Andra when she was young and tender-hearted and all racked with grief and fear out of anxiety for her lover. Women's wits had been turned for less—even in his short and narrow practice he had seen it. There was no second sight in Hampton Falls, but sometimes there was madness there. The cures in the causes! What had caused it in Ellen then, for she had been under no strain so far as he knew?

He put the book down and went to fill his glass from the dark green bottle.

"Oh Doctor! Doctor!" he heard Leitis wail from the landing at the turn of the stair.

The urgency in her voice told him he was not being summoned for any little thing. She did not want him to kill a mouse or poultice a sore toe. He flung his door open and ran through the gallery, down the stone treads to her side. There he stopped. Ellen stood a few steps below them, wet all over, hair, and skin, and clinging dress, come forth so hastily that she had not even taken a shawl to protect her from the rain. Her face was pale as it had never been when the visions plagued her. She stammered and gasped, and Leitis mumbled.

"For God's sake, what's the matter?" exploded Randall. "You look like the Devil had landed and come ashore."

"The children," murmured Ellen faintly, tossing back her dank hair. "It's like Passover in the Bible. In every house they're dying, and those who arena' dying, canna' walk. It's terrible. It's all through the town."

That was the beginning of it: the way the strange serpent-stealthy plague that he had never seen before was loosed on Rona. That was the moment his life stopped being the ordered business of a sensible man and became a nightmare. Finally he learned from the hysterical Ellen that her mother had sent her, that Andra was with Christie, so he gathered his drugs and his deerskin chest, left the two women huddled by the kitchen fire, and set off for the clachan, down the wet road in the endless rain.

Christie's five children lay among blankets spread on the floor near a sputtering fire of damp peat, that Rob, looking stricken and helpless, was trying to coax into an open blaze. At the far end of the long room, three cows watched patiently, aware of the trouble as animals always are, and fowl crouched on the rafters above. The children lay motionless, making no outcry. Andra bent over Jamie, her long supple fingers massaging his throat and chest. But what surprised Randall was the fact that Christie's children should be taken down so suddenly, for they had not ailed before. Only that afternoon they had stopped him to ask about another flying stone. Christie sat silently, holding the baby, who gazed before him with round, solemn eyes. Randall went down on his knees among the blankets. Andra looked up at him and there was fright in her eyes. He had never seen fright there before; resignation, when Lavan seemed to be dying, but not abandoned terror.

"They cannot breathe," she whispered. "When folk cannot breathe even my grandmother did not know what to do then!"

She kept on working over Jamie, so he bent to examine Donny and the rest. Every now and then the little faces twitched. Donny's two eyes turned in opposite directions, and he tried to breathe as if he had forgotten how.

"Do you think," murmured Randall, taking pulses, "it is a lung congestion?"

The tawny-haired girl whose name he did not know was choking, and he thought of the throat-ail, but he knew it was not that. His exploring finger found no phlegm or membrane in her mouth, but she could not swallow, and clear saliva kept forming in little pools that ran over her chin and dribbled on the blanket. None of the children were conscious. Now a pulse would race to a wild two hundred, now drop almost completely away under his fingers.

Randall felt no emotion now save helplessness and mounting horror. He had never seen the like. It was not in Hampton Falls. It had appeared in none of the lectures and textbooks in Edinburgh.

Christie was crying with grief and fright, her tears falling all over the baby's downy head.

"What is it? Oh, what is it?" pleaded Andra, still rubbing the little naked chest, trying to get the boy to breathe.

"'Fore God, I don't know," muttered Randall, looking at Donny. A shudder went through him as he realized that the child was not breathing any more, that he would never watch the lift of another flying stone.

Christie's five older children died that night, but she and Rob and the baby remained undiseased and well. And once he stepped out of her cottage, Randall found himself besieged with anxious fathers, waiting for him, gaunt and red-eyed in their ragged coats, for in every house in the clachan the story was much the same. The mothers were not in the street. They were fighting death at the bedside, and he joined them there.

There seemed to be two separate and utterly different forms of the terrible sickness that attacked only the children. Fever, headache, nausea, pain, and increasing debility were common to all, but some passed into a state of utter helplessness of the back and legs. Many of these died, but after a time some faltering few began to get well, though they did not at once regain the body's use. But others, like Christie's, were stricken in the lungs and throat, forgot how to breathe, twisted, and choked and died. When the breathing apparatus went awry, there was no saving them.

For days the sickness went on. Randall forgot the feel of a bed and the taste of food, except for a hasty gulp now and then when one of the women brought him barley cake and herring or a bowl of hot soup. He did not return to Rhinn House, sleeping propped in a corner whenever he could not keep awake any more, and then only for a few minutes at a time. Sim brought him clean linen and wines and whiskey, for his other drugs had failed him now, and he had returned humbly to the oldest, surest stimulant of all. And it was stimulants he needed. Nothing in his medicine chest, nothing in his poor desperate groping wits could cure the disease. All he could do was try to keep them alive and trust the body to find its own cure.

On the third night he had faced that decision when they sat resting for a few moments at Nellie Gow's fireside after her youngest child had been laid out in a sea chest and carried to the little graveyard on the hill.

"Andra," he said, leaning against a heap of sods by the old black hearth, while Nellie and Ewen fed the children still remaining to them, well and carefree children, not understanding, enjoying the school holiday, "I never saw anything like it, never. I feel like I'd been hit on the jaw so hard I don't know what hit me. Colin is back from Stornaway. I sent him there this morning to see if their doctor would come."

"Will he?" asked Andra tensely, eyeing the children with their little earthen bowls, expecting any moment to see another fall.

Randall shook his head. "No. The bastard's afraid, and he knows he's as helpless as we are. Colin wanted to go to Skye, but he put him off and said there'd be no profit in it; that 'twas either a new disease raised up or an old one that had passed out of the memory of man. We'll have to fight it all alone."

"None of my herbs or potions will help it," said Andra. "I have tried them all, and the children are dying still."

"None of my drugs will help it. I might as well be a shoemaker, for all the good I do."

"I even went to Leitis," said Andra hesitantly, "to ask her if in the cellar—there was still some heather ale."

He looked up sharply. "Heather ale!" he exclaimed. "The most powerful stimulant I ever saw! Could she find any for you?"

"No. She did not know if there was any left or where it was, and if she did, she said, she would not dare touch it with Miss Margery away."

He shook his head. "I'm beaten, Andra. I don't know what to do, except to try to keep them alive as long as I can. Back home, my father's friend was a Dr. Bartlett. He's near fifty now, and a well man, but the doctors gave him up when he was twenty-three. He had a fever they didn't understand, and they said he was sure to die before morning, and they all went home. He sat up all night drinking apple cider by the teacup full. And it pulled him through. My father always told me—when I came on a bad time, to remember that."

"It is the same in all countries," agreed Andra with a wan smile. "My grandmother always prayed to be kept from any disease that whiskey could not cure."

So they gave the children whiskey. Some shuddered and turned their heads away, and spewed it out on their pillows. Some lapped it up and called for more, and lay happily drunk in their beds till the crisis passed over. Others could not move the throat muscles and were forever through with swallowing. Drunk or dry, some died and some got well, and Randall could see no pattern in the difference.

Only one of the stricken was man-grown, and Randall would have given a share of his own flesh and blood to have saved him. Once at the height of the sickness when several children were dying every day, and the wind bore always an undercurrent of the women's soft wailing, he thought of what Andra had said about heather ale, and he remembered how it had saved Lavan when he thought nothing ever could. If only Margery was there—she could unearth a hidden bottle or perhaps brew some more. Perhaps it was only that he wanted Margery. In any case, he hurried to Colin's house one day when the sunset lay in red pools like frozen blood on the sky, having an impractical notion that perhaps the young fisherman would take his boat out on the long voyage down the Minch to Barra and bring Margery home.

At first he thought Colin must be away fishing or cutting seaware, though most of the everyday affairs of life had come to a halt since the sickness hit Ballyrhinn. No one answered his knock on the door of the little hut by the water. Then, pausing a moment before he turned and hurried back to the next bedside where they awaited him, he heard a slight sound within. He pushed the door open.

Colin lay on his back on the floor beside the dead hearth fire. He kept swallowing convulsively and snapping his fingers. His eyes turned in his head, and his chest throbbed unevenly, as if he were breathing only on one side.

"Canna' breathe—" he rasped, clawing at his throat, grabbing the motionless half of his chest and trying to move it up and down.

"Colin, lad," muttered Randall. He went down on his knees beside his dying friend. Colin was past whiskey. Past everything but the help of God. Suddenly Randall found that he was crying. His tears dripped down on Colin's face just the way Christie's had dripped on her baby's head the night the plague struck.

Colin thrust out his jaw and drew his lips back over his teeth in a ghastly smile. With a terrible effort he reached out and gripped Randall's hand.

Then suddenly he no longer fought for breath, he groped for it. He could not find it any more. Surprise, bewilderment, final terror distorted his handsome young face. Randall felt the loosening fingers fall away. A mist rose before his eyes, and when it cleared, he was alone. Colin would go to the graveyard, but he would not have to watch there long. There were others on the way.

Randall stole an hour's sleep that night in the Dweeney cottage, unashamed to share with the old couple his grief and bitterness and sense of inadequacy and defeat.

"'Tis their time has come," said Nanny solemnly, "though such a smashery o' poor weans I never saw before. 'Twas no your fault."

"But Colin," said Randall inconsolably. "He was no wean! He was a damn fine lad! Why did Colin have to die?"

"And who's to tell Janet Gillander?" muttered old Johnny. "Janet that couldna' have him and wanted him so."

"I'd rather be telling her," said Nanny soberly, "than telling Meg Munro—Meggy who could ha' had him and wouldna' have him at all."

XVIII

The Strange Ways of God

THE LARGEST TAVERN in Stornaway was a two-storied house covered with slates, looking ample enough from the outside, but its parlor was full of gossiping women and its taproom cluttered with geese and fowls, and Margery felt glad to be away from it as she paid for her night's lodging and stepped out into the mild gray day.

She had come up the Minch from Barra on a fishing boat the day before, arriving long after dark, and found Tam MacVean gone on a trip to Polewe and no way at all for her to get over the few miles of sea to her home on Rona that she had taken such a longing for.

"Wait till tomorrow," they had told her on the wharf when she came ashore. "Jock MacLeod will sail ye there tomorrow, we've no doubt. He's away tonight to take Master Riddoch there. They've had trouble, and 't has come to the eye o' the Kirk."

"Trouble on Rona?" she had asked quickly. "What's gone amiss?"

But the fishermen would not tell her, nor would anyone she met in street or the little inn. "We heard some children were sick," the chambermaid whispered, as she lit the fire and turned down the bed, but when Margery tried to question her further, she had ignored the proffered coin and hastened away. Margery kept waking up in the night to trouble herself about it. Whose children were sick, and what ever ailed them? Why was it a matter for the Kirk?

Now in the morning light and clean sea air she felt reassured again. If there were children sick, Randall would cure them. It was no new thing for Kirk folk like Master Riddoch to go poking their ferret noses everywhere. Still, she would feel better if she knew her father was at home, instead of knowing, as she did, that he had gone on to Edinburgh. It was when she first received his letter the week before, telling her of the change in his plans, that she had begun to be homesick. Before that, her stay on Barra had been happy enough. Perhaps not happy—but she had found out much that it was better for her to know, and after all, she had really gone there for that.

She walked slowly down the narrow street between the stone houses with crow-stepped gables, carrying only her purse and a rose-colored bandbox and her fur cloak over her arm. The harbor was full of idle boats, for it would be more than a month before the spring herring began to run. Surely someone should be willing to take her over the short stretch of open sea. Waiting in Tam's usual place she found a stranger, a middle-aged man with a battered brown face and a worse battered boat, who said that he was Jock MacLeod and would ferry her for the usual sum. As they pulled out on the soft gray water into the gray mist hanging low, she began to question him, but she might have saved her breath. He ignored her for a while and then turned, his deep-set eyes glaring, his low voice a growl.

"Lass," he said, "I mind my own lot in life. What goes on with my neighbors, I dinna' ken. Do ye expect to complete this voyage, ye'll give over asking me."

There was nothing she could do after that, except smile at him and save her questions till she got home. The wind blew steadily, moving them forward at a good rate, but it did not clear the mist that rose here and there like puffs of smoke from the surface of the sea. Her thoughts went back to the sunlight of yesterday, the trip up the Minch following the long line of blue islands, all little farms and ruined church towers, bare rocks, and inlets full of fishing boats, like the harbor at Stornaway. Her thoughts went back to Barra and the circumstances of her brief visit there.

Her cousin Roderick was much older than she, a tall vigorous man, growing early gray, with three sons at school in England where he had spent most of his life. He and his pretty wife, Mairi, made her as welcome at Kismull Castle as if she had never been away from her mother's home. For the first few nights they talked of the old days, and the women played and sang old songs to the spinet, and in the daytime they went riding on small sturdy horses all along the twelve-mile ring road round Barra, Margery feasting her eyes on the high rocky country as if she might never see it again and would try to hold every contour of it in her heart when she went away. They talked of her coming marriage and made wild laughing guesses about what her life would be like in America; laughing, because you never gave way to apprehension if you were a MacNeill of Barra and had "Vincere vel mori" carved above your door.

Over the wine at dinner Roderick told his wife with great hilarity of the day in Margery's childhood when she had insisted she wanted to learn to milk a cow because all her playmates, the crofters' daughters called her a bluntie—a stupid one—for not having the knack. Rona had forbidden it, for fear lest the beasts kick or trample her. His wife was still in bed, recently delivered of a dead son, and he treasured his little daughter all the more because of this new loss. Margery had stamped her foot, then grinned and turned away. At the next mealtime she was missing. She was gone three days, straying from farm to farm on the stony hillsides, known and welcomed everywhere. When she came back she was tired and dirty, but still grinning, and she could milk a cow like the veriest dairymaid. Rona had been proud of the exploit later and boasted of it among his friends in Edinburgh.

When Roderick finished the little story, Margery lifted her eyes over her wine glass and found that Mairi was smiling at her.

"Oh, Margery," she said, shaking her head dubiously, "I am afraid of what will happen if the time ever comes when you cannot have your own way."

Margery thought unhappily of the invisible barriers that kept raising themselves up between her and Randall in spite of all she could do.

"Oh, there are many times, Mairi," she murmured, "when I do not have my own way nor anything like."

Roderick, too, was smiling. "This American?" he questioned her. "What will he expect of you? I know little of their customs for the behavior of women there, but what I hear does not reassure me. It seems they are a savage breed, scarce fitted to offer delectable companionship to gentlemen."

"Why do you say that?"

He poured more wine into their glasses.

"I suppose it is because of a gruesome little story I heard in a London coffee house years ago. As I remember, it happened in the very province your young man comes from—New Hampshire, is it not?"

"Yes. Randall is from New Hampshire. What happened there?"

"Why it seems some doughty female—Dustin, I believe her name was, Hannah Dustin—slew ten Indians and brought their bloody scalps home for trophies. Unwomanly! Appalling! I have always been sorry for her husband. If New Hampshire men come to Scotland for their wives, it is understandable."

"I think that must have been very long ago," said Margery, trying to reassure him. "I do not think Randall will expect me to scalp anyone. I doubt if his mother is accustomed to do so."

"You shall have your choice of the family claymores to fend with, Margery dear," said Mairi with a bubbling laugh. "Let us go out on the parapet for a while. There is still some sunset left in the sky."

So they walked the battlemented walls of Kismull after that, and finally rested themselves on benches placed in a corner where the cold winds did not blow. Then, under the stars, she had finally told them her reason for coming to Barra; told them all Kenneth's stories about the American uprising that would put the Stuarts back on the throne, and wanted to know how much of it was true.

"Very little of it," said Roderick, at last, when she had made an end. "There is no new undertaking in favor of the Prince that I have heard of, and I am in touch with those who know. Every day his body and spirit decline, for which I am sorry. I was a boy when he was a young man, and I was brought up that he would deliver Scotland to the old ways again. A new star flashed in the sky the night he was born, and a great wind ravaged all Hanover. We took it for a sign."

"My mother has told me," murmured Margery.

"Yes, she would have told you. Tall, young, beautiful Gillian, gallant as a man! We could not rise when Lochiel called out the clans, because we owed fealty to the MacDonald of Sleat, and of all the MacDonalds only Clanranald had the courage to go. But we sent our piper to guide the Prince's ship into Eriskay, and three hundred guineas in our free gift. With the piper, your mother went along."

"That she never told me," said Margery wonderingly.

"Aye. She could keep her own counsel, Gillian could, when she chose. She knew your father would not approve, and she had set her mind to him even then. But when the Prince landed, Gillian was there."

Margery stirred restlessly against the stone and looked out over the sea into the dark. Much as she reverenced the stories of old times, she wanted to know now about nearer matters of today.

Roderick noticed her impatience and broke off sharply, then went on in another vein.

"It is true, there is an uprising in America. It will not be easily settled, and what may come of it, I cannot tell. But the Stuarts will never find followers there. Charles was an enemy of all Whiggery and born to destroy it, only he failed therein. America is a Whig's country, as all men in Scotland know."

Margery made a wry face. "So Cousin Roderick—the matter our schoolmaster told me was all a lie?"

"So much as makes no difference, yet there is a kernel of truth therein. A year or two back—three years, was it not, Mairi, that we wintered in Edinburgh—there was a score of young gallants and hard-bit old men who formed themselves into a group called the Royal Oak, and declared their purpose was to bring back the Stuarts again. That they ever did much beyond wearing blue bonnets, get themselves a Latin motto, and drink wine, I never heard—though they may have. It is true that Mac-

Donald of Kingsburgh has taken his wife to America, but I think they hope to advance their private fortunes there. There have been many who said it would be well if we could take advantage of a rising in America. I expect such rumors will be flying about these hundred years after we are gone. Just so long as there is a drop of Stuart blood anywhere, there will be those who are loyal to it—loyal, and gallant, and inept, likely, as their ancestors were. But as to your schoolmaster's stories—no! Why did the fellow lie to you?"

"I think I know the reason," said Margery grimly.

She was ready to leave Barra then, but she did not go till her father's letter came, saying that he himself would have to remain more than a month away.

She came out of her reverie and felt the boat nudging against the familiar wharf, saw the cottages of Ballyrhinn through the mist that was thinning on the hill. Jock MacLeod grumbled inarticulately as he helped her ashore with her belongings, took her money, and turned away. Then as she stood watching him, he looked back and spoke over his shoulder.

"I'm sorry for what's happened, lass," he said. "None of us wanted to be the one to let ye know." He leaped into his boat, shoved off with an oar, and disappeared in the thick grayness that still hung over the sea.

Margery shifted her cloak and bandbox so they would be the least trouble to her and walked slowly from the wharf into the town. She met nobody. It was not unusual to go the length of Ballyrhinn in the middle of a busy forenoon and meet no older children or grown folk. Kenneth would be holding lessons in the loft over the byre, the men cutting seaware, and the women spinning this season's wool for exportable tweed. But the little children should be playing at every doorstep, running their short, busy errands, gathering around like a flock of bright birds when they saw she had come home. MacNayr's old dog ambled by, and a pair of golden plovers settled behind Widow Gillander's house to search for crumbs or insects in the soft ground. Smoke went up from nearby chimneys, doors stood open, and she caught the murmur of voices, the sound of the spinning wheel, now and then a cough. She told herself she was foolish to think that anything could be seriously wrong, but she stopped dead still, nevertheless, and stood there in the middle of the winding turf street.

Then she saw Kenneth. He was coming down the slope from Rhinn House, his head bowed, cutting idly at the furze bushes with a stout stick as if he had nothing better to do. She had been angry with Kenneth, thought to fly at him when they met and give him the scolding he deserved, but she could not feel angry now—not until she knew where the

children were and what it was folk would not tell her in Stornaway.
"Kenneth!" she said.

He stood still and lifted his head, and she saw that his eyes were
sunken and his skin had a mouldy, grayish look. His face did not light
up at the sight of her as it was wont to do.

"So ye've come home, Margery," he said.

"Yes. I've come home. Tell me, Kenneth, why is everything so strange
—even you? You're not keeping school."

"No," he answered hoarsely. "No, I'll likely be keeping school no more
here."

"I heard some children were sick. Whose children? How many? Will
they soon be well again?"

He drew his hands across his eyes. "Margery," he said, "'t has been
terrible here. There's a-many gone."

"Gone? Gone where?"

It was not that she could not see, it was that she would not, and
Kenneth knew. He drew back a little.

"They ha' gone to the graveyard in boxes," he told her grimly. "There's
been a sickness let loose amongst the children such as was never known."

Suddenly it seemed to Margery that the whole hillside, lanes, and
byres, and cottages, tilted slantways before her eyes. She was near faint-
ing, she knew, but she tried to control herself. Kenneth kept on.

"Eighty-seven children there was on Rona," he droned, as if he were
reciting catechism. "We ha' buried forty-three, and twenty-nine canna'
use their limbs nor faculties. That leaves fifteen whole. Fifteen and no
more."

"But what was it, Kenneth?" she breathed in horror.

"Why there's none knows, not even your braw doctor lad. They sickened and they died, and there was naught any man could do."

Down the street a child cried fretfully, and Margery thought it was a
most precious sound.

"Where were you going, Kenneth?" she asked falteringly.

"To tend Johnny Dweeney," he answered dully. "He canna' leave his
bed, and no woman can spare the time from tending o' her own."

Hunching his shoulders, as if it were a cold day instead of a mild
damp one, he strode off. Margery stood still and watched him. Neither
had had the heart to speak a personal word to the other. He had made
no advances, and she had not spoken the reproach that was in her mind.
She did not know what it was, but she had the uncanny feeling that
something more than the death of his pupils troubled him. For herself,
she wanted to find Randall now, to cling close in his arms, and hear
the worst that had happened, to hear that he loved her in spite of all.

But where would Randall be? At Rhinn House, consulting his books and mixing his medicines, or among the crofters, giving comfort where he could, fighting lest another child should die? Perhaps it would be best to go to Andra. Whatever was right and fitting for her to do, Andra would know. Walking as if her own limbs were about to fail her, Margery went to Andra's house and tapped on the stone by the door.

No one answered for a long time, and then Ellen came out of the byre. She had a willow basket in one hand with flecks of turnip and mashed whins in the bottom of it, for she had been feeding their one cow. There were dark hollows under Ellen's eyes. Otherwise she seemed much the same.

"Well, Margery," she cried. "Randall didna' tell me ye were coming home."

The words were harmless enough, but something about them made Margery feel worse than she had before, and she was already half ill. She leaned against the rough stones of the cottage wall.

"Randall does not know," she murmured. "Do you know where he is, Ellen? I would go to him, if I knew."

"I think he's at Rhinn House," said Ellen pertly, "having a proper fight with Master Riddoch."

"A fight with Master Riddoch? Why?"

Ellen shrugged. "I dinna' know. Old Parson came here late last night and went up to the hall as he does when your father be there. My mother sent me this morning to fetch a salve Randall had promised to compound, and I heard them squalling at each other across the breakfast table like two tomcats on the thatch at the full moon. So I came away. Would ye like a cup o' tea, Madge. Ye look scarce able to stand on your feet."

Margery gazed across the clachan and up the hill to Rhinn House. It seemed like an endless way, and she knew she had to go there. But first she would speak to Ellen. Perhaps Ellen would tell her more than Kenneth had.

"No," she murmured, "I do not want tea. But tell me—what happened to the children?"

"Ye hadna' heard?" cried Ellen with new eagerness that she should be the one to impart the story. "Why, first they were ailing for a week—many of them. Then they began to die. Christie lost five."

"Oh, no!" gasped Margery, sinking her head in her hands.

"Nell Gow lost three. Everywhere it was the same. Some lived as had better ha' gone, for they canna' get their legs under them, and who's to tell if they ever will again? And ye know, my mother foresaw it all!"

Margery looked up. "When? After I went away?"

Ellen shook her head importantly. "Awww no! Last summertime, long gone. Do ye remember that night at the hall—the night after Parson had touched her with holy water to take the sight away?"

"I remember that night," said Margery slowly. "She had a vision that night. She would not tell us what she saw."

"No, and didna' tell it after—only to Randall, and I heard."

Margery knew what bothered her. It was Ellen's familiar use of the name.

"When a taischer sees a firebrand fall through the air and light on a body's sleeve, she knows its arms will hold a dead child soon. My mother says she saw firebrands falling all over the clachan that night. No wonder she didna' tell. Folk might ha' moved away, or burned her in tar!"

Margery was past everything except wondering how she could get home. It had to be done, and finally she pulled away from Ellen and stumbled along the lane, praying that she would not fall, that she would not meet any grief-stricken parent to whom she should offer comfort, feeling unable to face such a piteous sight. She crept past her cape and bandbox, letting them lie. She had just set her foot gratefully on the edge of the lawn at Rhinn House when John Riddoch rushed past her, almost knocking her down. He drew away sharply to avoid a collision and then stood still and stared at her with blazing eyes, an angry little turkey cock of a man, with turkey's swelling red throat.

"Hoo, lass," he shrilled. "Is your father no coming home?"

"No," she told him wearily. "My father is not coming home, not for a month. Good-by. I am sorry. I am feeling ill."

A cloud seemed to reach out for her then, and she drifted on it toward the house. Then she heard Randall calling, "Margery!"

In a moment she had collapsed in his arms, a rain of wet tears pouring over her face.

"Oh Randall," she wept, "the children! The children!"

"I know," he said brokenly, and she heard the tears in his voice that he would not allow himself to shed. "There's been hell to pay with the children. Thank God, Margery, you've come home."

Later, sitting together in one great chair by the bay window that faced the west terrace, he told her the course of it, and she listened calmly enough, commenting here and there as she could sense he wanted her to do. It was true, what Kenneth had told her. Forty-three of the soft rosy little bodies had gone to feed the old earth of the graveyard above Ballyrhinn. Their souls—and here Randall broke off to speak words about John Riddoch that should not be applicable to any minister of God. He had come there insisting that the disease was a visitation upon the island for its lewd and sinful ways in not seeking more earnestly for the establishment of a parish and a Kirk. He wanted to set the people fasting, but Randall had argued that they were weakened by grief and hard work and hunger and could not support a fast. Riddoch had been leaving in rage thereat when Margery saw him go.

He told her of Colin's death, and she was aghast and cried a little. Janet had cried for three days, but Meggy had only turned white and shed no tears. Then he spoke of those who had lived but lost their body's use, and for them he was hopeful. They were in no immediate danger, and there were cures to try: salves, and poultices; and applications of electric fluid had been used with much success for elderly paralytics in America. Later, he thought, he should take a trip to Edinburgh to consult the doctors there.

They did not speak of their love for each other, for there was no need. They felt sure and confirmed in it now, welded together by more than the body's fire.

The first moment that she felt her old courage and spirit returning, so that she could bear to let him go, Margery asked if he was not needed in the clachan. He rose at once, sighing.

"Yes. I am overdue there now. No one is in critical need. The disease has waned, and no new cases have appeared lately, but life there is all broken apart and will be, for a time. I go to each family every day to try to comfort those who have lost all, and assure those who have children alive but crippled that there is hope and a good chance. Andra is tireless in the work. She has been invaluable to everyone, most of all, to me. There was nothing we thought of that we did not try, but our remedies did no good. Some died and some lived, and it all fell out according to the strange ways of God. We had little part." Then suddenly he remembered something. His eyes brightened and he cried out, "Heather ale!"

"Heather ale!" Margery stared at him.

"Yes. I did not think of it, not being able, I suppose, to think beyond the *Pharmacopoeia*. But Andra remembered, and she came here seeking for some. Leitis said she had none by."

"Would it have helped?" asked Margery faintly. "Leitis is right. Lavan and Caitlin had the last of my grandmother's brewing."

"If you had been here, could you have made some, Margery?"

She shook her head. "I could not. It is not the time of year. It can only be done when the young heather first comes in bloom."

He smiled at her, a sad little smile. "I do not suppose you will tell me how it is made?"

"I thought you understood. You know I cannot tell you."

He kissed her upturned face. "I do not know whether I understand you or not, but I love you, Margery."

She walked to the door with him, followed him to the edge of the terrace. The fog and grayness had cleared away, and the sun shone out, almost springtime warm. The hillside had begun to green a little, and down it, skipping gaily from tuft to hummock, went Meg Munro's daftie, flinging his arms about, piping a shrill, wordless tune.

"I never thought of the daftie," said Margery wonderingly. "I supposed he was dead like so many, being a weak thing all his life, and ailing often before."

She looked up at Randall. His eyes followed the half-wit cavorting on the hill.

"So many—" he murmured, "so many twisted or dead—the strong, the quick, the beautiful, bright-witted children! But the daftie was never sick at all!"

XIX

By Health and All-heal

SPRING CAME IN with late March, cold and stormy and reluctant, but every day the sodden turf of the island showed a little more green. Sim pottered in the daffodil beds, and Leitis spread out the household linen for bleaching whenever there came a few hours of clear bright sun. Kenneth sulked in his room most of the time, reading sermons and drinking whiskey, and went prowling off after dark, nobody knew just where. The lovers were aware of nothing except themselves and their work in the clachan among the families in the silent cottages, that had once been loud with the clamor of children, that had echoed with their shouts and laughter all day long. The serpent plague—silent and deadly as a serpent—had done its work and gone, leaving almost unbelievable havoc behind. No new cases broke out after Margery's return from Barra, and no more children died. Some few had entirely escaped it, suffering nothing more than a slight cold. Others were beginning to totter about again, the iron that had seemed to bind their muscles dissolving away. But nearly a score lay helpless on the straw by the fire pits, scarcely able to drive off the curious hens and geese that came pecking about them, or reach for a cup of water even when it was set close to hand.

Andra and Randall tried everything they could think of that had no harm to it: hot packs and cold packs, salves, and ointments, and massages. Margery tried awkwardly to do as they told her, but her chief role was that of comforter to the distraught parents, giving them her word that the disabled children should never want for aught, even if all their lives they never walked again.

If Ellen was still troubled with visions, Randall heard no more about it; in fact, it almost seemed to him as if she was keeping out of his way, for he did not see her again after the day of Master Riddoch's visit, not even when he went to say good-by to her the night before he left for Edinburgh. Part of him had been longing to go ever since the sickness loosened its grip on Ballyrhinn, for he felt a nagging curiosity and in-

tellectual need to know what Dr. Cullen would say when he heard an
account of it. Part of him was deliciously content to remain where he
was, where he could walk with Margery in the soft twilight or sit close
by the fire with her when the wind turned chill. There were no shadows
between them now, and no strangeness. In everything except the ultimate
intimacy of the flesh they were already one, and Randall felt he could
wait for that now. He was still too troubled over guilt for past incon-
tinency to indulge himself again. And Margery knew how to display
all her warmth and love without trying to tempt or tease him. It was
almost as if she understood, and yet how could a maid—and he had no
doubts that she was a maid—be so quick to understand?

She confessed to him her real reason for going to Barra, and he listened in amazement when he heard the account of Kenneth's stories,
wondering how she could be fooled by them for so long.

"But Margery," he said, as they sat together on the terrace after supper
the night she told him, "how could you believe we in America would rise
to support the kings we went there to get away from? We do not really
care who governs England. All we want is for her to buy our goods and
let us alone." Margery looked a little rueful and shook her head at him.

"I think—it was because I wanted to, that I believed it. And how am
I to know what folk are like in America? I only know what I hear, and
one can hear anything. Why, I'm told in your very province there was a
woman cut off the scalps of savages, just as fierce and bloody as if she
had been a man."

" 'Twas no such thing—not in New Hampshire!"

" 'Twas, too! Her name was Hannah—Hannah Dustin!"

"Oh! Hannah Dustin! She was from Massachusetts!"

Margery giggled. "I suppose that makes a difference!"

"Of course." His eyes twinkled, but his mouth was grave. "Would
you say a girl from Galloway was the same as a girl from Aberdeen?"

"Oh! No! Of course not! Of course she would not be!"

"Well, the difference between Massachusetts and New Hampshire
would be just as plain—to anybody who knew. Anyway, Hannah was
none so bad. The Indians had lugged her off into the woods up the
Merrimac. She only killed them so she could get away and go home."

"I see. But when I go there—will you expect me to scalp an Indian?"

He looked thoughtful. Under her banter there was apprehension he
could not wholly soothe without a lie, and he was through lying to her.
"Probably—no. But I should like to feel you could scalp one if it was
necessary."

Margery shuddered, but she seemed to understand. "Well, I suppose
I could—if it was necessary," she said.

She had taken Kenneth aside and told him quietly and with no show of anger that she had found there was no Stuart uprising in the wind, that likely there never would be. She had not accused him of trying to win advantage of her in that way, but she had suggested that there were children needing his services in other places than Rona, and perhaps he had better go. But Kenneth had not gone. He had made no excuses for himself, only muttered that he would wait until her father came home. But brief notes kept coming now and then from her father, pleading great stress of affairs due to the threatened war in America, always extending his absence a little more.

And so things went until the end of April, when the world was warm again, most of the oats and barley sown, and all the island covered with fresh springing green. Randall decided then that he must make the trip to Edinburgh and return quickly if he were to have any time to carry out Dr. Cullen's suggestions for helping the children, before he finally established himself in the city for the great event of Midsummer Day. He meant to consult the doctor about Ellen, too, and the night before his departure, he and Margery walked down to her mother's house to tell her so, but only Andra was there, sitting by the fire and brooding, her head bent low.

They tried to cheer her, but she only murmured of "trouble coming to me and mine." No, she answered their question, she had not been warned of it by the sight. It was in her heart that she knew. Ellen, she said, was up at the hut on Ardmory. Ellen was ailing. They had best leave Ellen alone.

Randall promised that they would not follow the cattle maid, but left word for her that he would try in the city to see if he could find something that would bring her relief, or perhaps even a cure.

"Would you want to be cured too, Andra?" he asked. "If I can learn of such a thing—?"

"I do not know," answered Andra simply. "God will tell me, I think, when it comes to the time."

She promised, as she had no need to do, that she would keep a watchful eye on the children while he was away.

Randall and Margery left her after that, to wander over the new grass, and embrace in the shelter of the crags below Rhinn House, and think of nothing but each other and their own love.

The next morning in the gray light before sunrise, Iver took him to Stornaway. He was silent on the trip, thinking that the last time he made it, Colin MacKay had ferried him across. They had laughed and sung ribald songs and taken tobacco together. Now Colin was lying in the little graveyard with its broken stone crosses, its ancient unmarked stones, and he, Randall, was still breathing and alive and setting his face east toward a new day. He looked at Iver and thought of his wife. Lavan had ailed, and Sally Anne had ailed, and one was taken and the other left, just as it had been in Bible times. Even as then, interpretations still belonged to God. He spoke of Colin to Iver, casually, as became a man, and asked where the dead lad's gear would go.

Iver answered as casually, pulling the oars hard against the windless sea. Colin had been a bachelor with no kin. Everyone knew he loved Meggy, and folk believed she should have all, but she refused to touch anything, saying she would leave the matter till the laird was at home.

The packet for Dunvegan was already waiting when they reached Stornaway. They shook hands, and Iver went back to Rona, and Randall sailed for Skye, and beyond that, Scotland.

Six days later he was going along Leith Walk with the great gray castle crouched on the rock ahead of him, striding into the Old Town between the tall lands, feeling as much a stranger as if he had never seen it before. It was dusk, a raw, windy, spring dusk when he started down the High Street. He had forgotten how finely attired the city folk were: the men in ruffled shirts and embroidered waistcoats, buckled shoes and powdered wigs, carrying short swords; the women all decked with ribbons and tiers of flounces, dangling bracelets and face paint. But the streets were not entirely given over to the fashionable. Bare-headed shop-keepers chatted in groups in the doorways; corduroy-clad men from Gilmerton were bawling coals and yellow sand. There were fishwives with Newhaven haddock to sell, chimney sweeps, and water-carriers, and town rats, tired at the end of day, trailing their Lochaber axes. Fine, full of color, was this Scottish city, but hogs rooted in the street kennels, and the reek of filth and human offal breathed out of every alley he passed by. He was homesick suddenly for the island smells of herring and wet wool and leather. The clean pine and salt-scented air of Hampton Falls seemed very far away.

He stopped under the grim shadow of the Tolbooth to decide where he was going next. The Laird of Rona, he knew, lodged at the White Hart in the Grassmarket. Margery had written to tell her father of Randall's intention to visit the city, so he knew he would be expected there. That was where he should go, but instead he found his feet carrying him willy-nilly down the familiar way to the flat in Rowan Tree Wynd in search of Sandy and Tom.

When he got to his old lodgings, he found one, but not the other, of the two he sought. Sandy was lying on the floor in front of the fire, a treatise on midwifery spread in front of him, and a glass of ale at his elbow. He did not stand up when Randall opened the door and walked in; only lifted his head and cocked an eyebrow and said, "Tally-ho, Woodbury!"

A strange lad, dark and sallow and stocky, sat at the writing table. He looked up, shoved aside his work, and waited to have the intrusion explained. Sandy took his time about it.

"So ye're back from the island, lad. Is it to stay with us this time? We've room for ye here, since Culpepper took himself off last week."

"He's lodging elsewhere?" asked Randall in disappointment. "How've you been, Sandy, lad? All the way here I've been longing to see the two of you."

"I been well," said Sandy thoughtfully. He waved his hand toward the dark lad at the writing table. "This is Watt Ferlie from Arrochar. After ye left us, he came. He pays a wee bit o' rent—when he can bide here no other way."

Watt and Sandy smiled at each other. "And this," Sandy went on, "is he I've oft told ye of, Woodbury, our American lad."

Watt Ferlie stood up and came over to shake hands.

"Where's Tom?" asked Randall after the introduction. "Why'd he leave here? Wherever he is, let's send and get him. I've ale money in my pocket."

Sandy shook his head dolefully. "Ye canna' send for Thomas, unless a dolphin be your messenger. He's on the sea."

"You mean he's going home?"

"Aye. The colonies be all in a turmoil, and there's constant discussing of it. I find I canna' fash myself about the colonies. They can raze and plow 'em and sow 'em with salt, for all o' me."

"Was that why Tom went home?"

"Well, he didna' discuss the whole matter. He had a letter last week that set him swearing. He read it over and over, and the more he read it, the more he swore."

"What was in the letter?"

"He didna' tell me. I only know it came from Virginia. All one night he paced the floor. Then on a sudden he struck his hands together and cried, 'By God, they go too far!' Next I knew, I was bundling him into the fly coach for Glasgow where he could take passage westward. Don't tell me ye're for the same, lad. I hear there's no an American left of fighting age in all Scotland, or England either. Like the rats out of a sinking ship, they've all gone trooping awa' for whatever's to do at home."

"I hadn't thought things were that bad yet," said Randall uneasily. "My father hadn't written me things were that bad!"

He sat down in the cushioned chair by the grate and took the glass of ale Watt Ferlie poured for him. His thoughts were all in confusion. He ought to go home if all the other lads had gone. But on Midsummer Day he was going to marry Margery. He had kept himself warm, cold nights on the ship's deck, thinking what a high time he'd have with Tom and Sandy MacCrimmon when he told them about his betrothal and invited them to the wedding. Now he found he could not speak of it at all. There was a chill round his heart and a tightness in his throat. Both lads were watching him. He kept on, choosing his words carefully.

"I'm only here for a day or two. I came to consult Dr. Cullen about a sickness we had on Rona. I've never seen the like." Suddenly he found he was telling Watt and Sandy all about the stricken children.

They listened, shocked and interested, insisting they, too, had never heard of such a thing. Gradually the talk warmed him. After a while they went to a tavern for oysters and toasted cheese, and he came back to sleep that night in his old bed where he could look out through the small casement at the far dark line of the Grampians and hear the bells of St. Giles chiming the hours through.

The next morning he went early to the White Hart to breakfast with the laird. Rona was glad to see him, and ordered a huge repast of fried potatoes, beefsteak, and ale. He wanted a detailed account of the sickness and could hardly hold back his tears when Randall told him how many of the children were crippled or gone.

"Find out aught ye can that may aid them, lad, and dinna' worry for the cost. Trading worsens every day, but I've new matters afoot now that should send many a fine guinea into my purse."

"What are they?" asked Randall, since the laird's face indicated that he wished for the question.

"Supplying the army," he answered quickly, seeming much pleased with himself. "I've contracted with the King's purveyors to supply wool and leather. Warm coats and stout boots the soldiers will need, for the fighting in America."

"You mean—there be that many troops going—you're that certain there'll be war?"

Comyn shrugged his shoulders. "Some say it canna' last long. That we'll go through their armies like a knife through new cheese, and be home before harvest. I only know—we are outfitting many lads."

"Maybe I best be outfitted too," said Randall grudgingly, feeling that his world was flying apart, in spite of all his efforts to hold it together. "I heard from MacCrimmon all the Americans have gone."

Rona considered him soberly. "Lad," he said, "ye can see I'm no in a position to counsel ye."

"I know what you mean," said Randall slowly. "I know—I can see—

maybe you've changed your mind about having me for a son-in-law. If there's war, you know, I'll have to stand with America."

"If ye didna', ye'd be worth little. But ye know 'tis small account whether I change my mind. Do ye think the business will change Margery?"

Randall smiled as he remembered her promise to scalp red Indians if it became necessary. "No," he said, feeling his heart lighten, "I do not think that it will."

The laird nodded agreement. "Aye, she's a fine stubborn lass like her mother was in her time. When are ye going back to her?"

"By the next boat out of Leith—which is day after tomorrow. I've only to see Dr. Cullen and then be away."

"A good answer, one I was hoping for, and I'll give ye company home. I've only the one more task to attend to here, and that's to settle Margery's portion. What was ye expecting with her?"

Randall looked him in the eye. "Give her whatever you choose," he answered, "and if you give her nothing, that will do as well. My mother brought nothing to my father. A man's not paid for marrying in America. But if you give her aught—" Rona waited, watching him steadily "—I ask that it be not in land. We've no use for land in a country we will not live in."

There was no reproach in Rona's tone, only a complete lack of inflection that was worse.

"Do ye think it's fitting to rob a man o' his grandchildren?"

Randall sighed. He had thought this issue was settled. Now it was presented again, and again he would be no more yielding than any stone.

"No. I would not rob my father so. A man must first look to his own father."

Rona bowed his head. "Aye," he said. "And a lass must go with her husband. Ye've the right of it, lad, though 'tis a bitter drink to me. Well, I shall settle that it be not in land, Margery's portion."

Randall reached out awkwardly and cuffed the old man on the shoulder, the only way in which he dared show his sympathy.

"I promise sure that when you've a grandchild you shall see it. If you cannot come to us, we'll bring it to you."

They parted after that. Rona went to the banker's in the Exchange, and Randall walked down College Wynd to search in all the places he thought Dr. Cullen might be.

The doctor's tiny office was locked, nor could he be found at the Infirmary. Finally, in mid-morning, Randall stopped outside the door of a classroom, high up under the eaves of old Surgeon's Hall. The door was half open, and peering through he could see the front row of young men busily writing in their notebooks. He recognized a face here and there: Tam Earnshaw was squinting worse than ever and would soon come to spectacles, no doubt; John Craddock looked as if he had had too much to drink the night before. He could not see the lecture platform, but he could hear the high, nervous voice of the master, uttering, as he usually did, the stalest of facts with a kind of suppressed excitement.

"There is another particular in which Boerhaave's doctrine concerning the fluids appears to be imperfect and unsatisfactory, and that is in his doctrine De Glutinose Spontaneo. The causes which he has assigned for it are by no means probable, and the actual existence of it is seldom to be proved. Some of the proofs adduced for the existence of the *plegna calides* are manifestly founded on a mistake. His *Generalia et incertae sedis* has hardly any connection at all. The titles Rheumatism, Hypochondriasia, and Hydrop follow one another when he does not attempt any general data—"

Randall found he could not listen. He walked hastily to the end of the dusty corridor and stood there at the tiny window, looking out into the blue spring day. He knew what he ought to do, right enough. If the English in America—and that was what must have been meant by it—had gone too far for Tom Culpepper of Virginia, they had gone too far for Randall Woodbury of Hampton Falls. He, too, should leap abroad the fly coach for Glasgow. He, too, should take passage home. But he had given his word to marry Margery. He had given Margery his love. How was it that within one poor addled brain the private man and the public man must be so bitterly at war? He waited there, trying to calm himself, but he might as well have tried to calm a storm at sea.

When the students trooped out of the classroom, Randall waited until they had all gone pounding downstairs. Then he walked to the doorway and went in. Dr. Cullen sat back at the preceptor's desk, fiddling with his notes and waiting for the next class to gather. No detail of him had changed, so far as Randall could tell. He remembered the pointed nose, bushy white wig, and hunched shoulders under the flowing gown. The doctor started at him as if he were a small boy called for a reprimand. He spoke in his usual quick impatient tones.

"Well, sir?"

Randall hesitated, trying to decide on the best approach. Finally he said, "Do you remember me, Dr. Cullen?"

The doctor peered closer.

"Ah, yes. The New Hampshire lad. Why are ye not gone, sir, after your countrymen?"

"I went away nearly a year ago," Randall reminded him. "I went away with the Laird of Rona, do you remember—to his policies to inoculate the people there."

"Ah, yes. I talked with Rona last week. We shared a fish dinner in Anchor Close. He told me an unlikely tale."

The doctor's face had turned scornful and angry. Randall could not understand why, but he decided to move slowly.

"What did Rona tell you?"

"He told me that ye reported through his daughter's letters some nonsense of a swift paralysis striking young children."

Randall felt relieved that the doctor already knew, but his relief did not last, for the older man kept relentlessly on.

"I didna' tell him, for it would outrage the ethics of the profession, but I tell ye, sir, I consider it a false report and a grievous perversion of truth. Ye are guilty, either of stupidity or maliciousness. Young children do not become paralyzed! They are not susceptible thereto. Paralysis is the result of age or gross injury! Otherwise—" and he shook his head, "—I have never heard of such a thing!"

Randall had not expected this senseless rebuff. He stared at the doctor for a moment, then he felt a cold anger rising within him.

"Whether you have heard of it or not, it has happened so," he said. "The children cannot move their legs or walk. I wish that you could come through Ballyrhinn with me, and see them lying there!"

Dr. Cullen turned his eyes away, picked up a scrap of paper from his desk, and began to shred it with long, nervous fingers. After a moment he replied, "Ye were always a good student, sir, and I took ye for an honest man. A bit impatient and unappreciative of theory; too quick to take the shortest way; but decisive, and well-trained, and of a certain skill, of a great human sympathy."

"Thank you, sir," said Randall, taken by surprise again.

"What I heard of the matter from my old friend is hardly credible, but—suppose ye tell it to me in your own way. How did the sickness fall?"

This was what Randall had been waiting for, and his words began tumbling over themselves they poured so fast out of his mouth. He told of the slow onset of the disease, the week of colds and lamenesses, then the terrible night when he had been called to the deathbed of Christie's children.

"And nearly a score are lying there still, sir. Their fever has gone, and much of their pain, but they cannot move without the help of others, no more than puppets. I cannot cure them by standing at their bedsides and telling them the thing has never happened before."

"There is a doctor in London," answered Dr. Cullen slowly, "who has

observed a slow debility coming on young children over a period of
months that renders their limbs inert and flaccid. But he reported no
deaths and no raging fevers, such as ye describe."

"Has he found a cure?" asked Randall.

Dr. Cullen shook his head. "No. Some of the children were able to
walk later, supported in iron frames."

"Oh, God!" Randall cried out.

"Hush, lad," said the older man, not unkindly. "A doctor mustna' be
too greatly affected with human sympathy. I ha' always maintained that
the cures will be found in the causes. Have ye any theory as to what
brought the thing about?"

"There was no uncommon weather," said Randall slowly, "and no
unwholesomeness of food, either plant, or animal, or fish from the sea.
Food was scanty, indeed, and it was a cold wet season, but I am told
it is always so there at that time of year. It seems that it must have come
with some boatload of strangers. Ships often put in there to trade or fill
their kegs with fresh water. It is on the main sea road from Ireland to
the North."

Dr. Cullen nodded, and Randall went on.

"I remember reading when I was here at the College of a doctor in
Vienna some years ago—Plenciz was his name, or some such foreign
thing. He maintained that all epidemic diseases are caused by specific
living microcosms—"

Dr. Cullen gave a rude sound and spat on the floor of the classroom.

"How could he get such evidence save through a microscope. Ye know
I do not trust microscopes—"

"I remember you lectured against them, Dr. Cullen."

More and more baffled by the doctor's replies, Randall paced back
and forth in front of the desk. If I were a woman, I'd be wringing my
hands, he told himself inwardly. Aloud, he said, "Then you cannot advise me how to treat the children, sir. You can recommend nothing
but iron frames strapped for all their lives about them?"

"I ha' heard of no other thing."

"Thank you, sir, for the benefit of your vast knowledge," said Randall
bitterly. He turned to leave. Then he remembered there was still another
question.

"Dr. Cullen, forgive my rudeness. I have brought one more matter to
trouble you."

"I am listening to ye because it is my duty," snapped the doctor. "It
surely isna' a pleasure to me. What is this other matter?"

"On Rona there is a girl—and her mother, too—afflicted with the second sight—"

"What o' that? I ha' heard o' many such in my time. Seers be as common in the Highlands as scratched hands in blackberry time. Why do ye tell it to me?"

"I thought it might be a thing that—I thought there might be a cure for it in medicine."

"Ye wax preposterous, sir. The second sight is no matter for doctors. Do ye find it in my *Nosology?*"

"No. It is not in your *Nosology.*"

"Dinna' ye realize that every known disease is recorded there?"

"I can neither affirm nor deny. It well may be. You are learned enough. I do not know. It seemed to me that the sight might be a disease of the nerves or brain. I thought I would ask—"

Dr. Cullen stood up and began to pace the room with short nervous strides.

"The second sight is a gross superstition, and its practitioners should be banished out of Scotland. Lad, ye have a curious mind, but yo set it in the wrong way. If ye were as quick to observe what wiser men ha' written down as ye are to make ill and addle-pated investigations o' your own—"

Randall flushed. He felt all his determination and courage draining away like blood from a tapped vein. He would get no good here. He would have to go back to Rona and struggle with his problems alone. He could bring with him no help for the children, no help for Ellen to recompense her for his own stupid and cruel wrongdoing. He turned again to the stairs, but the doctor laid a hand on his arm. His voice quavered slightly, and his eyes flashed with a sudden light.

"Ye are going back to the island? Ye'll continue to practice medicine there?"

"For a month or two. Then—I had meant—to return here to school."

"Then, if ye are to be there, treating such mighty ills with no sworn doctor to guide and advise ye, to keep ye from doing your patients wrong —I think it is best that ye swear—"

"Swear?"

"That ye take the great Oath!" cried Dr. Cullen impatiently, "the oath of all our profession. The Oath of Hippocrates! 'Tis not given here to our doctors till they complete the work o' the school. But ye are there alone, and inclined to experiment and improvise. It may hold ye true to established practice—if ye swear. Stand in front o' me, sir."

Standing in the dusty classroom at the top of Surgeon's Hall, Randall faced the world-famous Scottish doctor and repeated the ancient oath. But his mind was busy with a half-forgotten thing. He was remembering a winter night in Hampton Falls, bitter cold, with wind howling down the chimney and snow drifting under the door. Two calls had come for his father; a man with a broken leg out Seabrook way, and a child fighting for breath in a farmhouse on the Kensington road. He was scarcely more than a boy, but he had been brought up in the practice of medicine. It was then that his father had sent him on his first case alone. But before he had gone, his father had made him stand as he was standing now—stand and swear.

"I swear by Apollo, the physician, and Aesculapius, and Health, and All-heal, and the gods and goddesses, that, according to my ability and judgment, I will keep this Oath. . . .

"I will follow that system of regimen which, according to my ability and judgment, I consider for the benefit of my patients, and abstain from whatever is deleterious and mischievous. I will give no deadly medicine to any one if asked, nor suggest any such counsel—" He could not remember the whole oath, he had been so young, it had been so long ago. But so far there was no guilt against him. He had followed it well. He continued to repeat after Dr. Cullen.

"With purity and with holiness I will pass my life and practice my Art." Well, he had done that, too, for the most part. Except for the one time—

"Into whatever houses I enter, I will go into them for the benefit of the sick, and will abstain from every voluntary act of mischief and corruption; and, further, from the seduction of females—!"

Randall did not hear any more that Dr. Cullen said. He must have mouthed it over, but only the final phrases beat at his eardrums hard enough to come through.

"—While I continue to keep this Oath unviolated, may it be granted to me to enjoy life and the practice of the art, respected by all men, in all times! But should I trespass and violate this Oath, may the reverse be my lot."

Dr. Cullen stepped back, a smile on his lean face. "That'll guide ye, lad. Keep it before ye, when ye're inclined to be rash and do the unfamiliar thing."

"Thank you, sir," muttered Randall, "thank you for all."

He bolted down the stairs and into the street. It was himself he was running from, himself and his sin, but he knew it was no use. He could never be free of them, never escape from what he had done. He slowed down as he reached the High Street on the way to Rowan Tree Wynd, walked with his head hanging, not seeing the shop windows or the passers-by. How true, he thought, was the old proverb, that when it rains, it pours; and when it pours, it does not bring down sweet rain, but blood, and hail, and fire. The guilt over his adventure with Ellen had been a dull, slow, heavy pain, but now he was not only guilty of physical uncleanliness; he was guilty of breaking a high and holy oath. How strange that he had never thought of it before! Never remembered the vows of that winter night in his boyhood that had defined forever what he must and must not do.

"From the seduction of any female—" And in the guise of her physician!

Now the pain of his guilt was a living, moving torment that pricked him not unlike the devils with pitchforks in the old moral tales of long ago.

Turning into the chilly shadows of Rowan Tree Wynd, dark and cold even in the bright May daytime, he looked up between the high walls at the narrow strip of blue sky.

"Apollo, forgive me," he muttered. "By Health and All-heal, I've done the worst I can! I've been a liar, a knave, and a fool!"

They were all evil companions to have about him, but he felt with ever increasing anguish that the liar was the worst of the three.

XX

A Bitter Bad Judge o' Women

ALONE by the door of her mother's house in the May morning, Ellen looked out at the blue tide flooding over the narrow sand. The tang of smoke troubled her nostrils, for up on the moors the men were burning the heather, as they did about this time every spring. She would remember this spring, she thought, when she had forgotten all the years that went before. She held her shawl about her in spite of the warm bright weather, and gave a sharp look up and down the road that wound through the clachan. No one seemed to be astir in Ballyrhinn but herself and the gulls, and the old dog on MacNayr's doorstep worrying disconsolately at a marrowbone. The women would be out on the machair, she thought, sowing beer-barley, or at home minding the sick children. There would be none to watch her and gossip at the way her body had begun to curve outward against the shawl.

It was a long time back that she had felt the first quickening, the flutter within her like the beating wings of a bird trapped in the hand. Since then she had bided indoors during the daytime, climbing up Ardmory every night to keep her usual vigil, and creeping down before the sunrise of each new day. She had not told her mother, but she was sure Andra knew. Ellen did not care. Soon everyone would know. Just as soon as ever Randall Woodbury came back from Edinburgh.

With a quiet little smile of triumph, she picked up a tin pail that stood by the door and started toward the cockle bed. How would he feel when he heard she carried his child, Ellen wondered. Well, no matter how he felt, he could do only the one thing. Master Riddoch and the Kirk would see that he did only the one thing. What would Margery do? Margery with her silks and laces, her feathered hats and high-heeled shoes, and all her wonderful well-bred things—and right under her nose Ellen had stolen her jo away—Ellen Deveron, the cattle girl!

Ellen knelt clumsily on the flat shiny leaves of scurvy grass that grew almost to the water's edge, but when she leaned over the wet tide pools to gather salmon bait as she meant to do, her head throbbed, and she felt again the fluttering in her side. So she put the pail down and sat beside it, idly sat there, thinking her own thoughts and watching the red and brown sails beat in from the sea.

She had taken her pleasure for more years than one would believe of a lass so young, taken it and remained sterile as a snowdrift all the while. Or perhaps not quite sterile, for she possessed more of her mother's knowledge of potions than she would admit, if anyone put the question to her mouth. Nothing violent and dangerous and wicked, of course. Only a tea of tansy and juniper when her body did not respond readily to the moon. She had never needed nor employed stronger measures, but the time had come when she had decided to let even those measures go. She was with child by her own choice, and she had her own reasons for that.

As she sat there in the grasses watching the sea, she heard the approach of heavy footsteps and turned her head. Kenneth Crary strode forward and flung himself down, not too close, but near enough for talk.

"Ye look like a storm rack, Kenneth," she said. "Could ye no win Margery back with the American gone?"

"I dinna' know that I want her back," he retorted, scowling. "Ellen, all can see ye've a child in ye. Ellen, is it mine?"

Ellen picked up a blade of grass and drew it slowly between her teeth before she answered him, waited a long time, not sure what she wanted to say.

Finally she replied, "Why would ye think it might not be?"

"Then—!" He moved quickly toward her. "Then, Ellen, it is mine! Ellen!"

Ellen pulled herself to her feet and stood very erect, almost flaunting the curves beneath the shawl.

"It dinna' matter whose it be," she said. "It'll get Randall Woodbury's name."

"Ellen—!"

"Go away from me," she hissed, staring at him till the pleading in his eyes died away and they seemed to mirror the fury in her own. He turned sharply from her and strode off, uttering a word Ellen did not choose to hear.

Picking up her empty pail, her shawl draped demurely now, she wandered along by the water side, further than she had intended, to the crags below Rhinn House, gathering limpets and mussels there. It was about mid-afternoon when, straightening up from her task, she looked to sea, and the sight she saw sent her hurriedly retracing her steps along the shore. She reached the little wharf just as Tam MacVean finished helping Randall Woodbury and Comyn Rhinn to set their baggage on the worn planking.

"Welcome home, sir," she said to Rona, curtsying as best she could. "You've been missed among us, and also the doctor lad. 'Tis happy I am to see the return."

"I've some ribbons for ye, Ellen," said Rona gruffly, "but they're shut away in my bag. There'll be gifts for all, and a feasting, verra' soon."

"Thank you, sir, you were always kind to me," Ellen answered, her head bent so that he could not see the scorn in her eyes. "Did you say a feasting?"

"Aye. 'Tis known my daughter's betrothed, but we've no yet feasted her well. We shall do it as soon as Leitis can prepare. Tell me, how are the bairns that ailed? Are they well?"

Ellen shook her head. " 'Tis my mother's opinion they'll never need shoes again," she said. Then she looked at Randall.

Her first thought was that he must have been ill—seasick, maybe, all the way from Edinburgh. His face was ravaged, and his gray eyes dark with suffering. Perhaps it was not seasickness; perhaps he, too, was smitten like Colin with the terrible creeping disease that stopped the breath. Perhaps she should fling herself on him quickly and point out his duty while he was still well enough to fulfill her plan. For indeed, he looked sick enough to die and find death welcome.

She took a tentative step toward him. "You look like Edinburgh had no agreed with you," she said.

He gave her a short answer. " 'Tis not the fault of Edinburgh," he muttered. He picked up a small canvas knapsack and strode ahead of Rona up the hill.

Ellen stared after him reflectively, the taste of the grass blade she had been chewing nervously still sour in her mouth. Then she went home, there being nothing else for her to do.

The feasting took Leitis more than a week to prepare for, even though she had Janet and Agnes Gillander to help in the kitchen. Ellen kept to the fireside and the shieling hut, for she had chosen the moment to reveal her plight to Ballyrhinn, and she knew that it must be close at hand. Randall did not come to her with any suggestions for curing the sight that he might have discovered in Edinburgh, and she did not seek him out to reveal her case in private with little discord. That was not Ellen's plan.

Finally Sim brought the word from door to door through the clachan that all were to sup that night at Rhinn House in honor of the American doctor and Miss Margery.

As Ellen preened herself before the small gilt-framed mirror that had been a birthday present from the laird's daughter, she was aware that her mother watched her with somber eyes. Taking no notice, or seeming not to, she fastened the belt of her green wool gown high under her breasts so that the fabric billowed out, hiding the swollen waistline below. Then she drew her shawl about her and asked in commonplace tones, "Are ye ready, Mother?"

Andra did not rise immediately from her stool by the fire. Instead she asked, her voice harsh with apprehension, "Ellen, do you think I don't know what's going on? What do you mean to do?"

Ellen looked her mother up and down and answered with a toss of her shoulders. "Whatever I do, it's no butter off your bread, is it?"

But Andra kept on. "Tell me, is Schoolmaster to blame?"

Ellen narrowed her eyes. "Why do ye say Schoolmaster?"

"He comes to you by night. I have seen him so."

Ellen smiled coldly. "If ye know so much by yourself," she said, "ye've no need asking me." She stepped through the doorway and started off toward Rhinn House. Andra sighed, heaped a dank, slow-burning sod on the fire, and followed, but not close enough to overtake her daughter.

It was a warm evening with stars and a crescent moon in a purple sky and scarce wind enough to stir the leaves of the rhododendrons and clipped yews by the terrace wall. Most of the crofters were there ahead of her, Ellen found, though not so great a company as would have appeared at a like occasion a year ago. Too many of the women were at home minding the children who could not stir forth for any feasting, and the handful of children able to turn out were already spoiled and shrill from being made too much of because there were too few of them left living any more.

Leitis had made no attempt to set places, but had loaded the great table with food of such a sort as everyone could pick up in his fingers and carry away to eat on the terrace or the broad stairs, the small parlors or the wide hall; oysters, pease porridge in earthen cups, haggis, roast chicken and goose, mutton collops, scones, and all manner of cakes and fruit pies.

"Ye're late for the blessing, Ellen," Tam Darran said, as she came up to where he stood with Ailis, his wife, at the edge of the crowd drawn around Sim and the whiskey barrel.

"I'll get no blessing here," Ellen murmured under her breath. Aloud she said, "There's the laird yonder, pouring claret, but where be the doctor and Miss Margery?"

Tam glanced about him. "They were here a moment back," he answered. "She looks bonny tonight. She's the fairest lass was ever seen on Rona, is Miss Margery."

He and Ailis smiled understandingly at each other.

"Her mother was fairer," said Widow Gillander, coming by with a tray of sweetmeats. "She married out of her kind, too—Gillian MacNeill."

"Peace to her dust then," said Tam, taking a long drink from the glass of whiskey in his hand.

"If ye want Margery," said Ailis, smiling at Ellen, "she went to the terrace wi' the doctor lad. She looked happy as never so."

"How did he look?" asked Ellen slyly.

Ailis frowned. "Well enough," she said after a moment. "I think Edinburgh no agreed wi' his constitution. I am sure it would not wi' mine."

Ellen drifted away from the Darrans, talking with one little group and then another. She saw Andra come in and go up to Leitis who stood in the kitchen doorway. The laird went over to the two women and offered them claret. Leitis took the glass and sipped it slowly, but Andra shook her head. Rona slapped her affectionately between the shoulders, drank the wine himself, and crossed the room to a row of high-backed chairs against the wall. The chairs were full of finely dressed folk, land owners from Harris and Lewis, maybe from as far off as Skye, all friends of Margery and her father, Ellen surmised. She turned her head at a sound from the far end of the room. The sound was the scraping of Ewen Gow's fiddle, and Johnny Dweeney's bagpipes joined it almost immediately in a dance tune. It was a round dance, and soon the crofters had formed in circles of eight and were turning about sunwise, in time to the high-pitched music of the two men. Everyone who had been on the terraces tried to come crowding through the door at once, eager to join the sport inside. Ellen refused to allow herself to be pulled into one of the circles. She withdrew to the edge of the throng and gazed about the room, deciding where would be the most conspicuous place for her to make her disclosure. Just in front of the fireplace would be best, she thought, and she took her way there slowly, sat down on a bench and watched the dancers, waiting her time.

Randall and Margery came in together, Margery in a white dress of some thin floating material that reminded Ellen of the mists that gathered on Ardmory after the sun went down. She was leaning on Randall's arm, smiling up into his eyes. Randall was not smiling. His dark broadcloth coat made his face look paler than it had the morning he returned from Edinburgh, and that was pale enough. He had his hand over Margery's, and stood as close to her as he could without an actual embrace. He looked devoted, but he did not look happy. One of the circles opened to admit them. Then the music changed. Over the sound of his own fiddle, Ewen Gow lifted his full, rich voice.

> *"Green sleeves and pudding pies,*
> *Tell me where my mistress lies,*
> *And I'll be with her before she rise—*
> *Fiddle and a' together."*

Soon everyone was singing.

Then the dance formation broke up, and folk began drifting back to the replenished table. Suddenly at a sign from the laird, Johnny blew one terrible wailing blast on the pipes and let them grow still. Talking and laughing stopped, and Rona lifted his voice in the silent hall.

"Friends, I think ye're all supplied now, with cup in hand, and I ask ye to drink to the marriage o' my daughter, Margery, to Randall Woodbury o' Hampton Falls!"

Ellen crouched tensely by the fire and watched Randall and Margery step forth and stand together, smiling all about them at the rush of cheers, the glasses lifted high.

It was Ellen's moment now. She jumped to her feet and slipped her belt so that it circled below her waist rather than above, catching the fabric of her dress in a way that made her condition plain. Then she gave a shrill, hysteric cry.

"I canna' endure it! I can endure no more!"

Sure now that all eyes had observed her, she crumpled down on the bench again. All heads turned her way, but there rose no sound except for a muffled gasp here and there. Margery was the first who spoke.

"Is it the sight, Ellen?" she cried, making her way swiftly through the crowd to the cattle maid's side, with Randall and her father close behind her.

"No," moaned Ellen, stumbling to her feet again so everyone could see her swollen body. " 'Tis no the sight! 'Tis as I said, I'll endure no more!"

"I'll talk to ye in private, girl," said Rona sharply. "Get to my study! Ye mar the feasting!"

Ellen stared boldly back at him. "No," she said. "I'll no be thrust aside, sir. I been wronged, as all can see, and it'll no be righted in your study. Ye didna' do the harm, and ye canna' set it straight."

Randall, she noted with satisfaction, had turned as white as Margery's gown.

The laird made a sputtering noise like a wet flame, and all the fine guests and the people of Rona waited, hushed and still.

Margery spoke again, tremulously.

"Yes, you have been wronged, Ellen, and whoever has done it shall set the matter right. I promise you that my father shall see he sets the matter right. But now—will you not drink to my wedding with the others?"

"No, I willna' drink to your wedding," shrilled Ellen, "when 'tis myself, not ye, should be bride to him—" and she mimicked Rona, "to Randall Woodbury o' Hampton Falls."

Margery was white now, and her eyes widened and stared out of her tense face. It was as if the room was empty of all others, and only the two girls there.

"Are you telling me that Randall—? Are you saying that he—?"

"Yes, it was he." Ellen bent her head and began to weep into her handkerchief. Stealing a quick glance over the edge of it, she watched Margery turn a stricken look toward Randall. The look on his face caused the laird's daughter to put her hand before her eyes. Ellen could see her mother, too, horror plain on her face, still standing with Leitis by the kitchen door. Kenneth loomed tall in the midst of the crowd, and necks were thrust out like those of silly, staring geese all about him. Kenneth looked as if he would like to take her in his hands and break her in two, and she was grateful for all the craning, curious folk between them.

Suddenly she heard Margery's voice lift again.

"I bid you all good night," said the laird's daughter steadily. "There will be no more songs and feasting."

Then Ellen heard the tap of Margery's silver slipper heels and raised her head. She watched the girl walk proudly from the room. Straight up the staircase went Margery, not once looking back at the disordered scene behind her.

Then Rona lifted his own voice.

"Ye heard my daughter!"

He said no more, but he had no need to. People were hastening away now, even the strangers in their fine clothes, whose boats were doubtless waiting. It took only a few moments to clear the hall and leave the three of them alone.

When Rona spoke again, his voice was low, but with a note of rising storm in it.

"Why did ye no give her the lie, lad? Give her the lie in front o' my daughter?"

"I do not know—if it be a lie," said Randall harshly, staring at a tapestry on the far wall.

"It could be your bairn she's carrying?"

"It could be."

Ellen stood sniveling, but they talked on as if she were not there, with such a terrible intensity in their manner that she dared not interrupt them.

Rona's voice was full of stony anger as he turned on the younger man.

"So ye gi'ed yourself to that one, and shamed my lass before her people?"

"'Tis no shame to your lass, sir," said Randall Woodbury. "'Tis I that am shameful. I been a knave and a fool, and I ought to shoot myself in the head for it."

Suddenly the stiffness of anger left the laird, and his face turned gray, and he looked tired, and old, and shaky.

"Dinna' talk o' shooting! Some would say I should be the one to talk o' shooting—or beat ye from my house—but naught would be helped by it. 'Twould no ease my lassie's pain, and that's all I care for. I thought I warned ye o' Ellen, but I didna' make it strong enough. No, ye're not a knave or a fool, but ye're a bitter bad judge o' women, lad."

XXI

War, Red War

SHE HAD allowed herself seven days—one day more than it had taken God to make the world. All that while she sat in her room with its white curtains blowing in the fresh wind that came up from the sea, the scent of early summer flowers rising from the terrace below. She had allowed no one to come near her but Leitis with a tray and a whispered murmur, "Oh dearie, dear!" Not her father, nor Kenneth, nor Andra. No one else had tried to come. At first she had lain on her bed weeping till her eyes were so washed with tears that the whole world looked to be the color of nothing at all. After a while she had ceased to weep, and sat there watching the days move westward over the sea and the daisy fields, the purple heather springing on the hill. At the end of seven days, she told herself repeatedly, she must go downstairs, the old, smiling Margery they would all recognize. Perhaps it might take longer than that to compose herself, but until she had done it, she would not go.

In the first night of weeping she had imagined terrible things while the very darkness seemed to hurt her like a thorny cloak, wrapping all her body, from which she could not twist away. Randall and her father were quarreling; Randall had taken a boat for America; Randall would marry Ellen out of hand. None of these things had come to pass. She knew, for she had asked Leitis while the old woman hovered about, urging her to take broth that tasted like bog water and bread that rasped her throat like sawdust when she tried to force it down. All that first night while she wept, she learned later, the two men, having finally got rid of Ellen, remained shut up in her father's study. Soon after daylight they had sent Leitis to fetch Andra, and she quickly joined them there, but nobody knew what went on. Only gradually, from words overheard as she served hot dishes at the table, did Leitis come by the bits of information she carried dolefully upstairs. Randall, it seemed, had made no attempt to deny Ellen's charges. He would provide for her and for the child, he said, but he meant to go at once to Edinburgh, and he would not take her there, he would never take her home. Ellen conveyed the message through her mother that she had sent off a note to Master Riddoch, laying her case before the Kirk. Then the two men at Rhinn House spent another sleepless night, deciding what to do. Should Randall leave immediately and provide for Ellen through the laird's good offices, or should he stay till the minister came and face the matter out? Randall had decided to stay.

Margery could not understand his decision, nor much that had led up to it. What had gone on between him and Ellen, she wondered, except the irrevocable thing? Had he taken Ellen with love, or only with desire? If it were with desire, she could understand. Not understand, perhaps, but forgive. After all, she had grown up in Paris. She had seen much evidence before this of the besetting weakness of man. But if he had taken Ellen with love! And Ellen—what had been her part in the matter? Margery thought she knew, but she tried to give the cattle maid the benefit of honest doubt, and failed therein. Why had Ellen chosen to make her outcry in public, to shame her lover and her friend before all? She remembered how the girl had stood there by the great hearth, triumphant in her disgrace.

Well it had happened, and it was over, she thought, and what would become of them now? Randall said he would not marry Ellen, but of that Margery could not feel sure. She had seen the power of the Kirk before, and she knew what Master Riddoch would say. Marry Ellen or not, he could not marry her, Margery. Not while he had marred their betrothal by getting another girl with child! Her world would not accept it, and neither would she. But did he still want to marry her? Had he ever wanted to marry her? He had not come to comfort her, but then, she had not expected him to come. And for herself, how did she feel? In a week's time she could be in Spain or France, on her way to the Stuarts in Rome. Her father would take her abroad, if she asked him, she knew. But a MacNeill of Barra could not run away.

So her mind moved circle-wise in its own misery until the eighth morning. Then she rose, combed her hair in curls, put on a sea-shell colored dress and went downstairs to the hall. Kenneth and Randall sat facing each other across a platter of bacon and eggs on the wide table. She walked steadily toward them over the stone floor, just as if the sky had not fallen and the whole world dissolved away, her head up and her eyes smiling.

"Good morning," she said.

But neither of them answered her, looked her way, or seemed to know she was there. She was about to speak again and then checked herself, staring at the two men, realizing suddenly that they crouched there like dogs ready to spring forward in savage encounter. Kenneth's head and shoulders jutted ahead of his body, and Randall sat straight, one fist doubled and resting lightly in the palm of the other hand, his eyes watchful. Surprisingly, he was the first to speak.

"Go on, say it," he snapped. "You've looked it at me all the week. Say I'm a bastard, and have done!"

Kenneth started to answer him, choked on his own emotion, cleared his throat, and tried it over.

"Ye've gone further," he growled, "than can be eased wi' a bit o' name calling."

"What do you want—pistols at fifty paces?" demanded Randall. His voice had a jeering quality.

"I want naught but these," said Kenneth heavily, looking down at his thick hands clenched before him on the table.

Randall rose and shoved his chair away. "On the headland, I suppose? And one of us to come back before breakfast gets cold? Only one of us!"

"The headland's a braw choice," said Kenneth harshly.

Randall shrugged his shoulders and turned toward the door. Margery gave a little gasp, the only sound she was able to make just then, but nobody heard her. She could see in her mind the headland, and far below it the gray tides flooding up from Ireland, pounding on the sharp and cruel stones. She tried again, but she could not utter a sound. How was it that two men should go out to fight to the death on such a morning, out of a room bright with sunlight, full of the homely smells of peat smoke and crisp bacon!

Randall turned suddenly. "Kenneth, lad," he said, in quiet tones, but with no tremor or hint of weakness, "maybe, before we go—'tis best we settle what we're fighting over. For I swear, I do not know."

Kenneth's eyes stared fiercely from beneath their craggy brows. "If ye dinna' know what ye're fighting for, I'll show ye soon."

"Oh I know what I'm fighting for. I'm fighting to save my skin," said Randall evenly, "because I've a fondness for it. But what are you fighting for, sir?"

"I be fighting because ye come here and wronged a lassie," rumbled the Highlander.

"Aye, I've done that, God help me. But not a lass that was anything to Kenneth Crary. Ellen's not your sweetheart or your sister. Are you out to defend the honor of every maid in Scotland?"

Kenneth's cheeks turned a dark red. He bent his glance downward, not meeting Randall's eyes, and thrust his clenched fists into the pockets of his tartan breeches.

"She's a lass o' the clachan," he muttered. "There's no man in her household to make ye pay for what ye done."

"She's a tenant of the Laird of Rona," answered Randall smoothly. "The laird takes care of his tenants. He will see she's paid her due. But I'm surprised at you, sir. 'Twas Miss Margery you were wooing, and so was I, and now I've disqualified myself by my own folly and left you a free field there. You should be drinking me a toast and giving me the high hand of gratitude. I cannot see why you want to fight."

Kenneth muttered deep in his throat. Then he lunged forward. "By God, I'll fight when I choose, with no explaining," he blustered.

Randall lowered one shoulder and thrust it forward, put his fists up.

"Kenneth!" Margery heard herself crying sharply. "Kenneth—why are you fighting? You will tell me!"

The schoolmaster stopped then, his boot soles grating on the stone floor, and swung sharply round.

"Kenneth," she said calmly, staring into his distorted face and angry blue eyes, "I know why you are fighting." Suddenly, inevitably she did know, wondered that she had not known before, the way things were with him. She was but dimly aware of Randall watching in the background. Her attention was all for the other man, the man who had insisted so stubbornly that she take him for her husband. He made a gruff sound of surprise and dismay, but she kept relentlessly on.

"You are fighting Randall for what he did to Ellen, because it is Ellen you love. You hate him so because—"

"I hate him because he come here strutting and thinking to have the pair o' ye," muttered the Highlander. "That he would ha' done, had he no cooked his own goose, if Ellen hadna' been so smart to trip him, had—"

"Strutting and thinking to have the pair of us!" cried Margery, her own anger flaring. "And who's to say ye did not think to do the same? Will you tell me that you love me and not Ellen, Kenneth Crary? Will you look me in the eye and tell me so?"

Kenneth tried. She watched him, suffering for him, suffering almost as much as he; watched the convulsive movements in his throat as he swallowed, watched his tongue wetting his stiff lips, his eyes fixed on her, the fire in them slowly dying into dull shade.

After a brief struggle he hung his head. "I canna' lie to ye, lass," he whispered painfully, "I ha' loved Ellen long, God pity me!" He stumbled from the room as if his bones were hardly able to carry his limp flesh away.

Margery stood staring at Randall.

"Where—where is Father?" she asked him faintly.

"He's gone down to fetch the post from Tam MacVean," said Randall steadily. "How do you feel, Margery? I'm sorry you had to come on us fighting so. I guess 'tis the end of Schoolmaster. You were right in all you said to him. But I wonder now—what you will say to me—"

"Randall—I—I want you to know—that I am not angry. I do not think it was your fault. It was—something that came to be."

Still she could not look at him. She heard his voice replying, tightly controlled, but she could sense the hurt and despair in it.

"I am glad you are not angry. You have a right to be so."

"No. No, I do not have a right. Did it happen after—you were promised to me?"

"No. It was before that. And it was only the once. You must believe it was only the once, Margery."

The dreadful stiffness had gone out of his voice, and there was only pleading there.

"If you say it was only the once, I will believe it was that. Have you—" and then she looked at him and smiled weakly, and saw him smiling weakly back "—have you no excuse, Randall? Most men would have an excuse, I think."

"None but the excuse of being a fool. Will you take that, Margery?"

"Yes, I will take that," she said.

They were staring at each other now, deeply and somberly, and all smiles gone. She had accepted his word, but the acceptance did not put them back on the old footing again. Both of them tacitly understood that could never be.

"I could say that Ellen tempted me," he went on. "But then, I have wronged Ellen more than the one way. I went to her as her doctor. It was as that I sought her out. And where did my healing lead?"

"It led to ill for both of you," said Margery. "For all of us—" she caught her breath.

"Margery, I broke a great oath when I went in to her—a greater oath than my pledge to you. An oath which is held among doctors to be the greatest that any man has taken."

The anguish in his voice sounded more terrible to her because of his iron control over it. But she was bewildered, frightened. What was to come now?

"Is there a greater oath than a man's pledge to a woman?"

"Yes. There is a greater oath than that. I swore the oath of the physician. I swore by Health and All-heal! I swore by Apollo!"

"Why should you swear by Apollo? He was a god of the old heathen Greeks. We swear by the Bible, when we swear."

His eyes smiled at her, but his mouth remained a hard line.

"And you were the one who held fast by old time and told me I was a new man from a new country and could not understand tradition. I agreed with you then, but I had forgotten. Before the MacNeills came out of Scythia—if it was there they came from—we doctors swore by Apollo—as we still swear!"

After a moment she went on, speaking brokenly. "So—what is this great oath you swore by Apollo? What is it to you and Ellen and me?"

"I swore to lead my life in purity and holiness and so practice my art. To abstain from the seduction of any female that was a patient of mine. Twice I have sworn it. And you see how well I have done! Margery, I am no fit doctor! I shall never practice medicine again!"

"That hurts you," she said wonderingly, her eyes fixed upon him. "Of course it would. But it hurts you more than losing me, I think. I shall never understand the ways of a man."

"Margery," he said, with a gentleness in his voice that was almost a caress, "you understand so much when you admit you do not understand them."

She clasped her hands twisting the fingers in and out nervously. There was so much to be said, and at any moment Kenneth and her father might come up the hill.

"Will it not—make it all right for you to be a doctor—if you marry Ellen? Will you be forgiven for breaking your oath then?"

"I shall not marry Ellen," he said stonily.

"Why?"

"I do not love her. She does not love me. There was between us—only—such as I would not speak of. I was not the first—to come to her so. If, as your father thinks, she is common—! No, I cannot marry Ellen. But there is the child. How can I abandon my child—if it be my child—Margery? When I have none and never will have, now?"

"Why can you not father a child later on? You will find some other woman to wed when this is all past and blown by."

"You think I would want another woman—after knowing you?"

"You wanted Ellen—after knowing me."

"No, I did not want Ellen. I wanted love from a woman. But I waited too long—I waited too long to be sure. It was not Ellen, I think. It was not I. It was the devils in us that had their way."

Oh, thought Margery feeling herself almost dissolve with anguish, if you wanted love from a woman, why did you not come to me, my dear, my dear! But he had come to her, in a sense, when he asked her to marry him, and she had chosen to wait for guests and gifts and a fine wedding in Carruber's Close at Midsummer! Oh it was her fault as much as his! And then, suddenly, as a stricken swimmer will catch at what-

ever floats on the sea, her mind caught at the significance of a thing
that he had said.

"You think there might be a doubt—? That it might not be your
child?"

He answered bitterly. "It would be too great a favor—to hope that it
is not mine. For that, I could pray to Apollo, if I had not foresworn
him. It is not a Christian's prayer. I do not know. I shall watch carefully
the time the child is born. Perhaps Ellen will give it to me for money.
Your father thinks she will. I have not heard of her courting with any
other man."

"Neither have I."

She heard the scrape of her father's boots and the click of the latch
as he came in with a sheaf of letters in his hand. He looked at her anxiously and she managed to smile at him.

"Do ye feel better, lass? Ye're pale yet," was all he said to her.

Then he handed the first letter to Randall, tore open the second, and
began to read it with gruff noises of dismay.

"'Tis from Master Riddoch. He warns me to prepare to assemble
those residing on my policy. He is coming among us shortly to hold
Kirk Session to discipline one Ellen Deveron and one Randall Woodbury
for fornication and the begetting of a bastard bairn. He warns me to
prepare—"

Randall turned white. Margery struggled with herself to try to comfort him. There was no anger in her now, not even against Ellen, only
weariness and dull, heavy pain.

"Randall," she said. "You need not endure it. Why do you not go
away?"

He shook his head, tearing his own letter slowly open with his tense
brown fingers. "No," he said. "I thought to do so. 'Twould be easy to do.
But it's time to stand my ground and take a man's punishment if I have
to. In all this business, I been little enough a man."

"He will make you marry Ellen, Randall."

Randall shook his head. "No, he cannot make me do that," he said,
and unfolded his letter on the table.

Margery watched him as he read, with the thought in her mind that,
like her father's, this letter, too, must have come from the minister. It
was doubtless a summons to appear for Kirk discipline. He read it slowly
without lifting his eyes.

"By God, they've done it," he muttered. "I didn't think they would,
but they have. It'll be hell to pay and no brimstone ready now."

He turned to the beginning and read it through again. Then he
straightened up and threw his head back. All the shame and bitterness

seemed to have dropped away from him like a cloak let fall. His eyes lighted, and there was a hard little smile on his mouth.

"Randall," she faltered, "what is it? Tell me! There's a difference on you now!"

"A difference? Yes."

He stared at her with a remote look in his eyes that told her he was already up and gone. Then he held the letter out. "Read it," he said grimly, "read it out loud. Your father better know."

Margery took the letter in a trembling hand.

"Dear Son," she read with a strained voice that did not sound like her own. "It has fallen out as I feared, and blood been spilled at last. The British shot eight men this week on Lexington Green. There was further fighting in Concord, and how many was killed or wounded, we do not know. When Captain Burnham heard of it, he ordered the drumbeat to call the town company, gave the men something to drink, and started for there, thinking he might be needed. Marched that day to Ipswich, twenty miles in an afternoon. Later we heard he and his men were killed, but it was not so. Rumors fly all about us like hornets now. Word came to Newburyport that the town was threatened, and folk went fleeing across the countryside so madly I doubt they have yet got home. It seems certain we will go to the aid of Massachusetts, whether with men as well as arms, I do not know. I have been to meetings in Portsmouth and Exeter, and am told that the men in the back country are all aflame and companies forming there. I am tempted to say there is War in America, but all I can say in truth is that the King's troops have fired upon and killed our men. If my son were such as needed to be told, I would tell him he is wanted here at home—"

There was more, but she did not read it. She let the paper fall from her grasp and lie unheeded on the floor. After a moment Randall picked it up and crumpled it in his right hand. Her father cleared his throat. In the silence after, she heard the tall clock striking in the hall—nine o'clock of a bright June day.

"Ye're going home?" her father was asking.

Randall nodded grimly. "Can you see," he asked, "how I could do another thing?"

The laird shook his head. "No. There be few young men in your time or any other gets out of going to a war. It's expected of ye."

Randall's lips curved in a hard smile. "Well, Aristotle said war is the only school for the surgeon, though I've heard he himself didn't know a vein from an artery." Then the harshness went out of his voice, and he spoke as evenly as if he were asking the time of day.

"When will the preacher be here? Did his letter tell you?"

Rona unfolded the page again.

"Thursday," he said, after consulting it for a moment. "He says he'll be here Thursday, given a fair wind and a calm sea."

Randall nodded. "I'll stay then, and hear what he's got to say to me. And then I'll be off. I won't use this as an excuse to hide behind. I've done wrong, here, and I'll face it out like a man. I'll let him shame me. I'll sit on a cutty stool and stand up in a white sheet before the congregation—if that's what he wants. I'll give her everything he tells me—except marriage. And then—I'll be away."

"Randall," faltered Margery, "you're going home to America?"

"I'm halfway there now," he said, looking straight at her, and there was no tenderness in his eyes. "You read it. There's blood been spilled. They've killed our men."

Margery turned and walked blindly from the room. She was thinking what her father had once said of Culloden—that there was more died there than the men who fell. More than the eight American lads, she thought brokenly, had likely lost life and hope and future by that blow on Lexington Green.

XXII

When the Pot Boils

S<small>HE</small> <small>THOUGHT</small> it was the tramp of marching feet when she first wakened enough to hear it, but as sleep fell away and the smoke-blackened walls of her cottage stood out clear, she knew it for the beat of the northeast rain. Andra Deveron sighed and turned on her pallet so she could see only the wall beside her. She was not yet ready to rise and prepare breakfast, not ready to face her daughter Ellen on Ellen's great day. The bedraggled hens roosting on the beams at the far end of the room began to cluck sleepily, and the smell of herrings and peat smoke hung in the gray air, the smell of dank woolen, and wet shoe leather, and mildewed clay. For four days now the folk of Ballyrhinn had endured the slow, dreadful monotony of a summer rain. No great winds or tempests, only a gray mist on the hilltops, a flooding of the burn, a flat, slate-colored sea before their doors, and the constant tap and drip on the roofs over them. 'Twas enough to drive a man mad, said old Johnny Dweeney, and played slow and mournful on his bagpipes to shut the sound away. 'Twas the tears of heaven for all the season's dead, said Janet Gillander, packing her few trinkets, for she would soon be going away to take service in Dunvegan, since she could not bear the Isle of Rona any more with Colin buried on the hill. Most folk had grumbled about this untoward weather for the first day of it, and stayed indoors, hoping that dawn would break with a clear sky, but Andra had heard whispers among them last night that this must be a sign and an omen, that this was no common rain.

To her it was only a vague annoyance. She felt she had passed beyond feeling anything more. She lay there in the cold room, in the damp bed, and thought of that night in Rona's study when she had faced the two men. She had expected to find the sword's point between them when they had summoned her there, but instead they had stood together like father and son.

She had spoken only to Rona, not being able to take a second look at the suffering in the young doctor's eyes, and Rona, only, had spoken with her.

"Old friend," he told her gruffly, "we're in woeful trouble. Your lass has dinged my daughter down."

Andra replied as best she could, there being little to say.

"Nobody could do that," she said. "Nobody could dishonor Miss Margery. But she has been hurt, and I would give of my flesh and blood if it were not so."

" 'Twas your flesh and blood did the business," he told her bluntly. "Do ye ken if it be Randall's or no? What moneys do ye ask?"

"I do not know whose it be," she answered firmly. "Ellen has walked with more than one, but I do not know how far she has walked with any man. I will name no names," and she thought of Kenneth. "What I do not know, I will not say. We want no money from either of you."

"Ellen will want money," said Rona harshly.

Andra felt her face turn hot to the very line of her hair.

"If she asks money, I will beat her," she said. "I will take her away from here. But she is asking a worse thing, and I cannot tell her nay."

"What is she asking?"

"She is up in the schoolroom even now, where there are quills and paper. She is writing to Master Riddoch to come here that she may be purged of her sin before the Kirk. That will mean doctor lad, too, must stand—"

Andra heard Ellen turn in her bed and gave a long sigh. Her thoughts shifted from that night more than a week ago, seemed to walk slowly back through gray veils of rain. Ellen had indeed written to the minister, and he had sent word to the laird of his coming amongst them to settle the matter. This was the appointed day.

She turned her own head, raised up on the pillow, and looked across the room at her daughter. There in the thin, shut face lying in its tawny disordered hair, she seemed to see her own youth, her own sin. She was back in Belfast, the ugly town on the beautiful site, crossing the long arm of the sea on the bridge with its twenty arches, walking along the mall between the foul ditch and the fine old trees—walking always with a lad. Walking out to the bleach fields and the daisy fields beyond. "I will name no names," she had told Rona. In her own time, she had not always known the name. But now, in her mind, she felt sure that Ellen knew.

She started from her bed and cried out, "Ellen! Waken and tell the truth! Tell the truth before all, today!"

Ellen slowly opened her eyes, rubbed the sleep from them and sat up, shivering, pulling the blankets round her.

"What are ye yellyhooing for now?" she demanded. "Have a vision, if ye will! Have a hundred visions! There's none cares what ye see!"

Andra began to dress herself, but there was hot anger under her calm. "Ellen," she went on, "you've trifled with the sight. It may be evil or good, but 'tis put upon us from another world, and we must bear it as we can. You have pretended it and mocked me. I'll forgive you even that. But not another thing."

"What will ye not forgive me?" asked Ellen, yawning and reaching for the fish spine to comb her hair.

"You have come between two that love. That's sin enough if you do it in truth—and if you lie—"

"I told no lies," said Ellen smugly. "He has lain with me. He admitted to it. He thinks to go free, but Master Riddoch will no countenance sin."

Andra put the kettle to boil, flung in barley and a handful of leaks and kale.

"I suppose you think Master Riddoch will make him wed you," she taunted. "I saw the lad's face when you cried out against him. I saw it afterward. I know he'd rather die."

Ellen smiled and reached for her one silken thing, for Margery's cast-off dress. "He'll find it none so ill," she said. "It'll go no worse in the bed of marriage than it went in Puffin Town."

"Oh, Ellen," said Andra wearily, "there were other lads. And he belonged to her! Why could you no have let him alone?"

"Aye, there's other lads," said Ellen, "but none full of gold from America. Did ye starch my white kerchief, Mother? 'Twill look well at the neck of this gown."

In mid-morning they wrapped their heavy cloaks around them and walked up through the clachan, still in the drumming rain. The storm mist hid Caldune, and the sea mist hid Ardmory, but the sea and the Long Island were as sharp as on any clear, frosty day. Sails flecked the water here and there, all driving toward the island, and Iver Gall told them the reason, coming out of his house with his wife beside him as they passed by.

" 'Tis all through the isles," he informed them, waving his hand at the unwonted traffic on the flood tide, "in Barvas Parish and beyond. The scandal o' what's happened here has gone forth, and all as can get a boat to bear them will be here to see."

"But how can there be Kirk Session," demanded Lavan as they toiled over the sodden grass and wet clay, "with only Minister to preside and no elder to counsel him in all?"

Iver shook his head gloomily. "Aye, Lavan, all can see ye're trying for a way to let the lad off—" he looked at Ellen, but she smiled coldly and walked straight ahead, "—and I dinna' blame ye, but 'tis no easy to do. Rona be the lone man o' elder's power here, and he canna' sit in session when it touches so close to his own. 'Twill be all Master Riddoch's say."

In silence they walked on. It was less than a mile to Rhinn House, but it seemed to Andra as if she had been toiling upward forever in the rain. The cart track was thronged, for not a soul in Ballyrhinn had stayed at home, save those with helpless bairns to mind, and once when she turned her head, she could see strangers crowding out of their boats on the wet, weedy shore.

"Oh, why cannot the power come to me when I would have it?" she cried in her heart, and then looked about, fearing that she had cried aloud, but it was only the gulls screaming above the sand. "I have never made a mock of the sight, never cursed it, or sold it, or used it for my own ends. I have taken it when it came! But now—!"

"Oh God, send me a sight of truth," she cried, and it was as if a voice said within her, no stranger voice, but part of herself, "What would you see, Andra?" And she made the desperate answer, "How do I know what I would see?"

She looked intently ahead of her, her eyes wide, her gaze fixed, as old taischers had told her she must do when she willed a vision to come. But she saw only the wet grass and dripping trees, and the soaked, straggling crofters going towards Rhinn House through pools of water standing on the lawn. Borne along in their midst, now close to Ellen, now losing sight of her, she entered the hall, no longer brave with feasting and lighted torches, set for no festive season. A fire blazed on the hearth, but there was no other lighting save the narrow windows that let in the gray day. All the furniture had been removed, except for the high-backed chairs and a lectern at one side. In the first chair sat the Laird of Rona, his head up, staring straight ahead, acknowledging none of his friends and tenantry. By his side sat Margery in a somber dress, a thin smile on lips that were a little too red. Nanny Dweeney caught Andra's arm.

"Och, who'd ha' thought the poor lass would be here? There's no need! Where be he?"

Andra looked around for Randall and saw him standing, bareheaded, in a black-coat, in the kitchen doorway, between Leitis and Sim. There was no announcement, no sort of greeting or any sign. The laird and his daughter sat wooden-stiff in their chairs, and those who had come out of curiosity, or pity, or good will, stood about the cleared space of the great hall. Time went, and sometimes they chatted, and some moved restlessly from group to group, and then there would be a hush and everything go still, and in the stillness could be heard the rain, beating steadily on the slate tiles of the roof overhead.

Once Ellen came and stood by her mother's side, and spoke impatiently. "I'll go mad if the rain doesna' stop," she said.

Andra stared at her.

"Where is Master Riddoch? Has he come?"

"No. They be waiting him," Ellen twitched her skirts and looked toward the door. "If I'd ha' known 'twould ha' taken this long, I'd eaten more barley broth. They've no put out for us. Not so much as a cup of wine."

" 'Tis little they have to drink to," Andra said.

"They'll have less," retorted Ellen, and flounced off.

Time went, and the gray day was turning to black beyond the long windows, and Master Riddoch had not come.

Andra could feel a restlessness in the crowd about her, like the restlessness of cattle in the byre before a thunderstorm. They were awaiting the expected, the arrival of the minister, and the Kirk had never failed them before. Tam MacVean, they knew, would take no account of the downpour. There was a fair wind, and no fog, and nothing to keep a man from sailing over from Stornaway. The minister had promised. But the minister did not come. And still, overhead, went on the terrible, ceaseless throbbing of the rain.

Now it was Lavan who paused by her side and looked upward. "I'll go mad," she said, "if the rain doesna' stop."

The hush and the tension deepened, and the sky grew ever more dark outside. Once Andra thought she saw a lightning flash, but she could not be sure, and there was no burst of thunder, no change in the relentless pulse of the rain. She looked at Margery, all stiff and waxen, and thought that never outside a coffin had she seen a girl look so. Then her eyes sought out her own daughter. Ellen was not waxen. She looked restless and impatient, but her cheeks wore a coarse bloom.

"She's mine, I bore her. But she has done this evil thing! But she's mine, I bore her." The two thoughts were like two enemies with swords pursuing each other round and round inside her mind, and she could not tell which one had the victory, which one mattered more.

Nanny's lean fingers clutched her sleeve. "Andra, lass, my legs can no more bear me. I be tiring. Lead me to the fireside and ease me down."

Looking around her, Andra saw Ewen Gow. "Ewen," she called softly, "go and ask Sim for a stool for Nanny, and bring it to the fire."

He nodded and moved away. Andra helped the old woman to the hearth and stood there, supporting her with one arm. It took Ewen a long time, and the two women waited, close to the blazing logs that had been cut and transported from the coast of Scotland. Andra glanced at them, and found that she could not take her eyes away. "They are Highland pine," she found she was telling herself, "Highland pine, such as I walked under long ago—before ever my sin created sinful flesh and blood."

Suddenly she no longer saw the wide black frame of the hearth, nor the logs, nor the leaping tongues of fire. They were fading, slowly, slowly fading, and mingling into one orange tide that flowed past her, one long curving river of flame.

"In the fire!" she heard a shrill voice screaming. "I see! I see!"

The flame dulled to palest yellow, and then to the warm honey-color of a summer's day.

"I see a summer's day." She found she was telling herself the thing as she saw it. "A summer's day, all blue and gold, with the heather in July colors, lying like a purple shadow on the hill. There is a woman coming—a woman, my daughter. She has a bairn in her arms, a dark-haired bairn! A man stands at the left hand of her, and his hair is dark. It is Schoolmaster!"

Then the summer day swept away from her into the whirling river of flame. Pale at first, and then deeper. Then she was looking again into the hearth at Rhinn House, into the log fire. She put her hand to her eyes. She felt faint and sick, and there was a terrible thirst in her mouth. Surprised, she found she was leaning on old Nanny Dweeney, when but a moment before, Nanny had been leaning on her.

"Ah, lass," the old woman babbled, "I always said the sight was from God, and ye showed it plain. When the pot boils, the scum's cast uppermost! Hark ye to Rona now!"

Slowly, vaguely, and then with swift apprehension and alarm, Andra realized what had come to pass. Spent and shaken, she clutched the old woman's arm.

"Nanny! Did I tell what I saw?"

"Aye, ye told! What better could ye do? Hush ye, lass, so I can hear!"

She turned her head slowly, the way Nanny turned hers, and looked toward the front of the hall. Margery still sat in the carved chair, but now there was color in her face, and she leaned forward, watching her father. Rona was on his feet, and Andra thought she had never seen him stand so tall or call so loud.

"Ellen, lass!" he roared. "And Schoolmaster! Where be ye?"

Nobody answered him. There was no sound, only the endless beat of the rain.

Then half a dozen gasping folk near the front drew apart to left and right, away from Ellen till she stood all alone.

"Ellen Deveron," said Rona sternly, "Ellen, ye ha' lied!"

"No, I ha' na' lied," insisted Ellen weakly. "Ask him?" and she pointed to Randall where he stood holding to each side of the kitchen doorway. "Ask him if he didna' lie with me?"

"We dinna' question that. I put it to ye that when it came about, ye were already with child before."

"No, I wasna', I wasna'," piped Ellen feebly, beginning to cry.

Rona turned in disgust. "Where be the man?"

Then Kenneth loomed in the doorway behind Randall. He muttered something and the American stood aside, slowly, uncertainly, like one who does what he is told, without understanding. Kenneth strode forward, ignoring Rona, and went straight to the girl.

"Ellen," he said, "will ye no tell me the bairn is mine?"

Ellen kept on weeping noisily and paid no attention to him. He did not touch her, only stood by her side, scowling down.

"Andra!" She heard the laird's appeal over the heads of the gaping crowd. "Can ye no unravel this thing? Can ye no tell the meaning of what ye have seen?"

Andra went slowly forward. Again the two thoughts pursued each other round and round a circular tower that grew in the midst of her mind. "She is mine, I bore her! But she has done this evil thing! But I bore her, she is mine!"

When she stood at the front of the hall, she found there was only one way she could speak, one thing to say.

"Laird o' Rona," she said simply, "Comyn Rhinn, my friend. I saw my daughter Ellen with her bairn, the bairn she carries within her now, and that bairn is dark. There is no darkness in her blood. I am as you see, and my people's hair was brown. Her own father was saxon fair— as fair as Randall Woodbury."

It seemed as if the whole crowd was one man drawing a sharp breath. Rona bent forward eagerly.

"But her bairn is dark?" he asked.

"Aye. As dark as Schoolmaster. I saw Schoolmaster at her left hand. All taischers know that if a man stands thus to a woman he loves her and would wed her if she will."

"Ah, lass!" pleaded Kenneth, a look of torment in his dark face, "are ye needing more?"

Ellen had stopped crying. She stood irresolute. Her mother went relentlessly on.

"The bairn will be born when the heather is July high," she turned toward the kitchen door. "When did ye lie with her, Randall, lad? Early enough to get a July bairn?"

"No," he murmured, slowly at first, and then eagerly, like a man who has been like to drown and feels firm land under his feet. "No. It was near December. It was too late for that."

Rona flung out his arms in a wide gesture freeing all.

"Take Schoolmaster or leave him, lass, but get yourself out o' here. Will ye tell the truth before ye go?"

Ellen cowered, weeping again. "Oh forgive me, sir," she pleaded. "It be Schoolmaster's indeed. But Schoolmaster is poor. Ye wouldna' know, but 'tis an ill thing, to be poor. We loved, and I was with child, but I thought the doctor could give it the better life—so I would try—"

"And meanwhilst, Schoolmaster was trying to wed my lass for her dower," said Rona bitterly, but the triumph in his face did not dull away.

"He never loved Margery. He loved me," babbled Ellen, "but we were poor. I thought—in America—"

"Sir," said Rona to Kenneth, "I shallna' tell ye again to take the lass and go."

Andra crept back and sank down on the stool that Ewen had finally brought for Nanny Dweeney. Crouching there, she watched Kenneth lead Ellen away. Sim was bringing in torches, and Rona started calling for whiskey and wine. The men crowded forward to shake Randall's hand. She had not seen Margery go, but she found herself gazing at Margery's empty chair. At that moment the front door swung open, and Master Riddoch burst into the room. His clothes dripped water, his hat was gone, and his gray hair plastered down.

"We was o'erset in a squall," he panted, "and clung to the keel wi' naught but our hands to make way wi'! But I am here as I promised, Kirk Session can begin."

"Have a drap o' whiskey, sir," said Rona happily. "We ha' no need o' Kirk Session now."

Hearing him, Andra was not so sure. She had stood for right and truth and revealed the sight as she saw it, but she had betrayed her child thereby. It would have been a stern choice, had she had to make it, but when she stood before Rona, there was only the one thing she could do. Nevertheless, she would be standing all the rest of her days, she thought, before the Kirk Session of her own heart; never condemned, perhaps, but never absolved and free.

XXIII

This I Learned in Scotland

"DINNA' look so sad, Randall," said Comyn Rhinn as they sat at breakfast over mutton collops and ale. " 'Twould start the tears aflowing from Castle Rock to look at ye. There's a cure for everything but stark dead."

"By God, sir, I can almost believe it, after the way things have fallen out," said Randall, draining his glass. "I thought for a while I was a done man, but it all came clear. If I've not got the wife I want, I've not got a wife I don't want, so things be none so bad."

He must try, he thought, to keep Rona from seeing how bad things really were. The laird looked at him keenly.

"Ye've no heard from Madge? She's sent no word down by Leitis, given no sign?"

"No."

"I thought she might, before ye went away."

"She'd better be quick then. In half an hour I'm meeting Tam. The packet sails a little past noon."

"Ye'll not go to her then?"

"How could I go to her, after I've used her so?"

"Aye, the lass has her pride, and so have ye."

"I've little to be proud of now."

"And if ye've little to be proud of, ye've no great cause to be ashamed, either. Ye was hot and young and easy gulled, and ye was seven ways a fool—but ye played it like a man."

Randall stood up. "I'd like those words on my gravestone, sir, when the time comes for that," he said with a smile. "Will you walk to the dock with me?"

Together they left Rhinn House in the soft gray misty day. Randall was empty-handed, for his sea chest with the small deerskin chest inside had already been sent ahead of him to Skye, where he could take ship for home. It had been a week since Andra had saved him from Kirk Session, saved him from her own flesh and blood. He had talked with Andra since, tried to thank her, but they had been embarrassed and constrained with each other, and he had given up, leaving little said. He had not talked with Margery. Again she had retreated to her room and stayed there, and sent no message down. Every ship that put in for fresh meat or drinking water brought stories of the threatened war with America. There was nothing now to hold him here, and even if there had been, he would still have had to go.

"We'll miss ye, lad," Rona was saying, as they strode down the hill, "but ye've taught Andra much that will help us—unless she herself should soon be gone."

"Andra? Is she going away?"

He knew well that Andra was not island bred, but she seemed as much a part of the place as its very turf and stone.

"Aye. With Ellen gone, she'll be free as she hasna' been in twenty years. She says she has not yet thought about it, but it may be she herself will go back to the place where she was young—to see if there still be aught of the old times there."

Randall felt his face turn hot and a tightening in his throat.

"And where has Ellen gone?" he asked.

"She's at home yet, but she'll soon be away. She's to marry School-master, ye know."

"I thought she might. I've no doubt they were lovers before she ever heard of me."

Rona nodded. "That they were, lad. Kenneth came to my study and asked forgiveness o' me. He told me the whole thing plain. When he came here he did at once the uncommon thing some lads do."

Rona paused, so Randall put the question. "What was that?" he asked.

Both men slowed their steps so as not to reach the clachan too soon. They had much to say, going down that hill.

"He saw two lasses together, and he fell in love with her that was poor and plain, rather than her that was rich and fair. The poor lass would lie with him, but she wouldna' wed him, wanting money. And so things were. Then between them they raised a plan. He was to wed the rich lass and spend her dower on the lass that was poor. And ye call yourself a knave! Why he's a shame to all Scotland, but he's run himself aground and foundered, and what could I do?"

"I'll bet I know what you did," said Randall. "I'll bet you made a place for him somewhere so he could take Ellen away."

The laird nodded. "Not with my factor. I wouldna' have him in my sight no more, but I'm sending him to Glasgow with letters to friends o' mine in the trade there. I writ the letters strong. He'll find a place. For all his knavery, I canna' hate the lad, for 'tis my belief Ellen was most at fault. Ye have both used my lass ill, but I canna' hate either o' ye."

"I think I know why," said Randall slowly. "I wooed her to her face, and behind her back, I was a fornicator. And Schoolmaster tried worse. But neither of us have wrought her any harm. We never could. Next winter she'll be the belle of Edinburgh, laughing gay, and dancing with better lads than me and Kenneth were."

He believed what he was saying. There was something unbreakable about Margery. She was the supple reed bending, not the oak that snaps in twain.

"Aye. My lass will recover. Quicker than ye, I think. But ye was conspired against, too."

"I?"

"'Twas with intent that Ellen came by the bairn in her. She confessed to Kenneth, and he to me. When she missed her first moon, and knew it was so indeed, then she laid the snare for ye."

"By God, I better get me to a monastery," muttered Randall, "if a woman can make that much a fool of me, I'm not safe in the world any more."

"Ye be going to a war, lad. Ye'll have other things to think of, and ye'll learn."

"I'm not at all sure of it," said Randall gloomily. "Some never do, you know. Sir –" and his eyes lighted with sudden interest, "—how much of this did Andra know?"

Rona looked at him in surprise. "Why Andra knew naught of it, she told me; only that she had seen Kenneth going up Ardmory in the night. Andra would no help Ellen bamboozle ye. Why did ye think Andra would know?"

"Because I still want to find out where the visions come from. I studied them in Ellen—that was what I sought her for, though it turned out so ill. I wonder why Andra saw just what she did see. Do you think it was in her mind somewhere, hid away where even she herself did not realize it—the truth about Ellen and Schoolmaster?"

Rona shook his head and his face darkened.

"Lad, since ye put it to me, I can no more spare your pride. I got to tell ye, ye been fooled still another way."

"Another way?" groaned Randall.

"Aye. Ellen's no taischer. What ye thought ye observed in her, ye didna' observe at all. Ellen ne'er had a vision in her life."

"She never—? Oh, but she did! She must have! How could she know that in America there would be war? It was before the ships had brought the news. There had been no talk of it here. Margery believed in her visions. She said they were true."

"Aye, Madge believed at first. Later, she was none so sure. She caught Ellen in your room once reading a letter. It told all she needed to know. War, red war! Aye, Ellen gave it back to ye the way your father writ it down."

"By God," said Randall, "he did write it down that way!" He stood still, looking at Rona. "And Ellen—she fooled me in all of it? Pretended to be so ill and frightened and sought my help! Answered my questions when I tried to study her! And all the time—she never had a taisch at all?"

"Never a taisch, lad," said Rona cheerfully.

"Well, God pity me for a fool!" said Randall Woodbury.

After a moment they began to move slowly down the hill. When the laird spoke again his tones were stern, but there was a gentleness there.

"Ye can be a bigger fool yet, lad, and that's if ye deny all belief in visions because ye been misled by those that werena' true. Ye come to Scotland to learn o' Wullie Cullen, but I think ye ha' learned more than Wullie ever taught. Ye ha' learned about the shifting ways o' women, and the difference between an old country and a new one; how to cut peat, and pull seaware, and speak a wee bit o' the Gaelic now and then."

"Yes, I learned all that. It's well enough to know."

"Aye, but if ye was to learn only the one thing here, I'd say, let it be this. Learn there be things in this world beyond our understanding, and 'tis best to leave them so and not inquire. And dinna' think two and two will always be four, for it sometimes doesna' work out that way.

"Believe in the mist, lad," and he waved his hand toward the soft grayness that hid the moorlands of Caldune. "A man shouldna' expect the universe to be clear to him like it was matter for bairns in a primer book. Because God has no revealed a thing, is no proof that it canna' be."

They were approaching the water now. Randall heard the lapping of the little waves against the sandy shore and the crooked timbers, heard Tam MacVean hailing him, and saw the small boat with sails hoisted, ready to pull away. He turned and stood for a moment looking up the hill at Margery's windows, and wondered if she were watching there. Oh Margery, Margery, his heart cried. But Margery gave no sign. Margery would let him go, and dance in Edinburgh next year with better lads than he.

He swallowed, and looked miserably about the clachan. The old greyhound ambled down the street, forlorn without the children who used to play with him, the children, crippled, or buried on the hill by the Cursing Stones. The sorrows of his own heart were enough for him, he thought. He could not bear the world's sorrows too.

Rona was gripping his hand. "Good-by. Good-by, lad. A good voyage home, and better weather!"

One moment the two men looked at each other, there on the edge of the ancient island and the even more ancient sea.

"I've no envy for any man on earth except your father, sir," said Comyn Rhinn.

"I'd put no man in his place but you, sir," said Randall Woodbury.

It was a good parting that left nothing more to say.

All afternoon the packet labored across the gray heaving waters of the Minch. Randall flung himself down in a corner of the small crowded cabin and lay there like a heap of old clothes, asleep more than half the time, worn out with emotion, prodded now and then by suspicious passengers who accused him of having taken too much ale. He went ashore at Portree in the foggy dark, made for the nearby tavern, and tumbled into bed after a supper of beefsteak pie and whiskey, only to fall back gratefully into heavy, untroubled sleep.

Next morning the sun shone for a little while, pale and yellow in a watery sky, and he went out and wandered through the narrow lanes and along the docks. He had shipped his sea chest to Captain MacClure, master of the *Bonnetta*, who was to sail to America sometime soon, Tam MacVean had told him, and before noon he located both the man and his vessel. Both appeared to him to be seaworthy, and he arranged passage, in spite of the fact that they were bound for Philadelphia, which would leave him with much ado to get home. But at least, he would be in his own country. He had had his fill of this one, and he did not intend to stay in it any more.

As it was, he had to remain for another week, while the *Bonnetta* was preparing to sail. Sometimes he roamed over the long moors behind the town, up to the hills where he could look west to the Long Island, a blue shadow on the edge of the farthest sea. He did not think of the Isle of Rona lying beyond that, nor of Margery's windows, dark as the towers of all the dead queens in the fairy tales. He had a sea to cross and a war to fight, maybe; all kinds of hell to face, and he did not dare abandon himself to any more pain. There was a grove of firs a little way out on the Dunvegan road, and sometimes he walked there at dusk, and thought how good it would be after a year in the almost treeless islands to go hunting again through the tall woods by Pickpocket Mill.

And without meaning to, only because he could not quite turn his back on their wretchedness, he made friends among the ever-growing group of dispossessed crofters encamped in the furze and bracken beyond the town. These poor folk, single men and women mostly, or married men who had been forced to leave their families behind them, had sold themselves as indentured servants in return for their passage to America, where as everyone knew, there were gowpins of gold and rich free land. They were worn with hard work and gaunt with hunger; ragged, living on tavern offal or chance handfuls of barley and boiled whey, but there was hope in their faces, and courage. They, too, were sailing on the *Bonnetta*, and would be his fellows there. So he treated their aches and illnesses, tried to answer their questions about his country, and wished he had money enough to buy every lass a hot meal and every man a bottle of wine.

His last night in Portree was a starry one, warm and soft, with a shimmering phosphorescence on the sea, and a rolling white mist that always seemed to approach, but never quite reached the shore. He sat late at his gable window in the small stone inn, feeling light and free and empty as a broken eggshell, cautiously looking inside himself to see if there was anything there.

"Ye have learned more in Scotland than Wullie Cullen taught," Rona had told him. He hoped so, for he had not really learned so much from Wullie Cullen. What he learned, he had learned alone. And what was that, he asked himself, there at the top of a strange house in a strange country in the summer night.

He did not want the answer to write down in a journal for his father now. He had not written in the journal for a long time. Maybe that was the first answer. He still loved and revered his father, but he did not rely on him any more, now that he had been out in the world, and succeeded a little, and failed much, and had a taste of being his own man. He had learned what it was to break his physician's oath to Apollo, and seen a whole townful of children die while he stood helpless before them, learned that a doctor is but brittle bail when the hour of reckoning is at hand. And he had meant it when he told Margery he could not practice medicine again, yet he had been treating the crofters all the week and meant to treat them on shipboard, meant to enlist as surgeon to the Army—if there was any army—when he got home.

Women, too, he had learned about. He had put one away forever, and sinned with one, and loved one and lost her, and behaved like a fool with all of them. He had told Margery he would never be in love again, and he meant it. And still—he was not yet going to make firewood out of his blue-green cedar tree. For he knew one thing now if he knew nothing else: that no matter what happened, a man must go on.

He woke to the sound of gray rain on the slates overhead, and a babble of voices in the street below. Looking out he saw the crofters straggling seaward, burdened with knapsacks and knotted shawls. One stout fellow carried a kid under his arm, and another had chickens in a small willow cage. A tall woman with brawny arms bore a flax wheel strapped across her shoulders. Axes and crooked hoes were among them, too. There might be gowpins of gold in America, but even there they would still be poor folk, they would still have to make their way.

He went on board the *Bonnetta* about nine o'clock, and she sailed soon after, going out on a slate-gray tide in a thin gray falling rain. Wrapped in a waterproof cloak of oiled silk he had bought in Edinburgh, Randall stood at the rail and watched the Isle of Skye fade into the mist behind him, felt that with it all Scotland faded too, a country that had never been and never quite could be. "Trust in the mist," Rona had said. Yes, he would trust in the mist, but he would not let himself think too much about it. Some day this would all seem like an unlikely dream he had had one night when he was a young man. Then a thrust of pain went through his heart, and he knew that he would not go so easily free.

Now all land was gone, all the comfort and security of good ground underneath, and the uneasy crofters huddled on the deck about him were beginning to sicken a little, as the *Bonnetta* passed out of the sheltering arms of the sea loch and began the monotonous rolling that would never end till they reached America, six weeks away. The wet sails billowed in the light wind, and the tall masts lost themselves in the grayness overhead. Randall walked to the prow and stood there, a little apart from the others. There would be no time now, for a while, and no season. If there was anything more lost and lone than an island, it was a ship at sea, and if there was anything more lost and lone than a ship at sea, it was a man. He had reached the end of unhappiness, he thought, having gone as far in it as one could go.

And as he thought that, he felt a light touch on his arm.

"Is this the way to Hampton Falls, sir?" asked a blithe voice with the suggestion of hidden laughter in it.

He turned sharply. By his side stood one of the crofter women in a gray duffle gown and stout brogues, her head wrapped in a plaid shawl. But under the shawl he saw a swirl of dark hair, and two hazel eyes, and Margery's sweet smiling mouth. He found there was nothing he could say, except her name.

"Yes, it is Margery," she told him gently. "Did you really think you could go away from me?"

How different the words had sounded, he thought, when he had heard almost the same from Sally Anne.

"You kept away from me," he told her in injured tones, as if the fault were hers, and they both knew it.

"But I thought you would come and find me. I did not think you would go off to America without saying good-by."

"Is that what you came here to say?"

"You know we will never say good-by, Randall."

He took her in his arms and kissed her then, feeling that it was the least that he could do; stood there against the rail, holding her, as the *Bonnetta* began to lift with the swelling pulse of the deep sea.

"How did you get here?" he asked after a few moments. "What did your father say?"

"Shall I tell you how it was? Of course, for you will want to know. I looked from my window and saw you go down the hill, you and my father together, walking so slow. But you were carrying nothing with you. I thought you were but going to the clachan. I did not know you were going away. Then I saw him come back alone."

"And it mattered to you?"

"Oh, Randall, you know that it did! You only want to hear me say it, so I will. I ran downstairs then and asked him, and he told me you were gone."

"You could have followed me at once. You could have caught me in Stornaway."

"Yes, I thought of that. But I did not want to do it. I was afraid you would send me home, so I came to you another way. Tam took me to Portree and booked my passage, and found me lodging in a cottage, and I stayed there out of sight until it was sailing time. I watched you from my window when you came aboard, and I followed and hid among the crofters till we were well at sea. You cannot send me back now."

He looked down at the dark salt waters cleft into white by the plunging keel, the waters going deep fathoms down; he thought of Rona, every moment slipping further behind them in the mist. He smiled down into her eyes.

"No," he said. "I cannot send you home now."

Then he asked again, "What did your father say?"

"He said, 'It's a Whig's country, Madge. Ye want to be sure ye can live in a Whig's country before ye go.' I said, 'If it's a Whig's country, it's time somebody went there to breed up Tories for them, and it might as well be I.'"

He tightened his arm about her, and she stammered a little, and then recovered herself and went on.

"We tried to do it gaily and without tears—the parting, I mean—since we knew it had to be. But I cried at the end of it, to think I must leave him all alone."

"What did he say when you cried?"

"He said not to worry for him. That he was none so old, and maybe he would take him a young lass and raise up another daughter, perhaps a son. I think he said it to cheer me."

Randall was still smiling down at her. "Perhaps he did, but you cannot tell. He's none so old, not much past fifty. Was that all he said?"

"He said a lass who would not leave her father to follow her lad was no fit woman at all."

"So he let you come?"

"Aye," said Margery cheerfully. "He wanted to send me after you in a proper way, with trunks and boxes and a maid to wait on me. But I came like this, with what I could take away in my shawl." She pointed to a dank woolen bundle behind them on the deck.

"It will be enough," said Randall.

She nodded contentedly. "That is what I told him you would say."

For a long time they stood there close together. Holding her in his arms, knowing that he would always hold her so now, in spite of all that had happened, Randall felt he was like a man who had been desperately sick and was beginning to get well. After a while he said, "Margery —does it not matter to you—that Ellen—that I—?"

She shook her head. "We will speak no more of Ellen," she said. "We are going to America, and she was never heard of there. We have left Ellen behind. But there is another thing—"

He looked down at her, puzzled and apprehensive. "Another thing?"

"Yes. You have told me once, but I want to hear it again. You will never steal from my bed after we are wedded and go out calling in the darkness for your Sally Anne?"

"No, I will not call for Sally Anne. I never would have, only I wanted to settle the matter, to find out if her spirit could come back."

Margery nodded wisely. "Yes, such things have been. There is an old Scottish song, 'The Crochallan Air.' It is about a lad who lost his young wife, and afterwards he would sometimes see her at twilight calling the cattle home."

"Do not worry, for if she could have come, she would have done it already. We do not much believe in ghosts in America."

"You have much to learn in America," said Margery with a smile that took the edge off the words as she spoke them.

"So have you," he told her gravely.

"Yes, I know," she answered. "Oh Randall—I never thought—it seemed that everything was broken so—"

She drew closer into his arms and he held her, soothing and kissing her. They were gentle kisses, rather than passionate. There would be passion in him later, when he had recovered a little more from near-disaster, when he felt himself to be a well man. Yes, he thought, they had much to learn in America, and he suddenly remembered one thing.

"Margery," he said, "you are going to marry me, are you not?"

"Yes, I am going to marry you."

"So will you tell me how to make heather ale—now?"

She bit her lip and looked at him with sober eyes. "You want very much to know, Randall?"

"Yes, though I do not know why, for no heather grows in America."

"But it will. I feared lest I should grow homesick for it, so I brought some cuttings in my shawl."

"You must never be homesick. I will not let you be. But tell me! How is it made?"

"Well—then—I suppose—since you want to know so much—it is this way: it is like brewing, but you must take the tops of the young heather —two-thirds heather and one-third malt, and add hops."

He had whipped out a pencil and a tiny ledger, and before she could finish the words, he was writing them down.

"You might change your mind," he said smiling, "and never tell me again. But I have it now."

"Yes," she answered soothingly, "you have it now."

Something about her tone or her quick glance downward made Randall reach out, take her chin in his hand, and hold her face up.

"Margery," he said, "you have not told me all. There is something else that must go in."

She looked straight at him because she had to. "Yes," she said slowly, "there is something else."

"What is it? Tell me?"

But Margery shook her head teasingly and gave him a look that went deeper than the laughter in her eyes.

"I will tell it to my daughter—or my son."

When he took her to him this time, he felt that he was a well man.

"Oh, Margery," he murmured against her hair, "you came to me, and I thought you never would. I'll never let you go away from me again. I'll never go—"

Behind them sounded the clatter of boots and the rasp of a gruff throat being cleared with as much noise as possible. Randall turned quickly about. Captain MacClure stood there, his face red, urgency and embarrassment showing on it plain.

"Excuse me, Doctor," he rumbled, "but there's a crofter lassie fallen in labor, and no midwife by. They've none such among them, and this trip we've fetched no doctor. I had her carried to the hold, and I don't like the look o' things, not at all, I don't. If ye could go down to her now—if 'twould no be interrupting ye—"

Slowly Randall took his arms from about Margery and gazed into her eyes.

"You'd best find yourself a place out of the rain," he said. "I may be a long while."

He turned and left her then, and followed Captain MacClure across the deck and down the ladder to the reeking hold. He had sworn by Apollo.

About the Author

SHIRLEY BARKER, born in Farmington, New Hampshire, was graduated from the University of New Hampshire and received her master's degree in English at Radcliffe. A member of Phi Beta Kappa, she also gained a master of library science degree from Pratt Institute Library School.

Miss Barker's first novel, *Peace, My Daughters*, was published in 1949. This was followed, in 1950, by the Literary Guild Selection, *Rivers Parting*, and, in 1952, by a book of poetry, *A Land and a People*. Her most recent novels were *Fire and the Hammer*, *Tomorrow the New Moon*, and *Liza Bowe*.

She has written many short stories, articles, book reviews and poems; she is now at work on a new novel at her New Hampshire home.